NUMERICAL ANALYSIS
OF PARTIAL DIFFERENTIAL
EQUATIONS

NUMERICAL ANALYSIS
OF PARTIAL DIFFERENTIAL
EQUATIONS

Charles A. Hall
Thomas A. Porsching

Institute for
Computational Mathematics and Applications
University of Pittsburgh

Prentice Hall, Englewood Cliffs, New Jersey 07632

Library of Congress Cataloging-in-Publication Data

HALL, CHARLES A., (date)
  Numerical analysis of partial differential equations / Charles A. Hall, Thomas A. Porsching.
    p.   cm.
  Includes bibliographical references.
  ISBN 0-13-626557-X
  1. Differential equations, Partial—Numerical solutions.
I. Porsching, Thomas A., (date).   II. Title.
QA374.H29   1990   89-16245
515′.353—dc20   CIP

Editorial/production supervision
  and interior design: *Kathleen M. Lafferty*
Cover design: *Lundgren Graphics, Ltd.*
Manufacturing buyer: *Paula Massenaro*

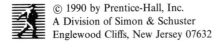 © 1990 by Prentice-Hall, Inc.
A Division of Simon & Schuster
Englewood Cliffs, New Jersey 07632

Printed in the United States of America

10 9 8 7 6 5 4 3 2 1

ISBN 0-13-626557-X

Prentice-Hall International (UK) Limited, *London*
Prentice-Hall of Australia Pty. Limited, *Sydney*
Prentice-Hall Canada Inc., *Toronto*
Prentice-Hall Hispanoamericana, S.A., *Mexico*
Prentice-Hall of India Private Limited, *New Delhi*
Prentice-Hall of Japan, Inc., *Tokyo*
Simon & Schuster Asia Pte. Ltd., *Singapore*
Editora Prentice-Hall do Brasil, Ltda., *Rio de Janeiro*

To our parents
George and Minnie Hall
and
August and Dorothy Porsching
for making it all possible

and to our wives
Mary and Eve
for sustaining it

Contents

Bibliography   299

Table of Conversion Factors   309

Glossary of Symbols   311

Index   315

Preface

In *Numerical Analysis of Partial Differential Equations* we present an account of the theory and methodology of the numerical solution of partial differential equations. This important subject forms much of the core of what is known more generally as "scientific computing," and it is one of the main areas that spawned the development of today's multimillion-dollar supercomputers.

Scientific computing was defined by Garrett Birkhoff[1] in 1971 as "the art of utilizing physical intuition, mathematical theorems and algorithms, and modern computer technology to construct and explore realistic models of problems arising in the natural sciences and engineering." In this spirit, our goal is to present some problems from these disciplines that involve partial differential equations, discuss algorithms for their numerical solution, and provide sufficient theory for an intelligent analysis of such algorithms.

We have attempted to avoid the "recipe format" in which numerical algorithms are given with little or no theoretical justification. At the same time, it is not our intention to sacrifice practicality on the altar of abstract analysis. Thus, in this textbook we hope to strike a middle ground and provide a development of material that is a balance between finite difference and finite element methods, has both a practical

---

[1] G. Birkhoff, *The Numerical Solution of Elliptic Equations*, SIAM, Philadelphia, 1971.

and an analytic nature, and contains basic theoretical results at a level that is understandable to beginning graduate students in engineering and the sciences.

This book is divided into two parts. Part I, A Course in the Numerical Solution of Partial Differential Equations, is self-contained and is suitable for a one-term (40 to 45 one-hour lectures) introductory graduate course on the subject. This material treats stationary and evolutionary partial differential equations. Numerical algorithms for the evolution equations are based on finite difference approximations, whereas those for stationary equations are developed via the finite element method. In this way we cover the two most popular and successful methodologies in use today. Part II, Some Additional Topics, contains subject matter that may be used to supplement or replace material from Part I. The two-part structure is intended to give the text a modular format and allow additional or alternate chapters from Part II to be "snapped" into Part I. The price of this flexibility is a certain amount of redundancy, but we hope, this has been minimized. We have endeavored to keep Part II largely independent of Part I. However, the material on finite elements in Chapters 8 and 9 should be preceded by a reading of Section 1 of Chapter 5, and Chapter 6.

The chapters include explanatory examples in the main body of the text as well as sets of exercises. There are traditional pencil-and-paper problems that test the understanding of the material developed in the chapter. In addition, there are Computer Exercises that require the reader to develop computer programs and/or use software available from other sources such as mathematical software libraries. Notes and Remarks sections appear at the ends of chapters to provide historical comments and additional references.

We have followed a standard method of referencing key items such as theorems, tables, examples, and equations. They are ordered by chapter, section, and their order of occurrence. For numbering purposes no distinction is made among lemmas, theorems, and corollaries. Thus in Chapter 5, Section 2, the fourth equation is numbered (5.2.4). Similarly, Theorem 5.2.1 is the first theorem (lemma or corollary) in Section 2 of Chapter 5. Notes and remarks are numbered according to their relevancy to a specific section.

Any attempt to treat a subject as large as the numerical solution of partial differential equations in a single work necessarily entails the omission of many interesting and relevant subjects. In this respect, we have consciously decided not to include extensive material on the solution of the algebraic equation systems arising from finite difference and finite element algorithms. However, Section 3 of Chapter 10 does contain a brief survey of such methods, and numerical methods for the solution of *general* linear and nonlinear equation systems may be found, for instance, in Stewart [1973] and Ortega and Rheinboldt [1970], respectively. Other topics for which the diligent reader will search in vain include finite element methods for hyperbolic equations, collocation methods, eigenvalue problems, and boundary elements, among others.

This book is an outgrowth of lecture notes developed by the authors over the years for courses on the subject at the University of Pittsburgh. It is intended for first-year graduate students in the sciences and engineering. Some material has also been used with success at the senior undergraduate level. Prerequisites include courses in advanced calculus, linear algebra and matrix theory, and differential equations.

During the course of writing this book, we have benefited from the suggestions and advice of many people. In this respect, we wish to mention our colleagues Charles Cullen, Vincent Ervin, Donald French, William Layton, Walter Pilant, and Patrick Rabier. We also acknowledge the Math 307B students, especially Monica Brodzik, Yiping Huang, and Victoria Radel, who participated in the debugging of preliminary versions of the text. We appreciate the comments of the following reviewers: Richard Falk, Rutgers University; Bruce Kellogg, University of Maryland; Robert J. Krueger, Iowa State University; William Layton, University of Pittsburgh; J. Tinsley Oden, The University of Texas at Austin; Dennis Ryan, Wright State University; and Olof Widlund, New York University. Finally, the authors thank Catherine Morrow, administrative assistant, ICMA, for her skillful assistance in the preparation of the manuscript, and Monica Brodzik for painstakingly reviewing the galleys.

Charles A. Hall
Thomas A. Porsching

PART I

A COURSE IN THE NUMERICAL SOLUTION OF PARTIAL DIFFERENTIAL EQUATIONS

1

Numerical Discretization: Finite Differences and Finite Elements

Although partial differential equations are used to describe many of the physical phenomena of science and engineering, few yield to closed-form solution. Numerical methods that have been developed to approximate solutions of partial differential equations can, for the most part, be grouped into two broad classes: *finite difference methods* and *finite element methods*. Our purpose in this book is to familiarize the reader with both classes of methods, to highlight their advantages and shortcomings, and above all, to present techniques that can be used for their analysis.

1.1 A MODEL PROBLEM

In this chapter we provide a description of both the finite difference and finite element methods applied to a simple transient convection–diffusion equation in one spatial dimension. This serves as an introduction to these methods and illustrates some of the computational pitfalls encountered in their implementation. Such pitfalls provide a partial justification for the need to analyze numerical methods.

Our model initial–boundary value problem is the following: Find $u(x, t)$ such that

$$\frac{\partial u}{\partial t} + v \frac{\partial u}{\partial x} - K \frac{\partial^2 u}{\partial x^2} = 0, \qquad 0 < x < 1, \quad t > 0 \qquad (1.1.1)$$

subject to the *initial condition*

$$u(x, 0) = 0, \qquad 0 \le x \le 1, \tag{1.1.2}$$

and *boundary conditions*

$$u(0, t) = 0 \quad \text{and} \quad u(1, t) = 1, \qquad t > 0. \tag{1.1.3}$$

We assume that the constants $v > 0$ and $K > 0$ are specified. The variable u can be thought of as the temperature of a fluid moving at a velocity, v, through a thin tube occupying the interval $0 \le x \le 1$. The temperature is forced to be 0 at the inlet ($x = 0$) and 1 at the outlet ($x = 1$) (see also the Notes and Remarks for Section 2.3). The constant K is called the thermal diffusivity of the fluid. The fluid is initially ($t = 0$) at a temperature of 0. We seek the temperature $u(x, t)$ at each position x in the tube and for each subsequent time t.

1.2 FINITE DIFFERENCE METHODS

An elementary approach to finite difference methods is provided by Taylor's theorem, which we state as follows:

Let $\phi \in C^{n+1}[a, b]$, where $C^{n+1}[a, b]$ denotes the class of functions that are $n + 1$ times continuously differentiable on the interval $[a, b]$. Then there exists a number $\xi, a < \xi < b$, such that

$$\phi(b) = \sum_{i=0}^{n} \frac{\phi^{(i)}(a)}{i!}(b - a)^i + R_n,$$

where

$$R_n = \frac{\phi^{(n+1)}(\xi)(b - a)^{n+1}}{(n + 1)!}.$$

From this theorem it is easy to justify the following three approximations to $d\phi/dx(a)$:

1. *Forward difference:* $\dfrac{\phi(a + h) - \phi(a)}{h}$,

2. *Backward difference:* $\dfrac{\phi(a) - \phi(a - h)}{h}$,

3. *Centered difference:* $\dfrac{\phi(a + h) - \phi(a - h)}{2h}$,

where h is a positive increment. Indeed, if ϕ is sufficiently smooth, then (1) and (2) approximate $d\phi/dx(a)$ with an error that is $O(h)$ as $h \to 0$, while (3) approximates $d\phi/dx(a)$ with an error that is $O(h^2)$ as $h \to 0$ (see Exercises 1.1 and 1.2). We say that (1) or (2) is a *first-order*, and (3) is a *second-order*, approximation to $d\phi/dx$.

The second derivative $d^2\phi/dx^2$ can be approximated similarly using the formula

4. *(Second) centered difference:* $\dfrac{\phi(a+h) - 2\phi(a) + \phi(a-h)}{h^2}$,

which is also second order as $h \to 0$. These approximations are sufficient for our purposes, although it is worth mentioning that higher-order finite difference formulas can be derived as well as finite difference approximations of higher-ordered derivatives.

If L_h is a finite difference approximation to a differential operator L and

$$(L_h - L)[\phi](a) \to 0 \quad \text{as} \quad h \to 0,$$

then $L_h[\phi]$ is said to be a *consistent finite difference* approximation to $L[\phi]$ at a. For example,

$$L_h[\phi] \equiv \frac{\phi(a+h) - \phi(a)}{h}$$

is a consistent approximation to $L[\phi] = d\phi/dx$ at a.

Finite difference methods for solving initial–boundary value problems such as (1.1.1)–(1.1.3) determine approximations at a finite number of points in the domain and involve four basic steps:

1. Subdivide the domain, for example by the uniform mesh $0 = x_0 < x_1 \cdots < x_N = 1$, where the *mesh points* are $x_j = j\,\Delta x$ and the *mesh gauge* is $\Delta x = 1/N$.

2. Approximate the differential equation at each mesh point x_j by replacing derivatives by appropriately chosen finite difference approximations.

3. Impose the boundary and initial conditions on the system generated in step 2.

4. Solve the finite difference equations generated in steps 2 and 3.

Hence we replace a differential equation and any auxiliary conditions by a system of (in this case) linear algebraic equations. The solution of the latter constitutes an approximation at mesh points to the solution of the former.

We now apply the finite difference method to the model convection–diffusion problem given above. There are choices to be made for the temporal and spatial discretizations, and we discuss each separately.

1.2.1 Spatial Discretization

Assume for the moment that u does not depend on time t (i.e., $\partial u/\partial t = 0$). The result is the steady-state boundary value problem[1]

$$\begin{cases} vu_x - Ku_{xx} = 0, & 0 < x < L = 1 \\ u(0) = 0, \quad u(1) = 1. \end{cases} \tag{1.2.1}$$

---

[1] Here we use subscript notation for partial differentiation. Thus $u_x = \partial u/\partial x$ and $u_{xx} = \partial^2 u/\partial x^2$. This is a practice we shall continue to employ whenever it is convenient.

One can verify that the solution of this boundary value problem is

$$u(x) = \frac{1 - e^{Rx}}{1 - e^{R}},$$

(1.2.2)

where $R \equiv vL/K$ is called the *Péclet number*.

If the "standard" centered difference approximations are used, we obtain the second-order finite difference equations

$$v \frac{U_{j+1} - U_{j-1}}{2\Delta x} - K \frac{U_{j-1} - 2U_j + U_{j+1}}{\Delta x^2} = 0, \qquad 1 \le j \le N - 1,$$

(1.2.3)

where $U_j \approx u(x_j)$. This set of difference equations can be solved in closed form as follows. Let $P = R\,\Delta x/2$. Then (1.2.3) can be rewritten as

$$-(P + 1)U_{j-1} + 2U_j + (P - 1)U_{j+1} = 0, \qquad 1 \le j \le N - 1,$$

where $U_0 = 0$ and $U_N = 1$. Assume that $U_j = r^j$ for some nonzero number r. Substituting, we obtain the auxiliary equation

$$[(1 - P)r^2 - 2r + (P + 1)]r^{j-1} = 0,$$

from which it follows that $r = 1$ or $r = (1 + P)/(1 - P)$. If A and B are arbitrary constants, we see that

$$U_j = A + B\left(\frac{1 + P}{1 - P}\right)^j, \qquad 0 \le j \le N,$$

is also a solution. The boundary conditions then determine A and B and, for example, the closed-form solution of (1.2.3) is

$$U_j = \frac{1 - Z^j}{1 - Z^N}, \qquad 0 \le j \le N,$$

(1.2.4)

where $Z = (2 + R\,\Delta x)/(2 - R\,\Delta x)$. We note in passing that Z is the $(1, 1)$-Padé second-order rational approximation to $e^{R\,\Delta x}$ [cf. (1.2.2) and (1.2.4)]. The reader is referred to the Notes and Remarks section for a definition of Padé approximants.

Unfortunately, if $\Delta x > 2/R$, then Z is negative and U_j oscillates as j ranges from 1 to $N - 1$. For example, $R = 50$, $N = 10$, and $\Delta x = 0.1$ yields $Z = -7/3$ and $U_9 \approx -0.43$ (see Figure 1.2.1). However, the true solution $u(x)$ is positive, monotone, and ranges from 0 to 1. Of course, if Δx is chosen to be less than 0.04, then Z is positive and monotone, and we obtain much better agreement with the true solution. For more complicated problems in which v and R are position dependent, or for multidimensional problems, it is not easy to predict the size of mesh that will prevent oscillations. Also, this mesh size may be prohibitively small from a computational efficiency standpoint.

A popular means of avoiding this aphysical oscillatory behavior is through the use of *upwind differencing*, in which (1.2.1) is discretized as

$$v \frac{U_j^E - U_j^W}{\Delta x} - K \frac{U_{j-1} - 2U_j + U_{j+1}}{\Delta x^2} = 0, \qquad 1 \le j \le N - 1,$$

(1.2.5)

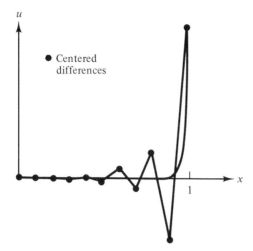

Figure 1.2.1 Center difference approximation.

where

$$U_j^E = \begin{cases} U_j & \text{if } v > 0 \\ U_{j+1} & \text{if } v < 0, \end{cases}$$

and

$$U_j^W = \begin{cases} U_{j-1} & \text{if } v > 0 \\ U_j & \text{if } v < 0. \end{cases}$$

The gradient of u is thus approximated by the gradient of the "fluid" entering mesh point j from the *upwind* direction. In our case $v > 0$ and the system (1.2.5) subject to the boundary conditions has the explicit solution

$$U_j = \frac{1 - Y^j}{1 - Y^N}, \qquad 0 \le j \le N, \tag{1.2.6}$$

where $Y = 1 + R\,\Delta x$ is now the (1, 0)-Padé first-order approximation to $e^{R\,\Delta x}$. This finite difference solution has the highly desirable property that it does *not* oscillate for any value of Δx (see Figure 1.2.2).

Our purpose here is not to resolve (or even debate) the issue as to whether centered differences with a "fine enough" mesh is a better strategy than upwind differences that are oscillation free for all meshes. Rather, we simply point out that there is much more to using finite differences than simply replacing derivatives by difference formulas.

Finally, we consider the behavior of the approximations (1.2.6) as $\Delta x \to 0$. We choose a sequence of meshes with $\Delta x = 1/N \to 0$ so that x^* is a mesh point for all N, say $x^* = j_N\,\Delta x$. Then

$$U_{j_N} = \frac{1 - (1 + R\,\Delta x)^{j_N}}{1 - (1 + R\,\Delta x)^N} = \frac{1 - (1 + Rx^*/j_N)^{j_N}}{1 - (1 + R/N)^N}.$$

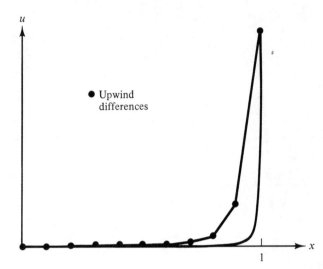

Figure 1.2.2 Upwind difference approximation.

Therefore, upon recalling that $\lim_{n \to \infty} (1 + x/n)^n = e^x$, we have

$$\lim_{N \to \infty} U_{j_N} = \frac{1 - e^{Rx^*}}{1 - e^R} = u(x^*). \tag{1.2.7}$$

For such sequences we have established the *convergence* of the solution of the finite difference equations (1.2.5) to the true solution (1.2.2). Of course, usually one does not know the true solution beforehand. These matters will be discussed in more detail in later chapters.

1.2.2 Temporal Discretization

We return now to the time-dependent problem (1.1.1)–(1.1.3). Assume as before that $v > 0$ and that upwind differencing is used for the convective and centered differencing is used for the diffusion term. The *explicit* (forward time difference) discretization is

$$\frac{U_j^{m+1} - U_j^m}{\Delta t} + v \frac{U_j^m - U_{j-1}^m}{\Delta x} - K \frac{U_{j-1}^m - 2U_j^m + U_{j+1}^m}{\Delta x^2} = 0 \tag{1.2.8}$$

for $1 \leq j \leq N - 1$, where Δt is the time step length and $U_j^m \approx u(j \, \Delta x, m \, \Delta t)$. We now show that the quantities $\{U_j^m\}$ are bounded independent of Δx and Δt if and only if

$$\Delta t \leq \frac{\Delta x^2}{2K + v \, \Delta x}. \tag{1.2.9}$$

TABLE 1.2.1   EXPLICIT TIME DIFFERENCING

Δt: 0.0009	0.001	0.0011
U_1^{50} 0.285E $-$ 01	0.299E $-$ 01	-0.141E $+$ 01
U_1^{100} 0.340E $-$ 01	0.342E $-$ 01	-0.105E $+$ 04
U_1^{150} 0.345E $-$ 01	0.345E $-$ 01	-0.767E $+$ 06
U_1^{700} 0.345E $-$ 01	0.345E $-$ 01	-0.237E $+$ 38

Condition (1.2.9) is called a *stability condition*. We shall encounter such conditions again in later chapters. If we assume that (1.2.9) is satisfied and rewrite (1.2.8) as

$$U_j^{m+1} = \left(\frac{K + v\,\Delta x}{\Delta x^2} \Delta t \right) U_{j-1}^m + \left(1 - \frac{2K + v\,\Delta x}{\Delta x^2} \Delta t \right) U_j^m + \frac{K\,\Delta t}{\Delta x^2} U_{j+1}^m,$$

then U_j^{m+1} is a convex combination[2] of the values $\{U_j^m\}$. As such, U_j^{m+1} is bounded above by the maximum and below by the minimum values of the U_j^m. This property of the difference approximation reflects the physical situation that the temperature at any time is bounded by the maximum and minimum values of the boundary and initial data. From a mathematical point of view, it essentially guarantees the convergence of the numerical solution.

If (1.2.9) is *not* satisfied, the time iterates U_j^{m+1} may grow in magnitude without bound. The easiest way to illustrate this is to consider a simple example. Let $N = 10$, $\Delta x = 0.1$, $v = 10$, $K = 4.5$. Then the time step restriction (1.2.9) is $\Delta t \le 0.001$. The explicit discretization is

$$U_j^{m+1} = (550\Delta t)U_{j-1}^m + (1 - 1000\Delta t)U_j^m + (450\Delta t)U_{j+1}^m,$$

from which we obtain values for U_1^{m+1} for three choices of Δt as shown in Table 1.2.1. It is clear that violating the time step restriction produces a useless solution. For small K, (1.2.9) requires that $\Delta t \le \Delta x / v$, but often v will be quite large, forcing Δt to be prohibitively small.

To circumvent such time step restrictions we can replace (1.2.8) by the *implicit* (backward time difference) discretization

$$\frac{U_j^{m+1} - U_j^m}{\Delta t} + v \frac{U_j^{m+1} - U_{j-1}^{m+1}}{\Delta x} - K \frac{U_{j-1}^{m+1} - 2U_j^{m+1} + U_{j+1}^{m+1}}{\Delta x^2} = 0 \qquad (1.2.10)$$

for $1 \le j \le N - 1$. That this discretization is such that the set $\{U_j^m\}$ is bounded for *all* choices of Δx and Δt follows from rewriting (1.2.10) as

$$U_j^{m+1} = U_j^m - \Delta t \left(\frac{2K + v\,\Delta x}{\Delta x^2} U_j^{m+1} - \frac{K + v\,\Delta x}{\Delta x^2} U_{j-1}^{m+1} - \frac{K}{\Delta x^2} U_{j+1}^{m+1} \right).$$

---

[2] $\sum_i \alpha_i U_i$ is a convex combination of the quantities $\{U_i\}$ if $\alpha_i \ge 0$ for all i and $\sum_i \alpha_i = 1$.

Now suppose that $\max_j U_j^{m+1} = U_i^{m+1}$. Set $j = i$ in the preceding equation and note that since the quantity in parentheses is nonnegative, we have $U_i^{m+1} \leq U_i^m$. This implies that $\max_j U_j^{m+1} \leq \max_j U_j^m$. Replacing m by $m - 1$, and so on, we deduce that the finite difference approximations U_j^m are bounded above by the largest of the boundary and initial data. An analogous argument in which $\min_j U_j^{m+1} = U_i^{m+1}$ shows that U_j^m is bounded below by the smallest of the boundary and initial data.

1.3 FINITE ELEMENT METHODS

Solutions of initial–boundary value problems, such as the one studied in the preceding section, can also be characterized as solutions of an associated variational problem. These matters are discussed at length in Chapters 7 and 9. For the present we consider the following simple construction.

If u satisfies (1.1.1)–(1.1.3), then certainly u satisfies

$$\int_0^1 (u_t + v u_x - K u_{xx})w \, dx = 0 \tag{1.3.1}$$

for any continuous function $w(x)$, called a *weight function*. If we further require $w(0) = w(1) = 0$, then applying integration by parts to (1.3.1) yields

$$\int_0^1 (u_t w + v u_x w + K u_x w_x) \, dx = 0. \tag{1.3.2}$$

Thus, (1.3.2) is a necessary condition for u to be a solution to (1.1.1). Furthermore, if u is sufficiently smooth and satisfies (1.3.2), it can be shown (Chapter 9) that u also satisfies (1.1.1). Hence, for smooth u, (1.3.2) along with (1.1.2) and (1.1.3) is an equivalent (variational) formulation of the initial–boundary value problem (1.1.1)–(1.1.3).

In the *finite element method* we determine approximations of the form

$$U(x, t) = \sum_{i=0}^{N} c_i(t)\phi_i(x)$$

to the solution $u(x, t)$ of the problem (1.1.1)–(1.1.3). Typically, the $\phi_i(x)$ are chosen as piecewise polynomials (see also Chapter 8). This method involves three basic steps:

1. Choose a finite-dimensional space S. For example, subdivide the domain into a union of *elements* by the uniform mesh $0 = x_0 < x_1 < \cdots < x_N = 1$, where $x_i = i \, \Delta x$. Then let

$$\phi_i(x) = \begin{cases} \dfrac{x - x_{i-1}}{\Delta x}, & x_{i-1} \leq x \leq x_i \\[2mm] \dfrac{x_{i+1} - x}{\Delta x}, & x_i \leq x \leq x_{i+1} \\[2mm] 0, & \text{otherwise.} \end{cases} \tag{1.3.3}$$

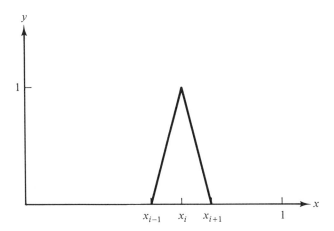

Figure 1.3.1 Hat function.

The ϕ_i are the so-called *chapeau* or *hat functions* (see Figure 1.3.1). The space S is then chosen to be the space spanned by $\{\phi_i(x)\,|\,0 \le i \le N\}$. This choice yields a space with desirable approximation theoretic properties. For example, it can be shown (Exercise 1.4) that if $u \in C^2[a, b]$, then there exists a function in S whose maximum deviation from u on $[a, b]$ is $O(\Delta x^2)$.

2. Approximate $u(x, t)$ by

$$U(x, t) = \sum_{i=0}^{N} c_i(t)\phi_i(x), \tag{1.3.4}$$

where by (1.1.3), $c_0(t) = 0$ for all t and $c_N(t) = 1$ for all t. Substitute $U(x, t)$ into (1.3.2) and choose the weight function $w(x)$ sequentially from some appropriate set, $\{\psi_j(x)\,|\,1 \le j \le N - 1\}$. A standard choice is $\psi_j \equiv \phi_j$.

3. Solve the set of ordinary differential equations generated in step 2 subject to the initial condition that $U(x, 0) = 0, 0 \le x \le 1$. For time-independent problems ($u_t = 0$), this system is algebraic.

In this way we use the finite element method to replace a partial differential equation and auxiliary conditions by a system of ordinary differential or algebraic equations.

1.3.1 Spatial Discretization

Assume that u does not depend on time t and consider the boundary value problem (1.2.1). The approximation in (1.3.4) reduces to

$$U(x) = \sum_{i=0}^{N} U_i\phi_i(x), \tag{1.3.5}$$

where the U_i are now constants. If we choose $\psi_j(x) = \phi_j(x)$ to be the hat functions defined above, (1.3.2) becomes

$$\int_0^1 \left[v \left(\sum_{i=0}^N U_i \phi_i' \right) \phi_j + K \left(\sum_{i=0}^N U_i \phi_i' \right) \phi_j' \right] dx = 0 \qquad (1.3.6)$$

for $1 \le j \le N - 1$. As mentioned earlier, the boundary conditions require that $U_0 = 0$ and $U_N = 1$. In this case $U_i = U(x_i) \approx u(x_i)$. We next note that for the hat functions,

$$\int_0^1 \phi_i' \phi_j \, dx = \begin{cases} -\dfrac{1}{2}, & i = j - 1 \\[2mm] \dfrac{1}{2}, & i = j + 1 \\[2mm] 0, & \text{otherwise} \end{cases} \qquad (1.3.7)$$

and

$$\int_0^1 \phi_i' \phi_j' \, dx = \begin{cases} \dfrac{2}{\Delta x}, & i = j \\[2mm] -\dfrac{1}{\Delta x}, & |i - j| = 1 \\[2mm] 0, & \text{otherwise.} \end{cases} \qquad (1.3.8)$$

For later reference, we also have

$$\int_0^1 \phi_i \phi_j \, dx = \begin{cases} \dfrac{2 \, \Delta x}{3}, & i = j \\[2mm] \dfrac{\Delta x}{6}, & |i - j| = 1 \\[2mm] 0, & \text{otherwise.} \end{cases}$$

Hence, the finite element equations (1.3.6) turn out to be *identical* to the finite difference equations (1.2.3). Such constructions are why many practitioners view the finite element method as a means of constructing difference equations. We elaborate on this idea in later chapters. This particular finite element approximation suffers from the same oscillatory behavior as the centered difference approximation if $\Delta x > 2/R$. As before, $R = v/K$.

As in the case of the finite difference method, there is an accepted procedure to guarantee that this does not occur for finite element methods. The weight functions $\psi_j(x)$ are now chosen to be different from the $\phi_j(x)$. In fact, we choose

$$\psi_j(x) = \phi_j(x) + \alpha \beta_j(x), \qquad (1.3.9)$$

where the

$$\beta_j(x) = \begin{cases} \dfrac{3(x - x_{j-1})(x_j - x)}{\Delta x^2}, & x_{j-1} \le x \le x_j \\[3mm] -\dfrac{3(x - x_j)(x_{j+1} - x)}{\Delta x^2}, & x_j \le x \le x_{j+1} \\[3mm] 0, & \text{otherwise} \end{cases}$$

are quadratic "corrections" to the functions $\psi_j(x)$. The constant α is positive if $v > 0$ and negative if $v < 0$ (see Figure 1.3.2).

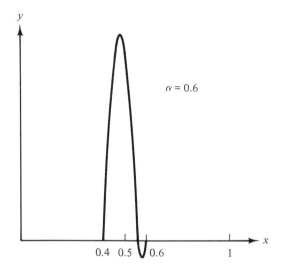

Figure 1.3.2 Weight functions for $\alpha > 0$.

Constructing the finite element equations (1.3.6) for the weight function of (1.3.9), we have

$$-\left[K + \frac{v \, \Delta x}{2}(\alpha + 1) \right] U_{j-1} + (2K + v \, \Delta x \, \alpha) U_j$$
$$-\left[K + \frac{v \, \Delta x}{2}(\alpha - 1) \right] U_{j+1} = 0 \qquad (1.3.10)$$

for $1 \le j \le N - 1$. As expected, $\alpha = 0$ reproduces the finite difference equations (1.2.3), but we also note that $\alpha = 1$ reproduces the upwind scheme (1.2.5).

The solution of (1.3.10) subject to the boundary conditions (1.1.3) is

$$U_j = \frac{1 - W^j}{1 - W^N}, \qquad 0 \le j \le N, \qquad (1.3.11)$$

where $W = [2 + (\alpha + 1)R \, \Delta x]/[2 + (\alpha - 1)R \, \Delta x]$.

If $\Delta x > 2/R$, then U_j oscillates for $\alpha = 0$, but is oscillation free for $\alpha \geq 1 - 2/(R \, \Delta x)$ (in particular, the upwind scheme resulting from the choice $\alpha = 1$ is oscillation free).

We conclude this section by demonstrating the pointwise convergence of the upwind finite element solution $U(x)$. That is, we will show that if $x^* \in (0, 1)$, then $U(x^*) \to u(x^*)$ as $\Delta x \to 0$, where $U(x)$ is given by (1.3.5) and the nodal values U_j satisfy (1.3.11) with $\alpha = 1$. The proof idea follows that of the upwind finite difference case, but is somewhat more complicated due to the continuous nature of $U(x)$.

We let $\Delta x = 1/N$ and choose $n \leq N$ such that $n \, \Delta x \leq x^* < (n + 1) \, \Delta x$. Then

$$|u(x^*) - U(x^*)| \leq |u(x^*) - U(n \, \Delta x)| + |U(n \, \Delta x) - U(x^*)|$$
$$\leq |u(x^*) - U(n \, \Delta x)| + |U(n \, \Delta x) - U((n + 1) \, \Delta x)|, \qquad (1.3.12)$$

where the last inequality results from $U(x)$ being a linear function on the interval $[n \, \Delta x, (n + 1) \, \Delta x]$. Suppose we can show that

$$\lim_{\Delta x \to 0} (1 + R \, \Delta x)^n = e^{Rx^*}. \qquad (1.3.13)$$

Then as $\Delta x \to 0$ (i.e., as $n, N \to \infty$)

$$U(n \, \Delta x) = \frac{1 - (1 + R \, \Delta x)^n}{1 - (1 + R \, \Delta x)^N}$$
$$= \frac{1 - (1 + R \, \Delta x)^n}{1 - (1 + R/N)^N} \to \frac{1 - e^{Rx^*}}{1 - e^R} = u(x^*).$$

But then also

$$U((n + 1) \, \Delta x) = \frac{1 - (1 + R \, \Delta x)^n(1 + R \, \Delta x)}{1 - (1 + R \, \Delta x)^N} \to u(x^*),$$

so that the convergence of $U(x^*)$ to $u(x^*)$ follows from (1.3.12). Thus, to complete the proof, it suffices to establish (1.3.13). But since $\Delta x = 1/N$,

$$(1 + R \, \Delta x)^n = \left[\left(1 + \frac{R}{N}\right)^N\right]^{n/N} \to (e^R)^{x^*}. \qquad (1.3.14)$$

Here we have used the fact that $0 \leq x^* - n/N \leq \Delta x$ and hence $\lim_{\Delta x \to 0} (n/N) = x^*$.

1.3.2 Temporal Discretization

When u is replaced by the approximation (1.3.4), the time-dependent problem (1.1.1)–(1.1.3) yields a system of ordinary differential equations (1.3.2), which we write here in matrix form as

$$M \frac{d\mathbf{C}}{dt} + A\mathbf{C} = \mathbf{S}. \qquad (1.3.15)$$

In (1.3.15), $\mathbf{C}$ is the $(N - 1) \times 1$ vector $(c_1, \ldots, c_{N-1})^T$, $d\mathbf{C}/dt$ is the entry-by-entry time derivative of $\mathbf{C}$, $\mathbf{S}$ is the $(N - 1) \times 1$ source vector containing contributions from boundary data, and A and M are $(N - 1) \times (N - 1)$ matrices with

$$M_{ij} = \int_0^1 \phi_j(x) w_i(x)\, dx,$$

$$A_{ij} = \int_0^1 \left[v \phi_j'(x) w_i(x) + K \phi_j'(x) w_i'(x) \right] dx. \tag{1.3.16}$$

M and A are called the *mass* and *stiffness matrices*, respectively. We choose the weight functions as $w_i = \phi_i$, $1 \leq i \leq N - 1$. This system can be solved by any of the standard methods for numerically solving ordinary differential equations. For example, we can approximate $d\mathbf{C}/dt$ by a forward difference to obtain the "explicit" time differencing scheme

$$M\mathbf{C}^{m+1} = (M - \Delta t\, A)\mathbf{C}^m + \Delta t\, \mathbf{S}, \tag{1.3.17}$$

where a vector superscript m designates the mth time step [i.e., $\mathbf{C}^m \approx \mathbf{C}(m\, \Delta t)$]. Note that unlike the finite difference case, a system of linear equations must be solved at each time step. Since M is nonsingular (Exercise 1.5),

$$\mathbf{C}^{m+1} = (I - \Delta t\, M^{-1}A)\mathbf{C}^m + \Delta t\, M^{-1}\mathbf{S}, \tag{1.3.18}$$

where I is the identity matrix. Moreover, since A is also nonsingular (Exercise 1.7), the solution of (1.3.15) may be written in terms of a *matrix exponential*.

For an arbitrary square matrix X, the matrix exponential is defined by the infinite series

$$\exp(X) = \sum_{i=0}^\infty \frac{X^i}{i!}.$$

It has many of the same properties as the scalar exponential function. For example,

$$\frac{d}{dt} \exp(Xt) = X \exp(Xt),$$

and also (Exercise 1.10)

$$\lim_{m \to \infty} \left(I + \frac{1}{m} X \right)^m = \exp(X).$$

Using the first property, it is straightforward to verify that the solution of (1.3.15) subject to $\mathbf{C}(0) = \mathbf{0}$ is

$$\mathbf{C}(t) = [I - \exp(-tM^{-1}A)]A^{-1}\mathbf{S}. \tag{1.3.19}$$

Now we examine the behavior of the vectors $\mathbf{C}^m$ as $\Delta t \to 0$. Let $P \equiv I - \Delta t\, M^{-1}A$, and $\mathbf{Q} = \Delta t\, M^{-1}\mathbf{S}$. Then (1.3.18) implies that

$$\begin{aligned}
\mathbf{C}^m &= P\mathbf{C}^{m-1} + \mathbf{Q} \\
&= P^2\mathbf{C}^{m-2} + (P + I)\mathbf{Q} \\
&= \cdots \\
&= P^m\mathbf{C}^0 + (P^{m-1} + \cdots + P + I)\mathbf{Q}.
\end{aligned}$$

If we choose $\mathbf{C}^0 = \mathbf{0}$ in agreement with the initial condition, and observe that $(I - P)^{-1} = (1/\Delta t)A^{-1}M$, then

$$\mathbf{C}^m = (I - P^m)(I - P)^{-1}\mathbf{Q}$$
$$= [I - (I - \Delta t \, M^{-1}A)^m]A^{-1}\mathbf{S}. \qquad (1.3.20)$$

We fix t and let $m \, \Delta t = t$. Then

$$\mathbf{C}^m = \left[I - \left(I - \frac{t}{m}M^{-1}A\right)^m\right]A^{-1}\mathbf{S}.$$

But

$$\lim_{m \to \infty} \left(I - \frac{t}{m}M^{-1}A\right)^m = \exp(-tM^{-1}A).$$

Hence

$$\lim_{\substack{m \to \infty \\ m\Delta t = t}} \mathbf{C}^m = \mathbf{C}(t).$$

This establishes the convergence of the numerical solution $\mathbf{C}^m(t)$ to the true solution $\mathbf{C}(t)$ as $\Delta t \to 0$.

On the other hand, if Δt is *fixed*, we can inquire about the behavior of the numerical solution as $m \to \infty$. If the eigenvalues of $M^{-1}A$, say λ_i, $1 \le i \le n$, lie in the right half of the complex plane, then $\mathbf{C}(t) \to A^{-1}\mathbf{S}$ as $t \to \infty$. However, it follows from (1.3.20) that $\mathbf{C}^m \to A^{-1}\mathbf{S}$ if and only if

$$|1 - \Delta t \, \lambda_j| < 1, \qquad (1.3.21)$$

since it is well known that this is a necessary and sufficient condition for

$$(I - \Delta t \, M^{-1}A)^m \to 0.$$

Of course, establishing (1.3.21) may not be an easy task.

We can also approximate $d\mathbf{C}/dt$ by a backward difference to obtain the "implicit" time differencing scheme

$$M \frac{\mathbf{C}^{m+1} - \mathbf{C}^m}{\Delta t} + A\mathbf{C}^{m+1} = \mathbf{S}, \qquad (1.3.22)$$

which can be rewritten as

$$(M + \Delta t \, A)\mathbf{C}^{m+1} = M\mathbf{C}^m + \Delta t \, \mathbf{S}.$$

Since $(M + \Delta t \, A)$ is nonsingular (Exercise 1.8), we see that for the implicit scheme

$$\mathbf{C}^m = (M + \Delta t \, A)^{-1}M\mathbf{C}^{m-1} + \Delta t \, (M + \Delta t \, A)^{-1}\mathbf{S}.$$

Using an argument similar to that of the explicit case, it follows that

$$\mathbf{C}^m = \left[I - \left(I + \frac{t}{m}M^{-1}A\right)^{-m}\right]A^{-1}\mathbf{S},$$

where $m \, \Delta t = t$. The convergence of the numerical solution $\mathbf{C}^m$ to $\mathbf{C}(t)$ is now obvious.

NOTES AND REMARKS

1.2 The (p, q) Padé rational approximation, $r(x)$, to an analytic function $f(x)$ is defined to be the ratio of a pth-degree polynomial to a qth-degree polynomial chosen such that the Taylor series expansion of $r(x)$ about the origin agrees with as many leading terms in the expansion for $f(x)$ about the origin as possible (H. Padé, circa 1890). The Padé rational functions are well known and are tabulated for various p and q in texts on approximation theory.

It is evident from Figure 1.2.1 that for large values of the Péclet number R the solution of (1.2.1) is essentially zero (i.e., its left boundary value) except in a small interval adjacent to the right boundary $x = 1$. This condition characterizes convection-dominated flow, and the narrow region in which u is significantly different from zero is known as a *boundary layer*. The contrasting situation is the case when $R \approx 0$. Now the flow is diffusion dominated and there is no boundary layer, since (1.2.2) shows that $u(x) = x + O(R)$.

1.3 One might ask why we should be concerned with the finite element method if we can only generate heretofore known finite difference formulas. First, it has been shown in Christie et al. [1976] that choosing $\alpha - (\coth R \, \Delta x/2) - 2/(R \, \Delta x)$ in (1.3.9) yields an approximation which exactly agrees with the steady-state solution of (1.2.1) at the mesh points.

Second, as we will see later, high-order approximations can easily be generated by choosing the functions $\phi_i(x)$ to be piecewise quadratic or cubic, and so on (see Heinrich and Zienkiewicz [1977]). Other advantages are discussed in later chapters.

EXERCISES

1.1. Using the Taylor theorem, verify that as $h \to 0$ the forward (centered) difference formula is a first (second)-order approximation to $d\phi/dx(a)$ if $\phi \in C^2[a, b]$ ($\phi \in C^3[a, b]$).

1.2. Verify that as $h \to 0$ the second centered difference formula is a second-order approximation of $d^2\phi/dx^2(a)$ if $\phi \in C^4[a, b]$.

1.3. Consider the following one-sided difference approximation to $d\phi/dx(a)$:

$$\frac{0.5\phi(a - 2h) - 2.0\phi(a - h) + 1.5\phi(a)}{h}.$$

Prove that for $\phi \in C^3$, it is a second-order approximation as $h \to 0$.

1.4. Let $u \in C^2[a, b]$ and define u_I, the interpolant of u, as

$$u_I(x) = \sum_{i=0}^{N} u(x_i)\phi_i(x),$$

where $\phi_i(x)$ is given in (1.3.3). Prove that as $\Delta x \to 0$,

$$\max_{a \leq x \leq b} \left| [u(x) - u_I(x)]^{(r)} \right| = O(\Delta x^{2-r}), \qquad r = 0, 1.$$

[*Hint:* In each subinterval $[x_j, x_{j+1}]$ use Taylor's formula to express $u(x_j)$ and $u(x_{j+1})$ in terms of $u^{(r)}(x^*)$, for each $x^* \in [x_j, x_{j+1}]$.]

1.5. Show that the matrix M in (1.3.17) is (symmetric) positive definite and hence nonsingular when the weights are chosen as the basis functions $\phi_i(x)$. Also show that M is nonsingular for a general choice of weights.

1.6. Let A_1 and A_2 be the $(N-1) \times (N-1)$ matrices with entries

$$[A_1]_{jk} = \int_0^1 \phi_j \phi_k \, dx$$

and

$$[A_2]_{jk} = \int_0^1 \phi'_j \phi'_k \, dx$$

and let $A = A_1 + A_2$. Prove that A_2 is (symmetric) positive definite. Prove that A_1 satisfies $\mathbf{Y}^T A_1 \mathbf{Y} = 0$ for all real nonzero $\mathbf{Y}$. [*Hint:* $\mathbf{Y}^T A_1 \mathbf{Y} = \frac{1}{2} \int_0^1 (g^2)' \, dx$ where $g(x) = \sum_{i=1}^{N-1} y_i \phi_i(x)$. Hence prove that $\mathbf{Y}^T A \mathbf{Y} > 0$ for all nonzero real $\mathbf{Y}$.]

1.7. Use Exercise 1.6 to prove that $A = vA_1 + KA_2$ is nonsingular.

1.8. Use Exercises 1.5 and 1.7 to prove that $(M + \Delta t \, A)$ is nonsingular for all Δt.

1.9. Prove that the eigenvalues of $M^{-1}A$ are real and positive if $v = 0$.

1.10. Let X be an $n \times n$ matrix. Prove that

$$\lim_{m \to \infty} \left(I + \frac{1}{m} X \right)^m = \exp(X).$$

[*Hint:* Let $J = \lambda I + N$ be a Jordan block of order n where $N = \text{Tridiag}\{1, 0, 0\}$, and let f be a scalar function which is $(n-1)$ times continuously differentiable. Then

$$f(J) = f(\lambda)I + f'(\lambda)N + \frac{f''(\lambda)}{2!} N^2 + \cdots + \frac{f^{(n-1)}(\lambda)}{(n-1)!} N^{n-1};$$

see, for example, Cullen [1966].]

Computer Exercises

1.11. Use the implicit formula (1.2.10) to calculate U_1^m for the values of m and Δt given in Table 1.2.1.

1.12. Choose $\Delta x = \frac{1}{33}$ and $R = 50$. Calculate the centered difference approximation (1.2.4) to (1.2.1). Verify that the finite difference solution is positive. Does it oscillate?

2

Prototypal Problems of Science and Engineering

In this chapter we discuss several model problems of science and engineering which involve different types of partial differential equations. In it we give some indication of how partial differential equations (PDEs) are classified and where they originate.

We do not expect the reader to work through all the details of these model problems. However, sufficient time and energy should be spent on one or more of them to gain an appreciation of the fact that partial differential equations are not spontaneous conceptions. The vast majority of partial differential equations studied are, in fact, products of the application of basic principles of science and engineering. An understanding of these origins of partial differential equations is, in our opinion, a necessary part of their numerical analysis.

2.1 CLASSIFICATION OF SECOND-ORDER LINEAR PARTIAL DIFFERENTIAL EQUATIONS

Many practical problems encountered in science and engineering involve the determination of a function $u(x_1, x_2)$ which satisfies an equation of the form

$$au_{x_1x_1} + 2bu_{x_1x_2} + cu_{x_2x_2} + du_{x_1} + eu_{x_2} + fu + g = 0 \qquad (2.1.1)$$

in some region[1] $\Omega \subseteq R^2$ whose boundary $\partial\Omega$ consists of piecewise smooth curves. Here a, b, c, d, e, f, and g are given functions of x_1 and x_2 which for the present we assume are at least continuous on Ω. In addition to satisfying (2.1.1), a solution of the underlying problem is required to satisfy *auxiliary conditions* (e.g., initial or boundary conditions), the form of which depends to a great extent on the *type* or *classification* of equation (2.1.1).

Equation (2.1.1) is said to be:

1. *Hyperbolic* if $ac - b^2 < 0$
2. *Elliptic* if $ac - b^2 > 0$
3. *Parabolic* if $ac - b^2 = 0$

Equation (2.1.1) resembles in form the general equation for a conic section and it is this similarity that motivates the terminology. As in the case of conic sections we seek to achieve standard forms for each of the classifications of (2.1.1) by an appropriate change of variables. Let

$$\xi = \phi(x_1, x_2), \qquad \eta = \psi(x_1, x_2) \tag{2.1.2}$$

be a continuously differentiable transformation in a neighborhood of a given point (x_1^0, x_2^0) in Ω. Let us assume for now that $b \neq 0$ in Ω. Furthermore, we suppose that the Jacobian of the transformation

$$\det J \equiv \phi_{x_1}\psi_{x_2} - \phi_{x_2}\psi_{x_1} \neq 0 \quad \text{at} \quad (x_1^0, x_2^0).$$

It then follows that (2.1.2) is locally invertible, so that

$$x_1 = \phi^{-1}(\xi, \eta), \qquad x_2 = \psi^{-1}(\xi, \eta).$$

Thus

$$u(x_1, x_2) = u(\phi^{-1}(\xi, \eta), \psi^{-1}(\xi, \eta)) \equiv V(\xi, \eta).$$

Using the chain rule for differentiation, we see that in some neighborhood of (x_1^0, x_2^0), (2.1.1) is transformed into

$$\alpha V_{\xi\xi} + 2\beta V_{\xi\eta} + \gamma V_{\eta\eta} + \delta(\xi, \eta, V, V_\xi, V_\eta) = 0, \tag{2.1.3}$$

where

$$\alpha = \phi_{x_1}(a\phi_{x_1} + b\phi_{x_2}) + \phi_{x_2}(b\phi_{x_1} + c\phi_{x_2}),$$

$$\beta = \phi_{x_1}(a\psi_{x_1} + b\psi_{x_2}) + \phi_{x_2}(b\psi_{x_1} + c\psi_{x_2}),$$

$$\gamma = \psi_{x_1}(a\psi_{x_1} + b\psi_{x_2}) + \psi_{x_2}(b\psi_{x_1} + c\psi_{x_2}),$$

and δ is a function that is linear in V, V_ξ, V_η.

---

[1] By a *region* we mean an open connected set.

Now the matrix

$$A = \begin{bmatrix} a & b \\ b & c \end{bmatrix}$$

has two real distinct eigenvalues

$$\lambda_1 = \frac{a + c + [4b^2 + (a - c)^2]^{1/2}}{2}, \qquad \lambda_2 = \frac{a + c - [4b^2 + (a - c)^2]^{1/2}}{2}.$$

Moreover, if ϕ is *any* function in $C^1(\Omega)$ that is nontrivial (i.e., $\phi_{x_1}^2 + \phi_{x_2}^2 \neq 0$) and satisfies

$$(a - \lambda_1)\phi_{x_1} + b\phi_{x_2} = 0, \tag{2.1.4}$$

then also

$$b\phi_{x_1} + (c - \lambda_1)\phi_{x_2} = 0. \tag{2.1.5}$$

Equation (2.1.5) follows from (2.1.4) since the left-hand side of (2.1.5) is just $[-\phi_{x_1}b^{-1} \det(A - \lambda_1 I)]$ and by the definition of λ_1, $\det(A - \lambda_1 I) = 0$. Hence $\phi \equiv (\phi_{x_1}, \phi_{x_2})^T$ is an eigenvector of A corresponding to λ_1. In exactly the same way, we see that if ψ is *any* function in $C^1(\Omega)$ that is nontrivial and satisfies

$$(a - \lambda_2)\psi_{x_1} + b\psi_{x_2} = 0, \tag{2.1.6}$$

then $\psi = (\psi_{x_1}, \psi_{x_2})^T$ is an eigenvector of A corresponding to λ_2. But $(\phi_{x_1}, \phi_{x_2})^T$ and $(\psi_{x_1}, \psi_{x_2})^T$ are orthogonal since $\lambda_1 \neq \lambda_2$. Hence, from (2.1.3) with

$$\alpha = \phi^T A \phi = \lambda_1(\phi_{x_1}^2 + \phi_{x_2}^2),$$

$$\beta = \phi^T A \psi = 0,$$

and

$$\gamma = \psi^T A \psi = \lambda_2(\psi_{x_1}^2 + \psi_{x_2}^2),$$

we have

$$\alpha V_{\xi\xi} + \gamma V_{\eta\eta} + \delta = 0, \tag{2.1.7}$$

an equation void of the mixed derivative $V_{\xi\eta}$. A primary motivation for eliminating the cross-derivative is that finite difference and finite element discretizations of (2.1.7) are much easier to construct and analyze than those for (2.1.1).

Note that any nontrivial C^1 transformation satisfying (2.1.4) and (2.1.6) is locally invertible since the orthogonality of ϕ and ψ implies that

$$(\det J)^2 = \det\left(\begin{bmatrix} \phi_{x_1} & \phi_{x_2} \\ \psi_{x_1} & \psi_{x_2} \end{bmatrix} \begin{bmatrix} \phi_{x_1} & \psi_{x_1} \\ \phi_{x_2} & \psi_{x_2} \end{bmatrix}\right)$$

$$= (\phi_{x_1}^2 + \phi_{x_2}^2)(\psi_{x_1}^2 + \psi_{x_2}^2) \neq 0.$$

Furthermore,

$$\alpha\gamma = (\det J)^2 \lambda_1 \lambda_2 = (\det J)^2 \det A = (\det J)^2(ac - b^2).$$

Hence, (2.1.7) and (2.1.1) are

1. Hyperbolic if $\alpha\gamma < 0$
2. Elliptic if $\alpha\gamma > 0$
3. Parabolic if $\alpha\gamma = 0$

Recall that we have arrived at these classifications under the assumption that $b \neq 0$ in Ω. However, if b vanishes in Ω, then the identity transformation, $\xi = x_1$, $\eta = x_2$, leads immediately to (2.1.7). In general, the transformation (2.1.2) applies only in a neighborhood of a given point, so that we have obtained what may be called a *neighborhoodwise* classification of (2.1.1). Indeed, unless a, b, and c are constants, the PDE (2.1.1) may change type as (x_1, x_2) ranges over Ω. Thus the equation

$$u_{x_1 x_1} + x_2 u_{x_2 x_2} = 0$$

is elliptic for $x_2 > 0$, hyperbolic for $x_2 < 0$, and parabolic for $x_2 = 0$.

In the remaining sections we discuss the origins of some typical problems involving partial differential equations.

2.2 THE VIBRATING STRING

Consider a perfectly flexible string that is stretched between two points of the x-axis. If the string is released from some initial configuration in such a way that the resulting motion remains planar, this motion is completely described by the string's subsequent displacement from the x-axis. If we denote this displacement by $u(x, t)$, and if we assume that it is everywhere small enough so that the tension T is constant over the length of the string, then at any time t the u component of the force, $\mathbf{F}(x, t)$, acting on the string at x is

$$F_2(x, t) = -T \sin \theta,$$

where $\tan \theta = u_x(x, t)$ (see Figure 2.2.1). But $\sin \theta = \tan \theta + O(\theta^3)$ as $\theta \to 0$, so that

$$F_2(x, t) = -T \tan \theta + O(\theta^3) = -T u_x(x, t) + O(\theta^3).$$

Utilizing the small displacement assumption again, we neglect the term $O(\theta^3)$ and deduce that $F_2(x, t)$ is approximately

$$F_2^*(x, t) = -T u_x(x, t).$$

From this it follows that the u component of the reaction at the point $x + \Delta x$ is approximately

$$-F_2^*(x + \Delta x, t) = T u_x(x + \Delta x, t).$$

Hence if the weight of the string between x and $x + \Delta x$ is neglected, the sum of the u component forces that act on it is essentially $F_2^*(x, t) - F_2^*(x + \Delta x, t)$.

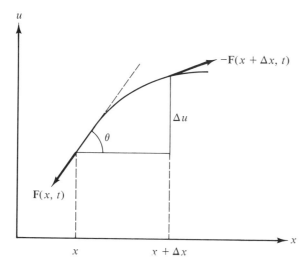

Figure 2.2.1 Element of string.

Let the linear density of the string be ρ. Then Newton's second law of motion (*force = mass $\times$ acceleration*) gives

$$F_2^*(x) - F_2^*(x + \Delta x) = \rho \, \Delta x \, u_{tt}(x, t) \qquad (2.2.1)$$

or

$$T \frac{u_x(x + \Delta x, t) - u_x(x, t)}{\Delta x} = \rho u_{tt}(x, t).$$

Letting $\Delta x \to 0$, we find that

$$\frac{T}{\rho} u_{xx} = u_{tt}$$

is an equation for the displacement u. Since both ρ and T are positive, we can write this equation as

$$u_{tt} - a^2 u_{xx} = 0, \qquad (2.2.2)$$

where $a^2 = T/\rho$. This hyperbolic equation is called the *equation of the vibrating string* or the simple *wave equation*. Note that the units of a are

$$\left(\frac{\text{mass} \times \text{length}}{\text{time}^2} \times \frac{\text{length}}{\text{mass}} \right)^{1/2} = \text{length/time}.$$

These are the units of speed, and in this connection it is appropriate to note that certain solutions of (2.2.2) may be interpreted as signals or waves that propagate along the x-axis with speeds $\pm a$ (see Section 3.2).

If the string is pinned at $x = 0$ and $x = L$, if its initial configuration is described by the curve $y = f(x)$, $0 \le x \le L$, and if it is at rest when released from this configuration, then it is clear that in addition to satisfying (2.2.2) for $0 \le x \le L$, $t > 0$, the displacement function $u(x, t)$ must also satisfy the following auxiliary conditions:

1. *Initial conditions*

$$u(x, 0) = f(x),$$

$$u_t(x, 0) = 0, \qquad 0 \leq x \leq L.$$

2. *Boundary conditions*

$$u(0, t) = u(L, t) = 0, \qquad t \geq 0.$$

2.3 HEAT CONDUCTION IN AN ISOTROPIC SOLID

Suppose that Ω represents a solid body in which heat is flowing. We describe this flow at any point in the body by a *flux vector* $\mathbf{J} = (J_1, J_2, J_3)^T$ whose direction corresponds instantaneously to that of the flow and whose magnitude is the rate of heat flowing through an element of surface normal to it. Thus J_i has the units of heat (energy) per unit time per unit area. We assume that the flow of heat has no preferred direction (*isotropic flow*). It is also natural to assume that the direction of flow will be in the direction of maximum temperature decrease from the point, and this is opposite to that of the gradient of the temperature $u(x, y, z, t)$ at the point. This is sometimes called the *fundamental hypothesis of heat conduction*. Therefore, upon combining these assumptions, we have

$$\mathbf{J} = -k(u_x, u_y, u_z)^T = -k \, \nabla u,$$

where the factor of proportionality k is called the *thermal conductivity* of the body and has units of heat/(time $\times$ length $\times$ temperature). If k is large, the material is a good *thermal conductor*, and if k is small, it is a good *thermal insulator*.

Now the amount of heat per unit time flowing into an element of volume V with surface area S is seen to be

$$I_1 \equiv \int_S \mathbf{J} \cdot (-\mathbf{n}) \, dS = \int_S k \, \nabla u \cdot \mathbf{n} \, dS,$$

where $\mathbf{n}$ is the exterior normal to S (Figure 2.3.1). In the case of isotropic solids, k does not depend on $\mathbf{n}$. Hence, according to the *divergence theorem*,

$$I_1 = \int_V \nabla \cdot k \, \nabla u \, dV.$$

Also, if the instantaneous volumetric rate of heat generation at the point $(x, y, z) \in V$ is $f(x, y, z, t)$, the total amount of heat produced in V per unit time is

$$I_2 = \int_V f \, dV.$$

The *specific heat* c of a solid is defined to be the amount of heat required to raise 1 unit of its mass 1 degree. The units of specific heat are heat/(mass $\times$ temperature).

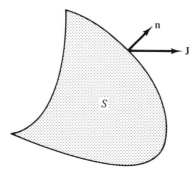

Figure 2.3.1   Flow through the surface S.

Thus if Δu is a temperature change that occurs in a mass m over a time Δt, the corresponding amount of heat that was added to the mass must have been $(c \cdot m \cdot \Delta u)$. In particular, if m is the mass of V, this amount of heat is

$$I_3 = \int_V \rho c \, \Delta u \, dV,$$

where ρ is the density. (The units of density are mass/length^3.) But another expression for I_3 is clearly $\Delta t(I_1 + I_2)$. Therefore,

$$\int_V \left(\rho c \frac{\Delta u}{\Delta t} - \mathbf{V} \cdot k \, \mathbf{V} u - f \right) dV = 0,$$

and since Δt and V are arbitrary, it follows that

$$\rho c u_t - \mathbf{V} \cdot k \, \mathbf{V} u - f = 0$$

or

$$\rho c u_t = \mathbf{V} \cdot k \, \mathbf{V} u + f. \tag{2.3.1}$$

If ρ and c are constants, (2.3.1) can be written as

$$u_t - \mathbf{V} \cdot D \, \mathbf{V} u - \frac{f}{\rho c} = 0,$$

where $D \equiv k/\rho c$ is the *diffusivity* of the material. This equation is of *parabolic* type.

If the functions in (2.3.1) do not depend on t, this equation becomes the *steady-state heat conduction equation*

$$-\mathbf{V} \cdot k \, \mathbf{V} u = f, \tag{2.3.2}$$

which is of *elliptic* type. If k is a constant, (2.3.2) is the *Poisson equation*, and if in addition $f \equiv 0$, we obtain *Laplace's equation*,

$$\nabla^2 u = 0. \tag{2.3.3}$$

The appropriate auxiliary conditions for the heat conduction equation (2.3.1) may be categorized as initial conditions, boundary conditions, and interface conditions.

1. *Initial conditions.* Equation (2.3.1) describes the time evolution of temperature as a function of position. We initialize this process by specifying a function u_0 such that

$$u(x, y, z, 0) = u_0(x, y, z). \qquad (2.3.4)$$

2. *Boundary conditions.* Since (2.3.1) holds for $t > 0$ and $(x, y, z) \in \Omega$, a reasonable specification of the situation on the boundary $\partial\Omega$ of Ω is as follows. Let $\partial\Omega = \partial\Omega_1 \cup \partial\Omega_2 \cup \partial\Omega_3$ where some, but not all, of the disjoint sets $\partial\Omega_i$ may be empty. Then we consider three types of boundary conditions:

   a. *Temperature specified or Dirichlet condition.* In this case,

   $$u(x, y, z, t) = g(x, y, z), \qquad (x, y, z) \in \partial\Omega_1, \qquad t \geq 0, \qquad (2.3.5)$$

   where g is some specified function.

   b. *Insulated boundary or Neumann condition.* Here

   $$-\nabla u \cdot \mathbf{n} = 0, \qquad (x, y, z) \in \partial\Omega_2, \qquad t \geq 0, \qquad (2.3.6)$$

   where $\mathbf{n}$ is the unit outward normal to $\partial\Omega_2$. This condition states that the thermal flux across $\partial\Omega_2$ is zero.

   c. *Radiation or mixed condition.* In this case,

   $$-k\,\nabla u \cdot \mathbf{n} = h(u - u_s), \qquad (x, y, z) \in \partial\Omega_3, \qquad t \geq 0, \qquad (2.3.7)$$

   where $\mathbf{n}$ is the unit outward normal to $\partial\Omega_3$, h is the *coefficient of heat transfer*, and u_s is the temperature of the surrounding medium. This condition states that the thermal flux across $\partial\Omega_3$ is proportional to the difference between the temperature of the surrounding medium and the surface temperature.

   There are other types of boundary conditions that are useful; for example, we can allow g to depend on time.

3. *Interface conditions.* If Ω is composed of more than one material, then along an *interface* between two materials the flux must be continuous. That is,

$$k_1(\nabla u_1 \cdot \mathbf{n}) = k_2(\nabla u_2 \cdot \mathbf{n}), \qquad (2.3.8)$$

where k_i and u_i are the thermal conductivity and temperature of material i and $\mathbf{n}$ is the normal to the interface. This condition is implied by (2.3.1) in that the flux, $\mathbf{J} = k\,\nabla u$, is assumed to be differentiable.

Equation (2.3.2) not only occurs in heat conduction applications, but also in descriptions of neutron diffusion (Glasstone and Edlund [1952]), fluid flow (Roache [1972]), and elsewhere.

Table 2.3.1 gives some representative values of the thermodynamic quantities that we have introduced. More elaborate tables can be found in the *ASHRAE Handbook* [1978].

TABLE 2.3.1 THERMODYNAMIC QUANTITIES

Material	ρ (lbm/ft^3)	c (Btu/lbm-°F)	k (Btu/hr-ft-°F)
Air	0.08	0.24	0.01
Aluminum	168.99	0.21	117.89
Concrete	150.00	0.25	0.79
Copper	558.99	0.09	221.90
Steel	489.01	0.11	30.62
Water	62.45	1.00	0.33
Wood	47.00	0.57	0.09

2.4 ELASTIC DEFORMATION

In this section we develop the differential equations describing the linear elastic behavior of a solid subjected to external forces. The derivation is for the two-dimensional case in Cartesian coordinates, although extensions to other coordinate systems and three dimensions are straightforward.

Consider a region Ω in the xy-plane representing a solid of unit thickness. Assume that loads are applied in the form of *boundary loads* (distributed on the boundary $\partial\Omega$ of Ω) and *body loads* (distributed over Ω itself). Gravitational forces or thermal forces due to heating are examples of body loads, while a weight attached to some portion of the boundary of Ω generates a boundary load on Ω. The boundary loads are designated $(\bar{X}, \bar{Y})$ and have units of force/area, while the body loads are designated (X, Y) and have units of force/volume. Under the action of these loads, particles are displaced by an amount $\delta \equiv (u, v)$ from their position in the unloaded or undeformed state. The vector (u, v) is termed the *displacement vector* and has units of length. The behavior of a material is said to be *elastic* if the material returns to its undeformed state when applied loads are removed. Otherwise, the behavior is termed *plastic*.

Forces acting on an infinitely small surface element dS of the material have the form $\mathbf{F}\,dS$ for some vector $\mathbf{F}$. Any point of dS may be assumed as the point of application of $\mathbf{F}$. The vector $\mathbf{F}$ is the force per unit area being applied and is termed the *stress*. Note that it has units of pressure. The load or *traction* $\mathbf{F}\,dS$ represents the force acting between parts of the body adjacent to either side of the surface element dS. For two-dimensional domains Ω, the force (and hence the stress) can be resolved into two components, one normal and one tangential to the surface dS. If we now consider dS as the boundary of a rectangular differential element $d\Omega$ whose side lengths are dx and dy as in Figure 2.4.1, then these normal and tangential components are conventionally labeled as indicated.

The *normal components* of stress are denoted by σ_x and σ_y, while the *shear components* are denoted τ_{xy} and τ_{yx}. Normal stress has a single subscript, which indicates that the stress acts on a plane normal to the axis of the subscript direction. The first letter of the double subscript on a shear stress component indicates that

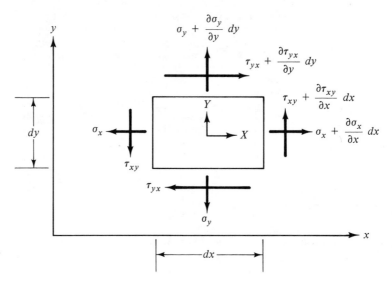

Figure 2.4.1   Differential element of material.

the plane on which the stress acts is normal to the axis in the subscript direction; the second letter designates the coordinate direction in which the stress acts. One can show (and we assume here) that $\tau_{xy} = \tau_{yx}$.

If a differential element of the material is deformed uniaxially, the engineering *strain* is defined to be the change in length per unit length along that axis. For more general loadings the strain is resolved into coordinate directions. Consider the differential element in Figure 2.4.2 in an undeformed state $ABCD$ and a deformed state $A'B'C'D'$. The length $\overline{AB}$ in the x-direction becomes $\overline{A'B'}$ in the deformed state. The

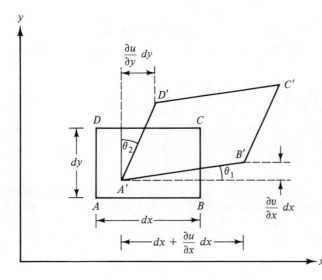

Figure 2.4.2   Strain–displacement relationships.

component of strain in the x-direction is denoted ε_x and by definition

$$\varepsilon_x = \frac{|\overline{A'B'}| - |\overline{AB}|}{|\overline{AB}|}.$$

Since $|\overline{AB}| = dx$, we have

$$|\overline{A'B'}| = (1 + \varepsilon_x)\, dx. \tag{2.4.1}$$

But from Figure 2.4.2 we have

$$|\overline{A'B'}|^2 = \left(dx + \frac{\partial u}{\partial x}\, dx\right)^2 + \left(\frac{\partial v}{\partial x}\, dx\right)^2. \tag{2.4.2}$$

Squaring (2.4.1) and subtracting from (2.4.2), we find that

$$0 = 2\left(\frac{\partial u}{\partial x} - \varepsilon_x\right) dx^2 + \left[-\varepsilon_x^2 + \left(\frac{\partial u}{\partial x}\right)^2 + \left(\frac{\partial v}{\partial x}\right)^2\right] dx^2.$$

Assuming that the strains are small, we can discard higher-order terms and obtain

$$\varepsilon_x = \frac{\partial u}{\partial x}. \tag{2.4.3}$$

Similarly, we see that the component of strain in the y-direction is

$$\varepsilon_y = \frac{\partial v}{\partial y}. \tag{2.4.4}$$

The *shear strain* γ_{xy} is defined as the change in the measure of an angle that is originally a right angle in the undeformed state. From Figure 2.4.2 the change in the angle DAB is

$$\theta_1 + \theta_2 \approx \sin\theta_1 + \sin\theta_2$$

$$\approx \frac{\dfrac{\partial v}{\partial x}\, dx}{|\overline{A'B'}|} + \frac{\dfrac{\partial u}{\partial y}\, dy}{|\overline{A'D'}|}$$

$$\approx \frac{\partial v}{\partial x} + \frac{\partial u}{\partial y}.$$

Here we have ignored the higher-order terms such as $\varepsilon_x\, dx$. Thus the shear strain is

$$\gamma_{xy} = \frac{\partial v}{\partial x} + \frac{\partial u}{\partial y}. \tag{2.4.5}$$

Equations (2.4.3)–(2.4.5) relate strains to displacements and provide the first of the three basic relationships that comprise plane elasticity theory:

1. *Strain–displacement relations*
2. *Constitutive laws of the material*
3. *Equilibrium equations*

Let us next consider the constitutive laws, which relate stress to strain. For a uniaxial specimen of cross-sectional area A (Figure 2.4.3), the strain $\varepsilon_x = \Delta L/L$ and the associated stress σ_x is proportional to ε_x, that is

$$\sigma_x = E\varepsilon_x. \tag{2.4.6}$$

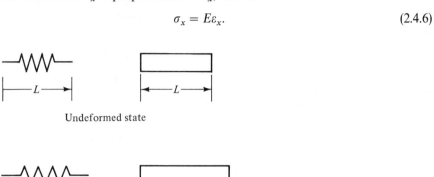

Undeformed state

Deformed state   **Figure 2.4.3**   Uniaxial specimens.

This is called *Hooke's law* after the English mathematician Robert Hooke (1635–1703). The constant E is the *modulus of elasticity* or *Young's modulus*, named after Thomas Young (1773–1829). If the specimen is a linear spring, then (2.4.6) states that the force F necessary to stretch the spring by an amount ΔL is $F = k \, \Delta L$, where the spring constant $k = AE/L$. As the stiffness of the spring increases, more force is required to extend it the given amount ΔL. Thus k increases, and since A and L are fixed, we see that Young's modulus plays the role of the "spring constant" for the material being considered. The units of E are the same as those of stress, force/area.

Now consider the response of a two-dimensional *isotropic* specimen to imposed in-plane stresses. A material is isotropic if its stress–strain relation is unaltered by orthogonal transformations of the coordinate system. Figure 2.4.4 illustrates that the

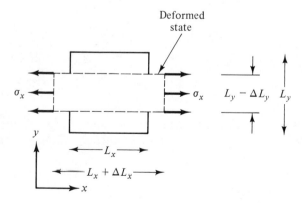

Figure 2.4.4   Normal stress components.

effect of a stress in one of the coordinate directions is a strain in both directions. Corresponding to the stress σ_x in the x-direction is a strain σ_x/E.

Simeon D. Poisson (1781–1840), a French mathematician, demonstrated that the specimen also contracts in the y-direction by an amount proportional to σ_x/E. The constant of proportionality v is called *Poisson's ratio*, and from Figure 2.4.4 we have

$$\frac{\Delta L_y}{L_y} = -v\frac{\Delta L_x}{L_x} = -v\frac{\sigma_x}{E}.$$

The roles of x and y are interchanged to describe the effect of an imposed stress σ_y. Now there are two cases to consider relative to stresses in the z-direction. Under a plane stress condition, $\sigma_z = 0$ and there is nothing to add. However, under a plane strain condition there is also a contraction in the x and y directions by an amount $-v\sigma_z/E$ due to an imposed stress σ_z. We assume the latter, that is, that the plane strain condition holds. (See the Notes and Remarks for a discussion of these two conditions.) Combining the three contributions to normal strain for a general loading, we see that the changes in length per unit length in the x, y, and z directions are, respectively,

$$\varepsilon_x = \frac{\sigma_x}{E} - \frac{v\sigma_y}{E} - \frac{v\sigma_z}{E},$$

$$\varepsilon_y = -\frac{v\sigma_x}{E} + \frac{\sigma_y}{E} - \frac{v\sigma_z}{E}, \tag{2.47}$$

$$\varepsilon_z = -\frac{v\sigma_x}{E} - \frac{v\sigma_y}{E} + \frac{\sigma_z}{E} = 0.$$

This response in normal strain is not influenced by the shearing deformation caused by the *shear stress* τ_{xy}. A shear stress corresponds to a transverse load. Consider, for example, the rivet in Figure 2.4.5 connecting two plates which are subjected to tension forces F_1 and F_2 as illustrated. A shear stress will develop in the section of the rivet belonging to the plane normal to the page and through $\overline{AB}$. Such shear stresses are also proportional to the associated shear strain,

$$\tau_{xy} = G\gamma_{xy}, \tag{2.4.8}$$

where G is the *modulus of rigidity* or *shear modulus*. The three elastic constants E, G, v are related by the equation $E = 2G(1 + v)$. Elastic constants for various materials are given in Table 2.4.1.

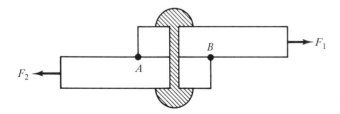

Figure 2.4.5 Shear stress in a rivet.

TABLE 2.4.1 SAMPLE ELASTIC CONSTANTS

Material	v	E (10^6 psi)	G (10^6 psi)	α (10^{-6})
Aluminum	0.35	10.0	3.7	12.8
Concrete	0.22	54.5	18.4	5.5
Copper	0.45	18.0	6.2	9.3
Steel	0.26	29.0	11.5	5.6

Solving the third line of (2.4.7) for σ_z and substituting into the first two eliminates the stress component σ_z and leaves two equations relating the in-plane strains to the in-plane stresses. Inverting the remaining two equations and combining the result with (2.4.8), we obtain (for plane strain) the *stress–strain relation* or the *constitutive laws* for the material as

$$\boldsymbol{\sigma} \equiv D\boldsymbol{\varepsilon}, \tag{2.4.9}$$

where $\boldsymbol{\sigma} \equiv (\sigma_x, \sigma_y, \tau_{xy})^T$, $\boldsymbol{\varepsilon} = (\varepsilon_x, \varepsilon_y, \gamma_{xy})^T$, and

$$D = \frac{2G}{1 - 2v} \begin{bmatrix} 1 - v & v & 0 \\ v & 1 - v & 0 \\ 0 & 0 & \dfrac{1 - 2v}{2} \end{bmatrix}. \tag{2.4.10}$$

The matrix D is the *material stiffness matrix*. If a mechanism exists to produce strains without the imposition of stress, $\boldsymbol{\varepsilon}$ can be replaced by $\boldsymbol{\varepsilon} + \boldsymbol{\varepsilon}^0$, where $\boldsymbol{\varepsilon}^0$ represents the *initial strains*. For example, if there are thermal strains due to heating, then

$$\boldsymbol{\varepsilon}^0 = (\alpha T, \alpha T, 0)^T, \tag{2.4.11}$$

where α is the *coefficient of thermal expansion* and T is the temperature. The associated thermal stresses are $\boldsymbol{\sigma} = D(\boldsymbol{\varepsilon} + \boldsymbol{\varepsilon}^0)$.

We next derive the *equilibrium equations* for the planar differential element shown in Figure 2.4.1 subjected to normal stresses σ_x and σ_y, shear stress τ_{xy}, and body forces X and Y. Since the body is in equilibrium, the sum of the forces in the x-direction is zero, that is,

$$\sum F_x = 0 = \left(\sigma_x + \frac{\partial \sigma_x}{\partial x} dx\right) dy - \sigma_x \, dy + \left(\tau_{xy} + \frac{\partial \tau_{xy}}{\partial y} dy\right) dx - \tau_{xy} \, dx + X \, dx \, dy.$$

After clearing terms, this gives

$$\frac{\partial \sigma_x}{\partial x} + \frac{\partial \tau_{xy}}{\partial y} + X = 0. \tag{2.4.12}$$

Similarly, the equation $\sum F_y = 0$ yields

$$\frac{\partial \sigma_y}{\partial y} + \frac{\partial \tau_{xy}}{\partial x} + Y = 0. \tag{2.4.13}$$

In the absence of body forces, this coupled system of second-order PDEs is equivalent to a single fourth-order PDE

$$\nabla^4 \Phi = 0,$$

where Φ is the *Airy stress function*. The stresses are then determined by

$$\sigma_x = \frac{\partial^2 \Phi}{\partial y^2}, \qquad \sigma_y = \frac{\partial^2 \Phi}{\partial x^2}, \qquad \tau_{xy} = -\frac{\partial^2 \Phi}{\partial x \, \partial y}.$$

We will not pursue this approach here.

Substitution of the stress–strain relation (2.4.9) into (2.4.12) and (2.4.13) yields the following *equilibrium equations in displacement form* for plane strain (single material):

$$\nabla^2 u + \frac{1}{1 - 2v}(u_{xx} + v_{yx}) + \frac{X}{G} = 0,$$

$$\nabla^2 v + \frac{1}{1 - 2v}(v_{yy} + u_{xy}) + \frac{Y}{G} = 0. \tag{2.4.14}$$

The auxiliary conditions for the equilibrium equations (2.4.14) of plane elasticity are of two types:

1. *Boundary conditions.* On a segment $\partial \Omega_i$ of the boundary $\partial \Omega$ with unit outward normal **n** and unit tangent **t**, typical boundary conditions are either
   a. *Displacement specified:*

   $$\boldsymbol{\delta} \cdot \mathbf{n}(x, y) = b_1(x, y) \qquad \text{for } (x, y) \in \partial \Omega_i$$

   and/or

   $$\boldsymbol{\delta} \cdot \mathbf{t}(x, y) = b_2(x, y) \qquad \text{for } (x, y) \in \partial \Omega_i,$$

   or
   b. *Stress specified:*

   $$\mathbf{F} \cdot \mathbf{n}(x, y) = b_3(x, y) \qquad \text{for } (x, y) \in \partial \Omega_i$$

   and/or

   $$\mathbf{F} \cdot \mathbf{t}(x, y) = b_4(x, y) \qquad \text{for } (x, y) \in \partial \Omega_i.$$

   On each segment $\partial \Omega_i$ of $\partial \Omega$, and in each of the directions normal and tangential to $\partial \Omega_i$, a component of displacement or stress must be specified in such a manner as to eliminate rigid body motions. Otherwise, a unique solution will not exist.

2. *Interface conditions.* The components of stress normal and tangential to an unloaded interface are required to be continuous (in fact, differentiable) by the equilibrium equations. If the interface is a material interface, this means that the normal and shear strain will be discontinuous across such an interface, a situation analogous to that discussed in Section 2.3, where thermal flux is continuous but the temperature gradient is discontinuous across material interfaces.

2.5 *FLUID FLOW*

A simple mathematical model of fluid flow may be developed from consideration of two fundamental physical principles: the *conservation of mass* and the *conservation of momentum* (i.e., mass × velocity). To simplify the situation, we assume that the flow is unidirectional, say along the *x*-axis of a Cartesian coordinate system. We fix our attention on a stationary differential control volume dV whose planar faces are perpendicular to the coordinate axes (Figure 2.5.1). At each point in space we identify a fluid density ρ (mass/volume), pressure p (force/area), and *x*-directional velocity component v (length/time). Since the flow is one-dimensional, these scalar quantities are functions only of x and the time t. We may interpret the quantity ρv as a point-wise mass flux [mass/(area × time)]. Then the net mass flux into dV through the faces perpendicular to the *x*-axis is

$$\rho v - \left[\rho v + (\rho v)_x \, dx\right] = -(\rho v)_x \, dx.$$

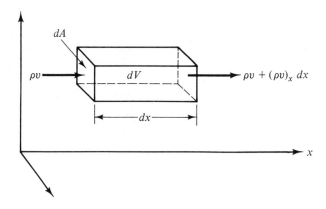

Figure 2.5.1 Differential control volume.

Since there is no flow through the remaining faces, the total mass transported into dV during a time increment dt is therefore $-(\rho v)_x \, dx \, dt \, dA = -(\rho v)_x \, dV \, dt$. According to the conservation of mass principle, this must represent the increase of mass in dV over time dt. But this quantity is given by $\rho_t \, dt \, dV$. Hence $\rho_t \, dV \, dt = -(\rho v)_x \, dV \, dt$, or upon rearranging,

$$\rho_t + (\rho_v)_x = 0. \tag{2.5.1}$$

Equation (2.5.1), which represents the pointwise conservation of fluid mass per unit time per unit volume, is known as the *continuity equation*.

We next consider the conservation of momentum principle. In the present situation it states that the net time rate of increase of momentum[2] in dV consists of

---

[2] More precisely, this is the component of momentum along the *x*-axis.

the time rate of increase due to momentum transport through the faces perpendicular to the x-axis plus the resultant of the pressure forces acting on these faces. Since the pointwise momentum per unit volume is again given by the product ρv (mass × velocity/volume), the net rate of increase in dV is $(\rho v)_t\, dV$. Furthermore, by an argument similar to the one given above, the net momentum flux into dV is

$$\rho vv - [\rho vv + (\rho vv)_x\, dx] = -(\rho v^2)_x\, dx.$$

(Note that the transported quantity is now ρv, whereas for mass conservation it was simply ρ.) Thus the momentum increase due to transport through the faces is

$$-(\rho v^2)_x\, dx\, dA = -(\rho v^2)_x\, dV.$$

Finally, the resultant of the pressure forces[3] on the faces of dV that are perpendicular to the x-axis is

$$p\, dA - (p + p_x\, dx)\, dA = -p_x\, dV.$$

Utilizing these expressions in the conservation of momentum principle, we obtain the *momentum equation*,

$$(\rho v)_t + (\rho v^2)_x = -p_x. \tag{2.5.2}$$

In Chapter 3 we will see that (2.5.1) and (2.5.2) constitute an example of a first-order *hyperbolic system*.

From Exercise 2.9 we see that an equivalent form of (2.5.2) is

$$\rho \frac{dv}{dt} = -p_x, \tag{2.5.3}$$

where d/dt, the so-called "material derivative," represents differentiation following the motion of a fluid particle. Equation (2.5.3) states that on a per unit volume basis the force acting on a particle of fluid is equivalent to the product of its mass and its acceleration. Thus the principle of momentum conservation is equivalent to Newton's second law of motion.

NOTES AND REMARKS

2.1 Linear differential equations in more than two variables can also be classified as hyperbolic, elliptic, and parabolic. In particular, consider the second-order differential operator L in n variables

$$L[u] = \sum_{i=1}^{n} \sum_{k=1}^{n} a_{ik} u_{x_i x_k}$$

---

[3] Pressure exerts a compressive force on dV.

at a point $\mathbf{x}^0 \in R^n$. We associate this with the quadratic form

$$Q = \sum_{i=1}^n \sum_{k=1}^n a_{ik} y_i y_k,$$

which is equivalent by an affine transformation to the canonical form

$$Q' = \sum_{i=1}^n \kappa_i \eta_i^2$$

in which each κ_i is 0, 1, or -1. The differential operator L is called *elliptic* at $\mathbf{x}^0$ if all the values κ_i are equal and equal to either 1 or -1. L is called *properly hyperbolic* if all values κ_i have the same sign, say positive, except one which is negative. If several signs are positive and several negative, L is called *ultrahyperbolic*. Finally, if Q' is singular (one or more κ_i vanish), L is called *parabolic* (Courant and Hilbert [1962]).

2.2 If an external force $\rho F(x, t)$ per unit length of the string acts in the direction of the negative u-axis, then (2.2.2) becomes

$$u_{tt} - a^2 u_{xx} - F = 0. \qquad (1)$$

For example, if the weight of the string is considered, $F = g$, where g is the acceleration of gravity. If air resistance is considered, F depends on the velocity of the string (see Exercise 2.1). Equation (1) also describes the displacement of a homogeneous elastic bar from its position of equilibrium after being flexed. Equation (1) can be generalized to two spatial dimensions as the equation of a *vibrating membrane*:

$$u_{tt} - a^2(u_{xx} + u_{yy}) = 0, \qquad (2)$$

where u is the displacement of a point on the membrane out of the xy-plane. The membrane is assumed to be thin and perfectly flexible with density (mass/area) ρ. The tension T per unit length across any line on the membrane is assumed to be large and the displacement u is assumed small relative to the dimensions of the membrane.

2.3 If Ω is not a solid, but a medium such as a liquid, heat is also transferred or transported by *convection*. The heat *convection–conduction equation* is

$$\rho c u_t = \nabla \cdot k \nabla u - \rho c \mathbf{q} \cdot \nabla u + f, \qquad (3)$$

where $\mathbf{q}$ is a known function of position and time and represents the velocity of the fluid through which heat transfer occurs.

2.4 Assume that Ω is three-dimensional, let w be the displacement in the z-direction, and append the strain components

$$\varepsilon_z = \frac{\partial w}{\partial z},$$

$$\gamma_{xz} = \frac{\partial w}{\partial x} + \frac{\partial u}{\partial z},$$

$$\gamma_{yz} = \frac{\partial w}{\partial y} + \frac{\partial v}{\partial z},$$

and the stress components σ_z, τ_{xz}, and τ_{yz}. The D matrix in (2.4.9) is then

$$D = \frac{E}{(1+v)(1-2v)} \times \begin{bmatrix} 1-v & v & v & 0 & 0 & 0 \\ v & 1-v & v & 0 & 0 & 0 \\ v & v & 1-v & 0 & 0 & 0 \\ 0 & 0 & 0 & \dfrac{1-2v}{2} & 0 & 0 \\ 0 & 0 & 0 & 0 & \dfrac{1-2v}{2} & 0 \\ 0 & 0 & 0 & 0 & 0 & \dfrac{1-2v}{2} \end{bmatrix}. \tag{4}$$

If the "thickness" of Ω in the z-direction is large in comparison with the representative x and y dimensions, then the normal component of strain in the z-direction ε_z and the shear strains γ_{xz} and γ_{yz} are zero and a *plane strain* condition is said to exist. On the other hand, if the thickness of Ω is small, the normal component of stress in the z-direction σ_z and the shear stresses τ_{xz} and τ_{yz} are zero and a *plane stress* condition exists.

2.5 It is not difficult to generalize the derivation presented in Section 2.5 to the case of three-dimensional flows (Bird, Stewart, and Lightfoot [1960]). The resulting system consists of a continuity equation and three momentum equations. Furthermore, it is possible to include more forces than the pressure in the momentum equations. For example, the weight of the fluid and the internal shearing force due to the fluid's viscous nature are frequently included. These matters are discussed at length in texts on the subject (e.g., Batchelor [1967] or Milne-Thomson [1955]).

Fluid dynamics provides a rich source of problems for both the theoretician and numerical analyst. The *nonlinear* nature of the governing equations makes the problems especially challenging. For a consideration of some of the theoretical aspects of fluid flow, the reader may consult the seminal work by Ladyzhenskaya [1969]; for compendia of numerical methods, see Roache [1972] or the more recent book by Peyret and Taylor [1983].

EXERCISES

2.1. If the vibrating string is damped by a force proportional to the velocity du/dt, show that the equation of motion has the form

$$u_{tt} - a^2 u_{xx} + bu_t = 0,$$

where b is a positive constant.

2.2. Verify that all functions of the form

$$F_n(x, t) \equiv \sin\frac{n\pi x}{L} \cos\frac{n\pi a t}{L}, \qquad n = 1, 2, \ldots$$

satisfy (2.2.2) and the homogeneous conditions $u(0, t) = u(L, t) = 0$, $t \geq 0$, and $u_t(x, 0) = 0$, $0 \leq x \leq L$.

2.3. Let Ω be a hollow cylinder of unit height whose inner and outer radii are a and b. Assume that the temperature at the surface $r = a$ is u_1, and at $r = b$ assume that there is radiation into a medium at temperature u_2, that is,

$$u = u_1 \quad \text{at} \quad r = a,$$

$$\frac{du}{dr} + h(u - u_2) = 0 \quad \text{at} \quad r = b.$$

Prove that the solution to the axisymmetric steady-state heat conduction equation [cf. (2.3.2)]

$$\frac{1}{r}\frac{\partial}{\partial r}\left(r\frac{\partial u}{\partial r}\right) + \frac{\partial^2 u}{\partial z^2} = 0$$

subject to the boundary conditions above is

$$u(r, z) = \frac{u_1[1 + hb \ln (b/r)] + hbu_2 \ln (r/a)}{1 + hb \ln (b/a)}.$$

2.4. Let Ω be a hollow sphere whose inner and outer radii are a and b. Assume that the temperatures at $r = a$ and $r = b$ are, respectively, u_1 and u_2. Prove that the solution to the steady-state heat conduction equation in spherical coordinates subject to these boundary conditions is

$$u(r, \theta, \phi) = \frac{au_1(b - r) + bu_2(r - a)}{r(b - a)}.$$

[*Hint:* Write (2.3.2) in spherical coordinates (r, θ, ϕ) and note that u depends only on the radius r.]

2.5. Show the 6×6 matrix D in (4) of the Notes and Remarks section reduces to the 3×3 matrix D in (2.4.10) when the plane strain condition $\varepsilon_z = \gamma_{xz} = \gamma_{yz} = 0$ is imposed.

2.6. Show that when a plane stress condition exists, the 3×3 matrix D analogous to (2.4.10) is

$$D = \frac{E}{1 - v^2}\begin{bmatrix} 1 & v & 0 \\ v & 1 & 0 \\ 0 & 0 & \dfrac{1 - v}{2} \end{bmatrix}.$$

2.7. Prove that rigid body motions (translations and rotations) are solutions of the equilibrium equations. [*Hint:* Such motions are described by

$$\delta = (a, 0)^T, \quad \delta = (0, a)^T, \quad \text{and} \quad \delta = \begin{bmatrix} \cos \theta & -\sin \theta \\ \sin \theta & \cos \theta \end{bmatrix}\begin{bmatrix} x \\ y \end{bmatrix},$$

where a and θ are constants.]

2.8. Let $\mathbf{r}$ be a 6×1 vector of constants, and $\boldsymbol{\varepsilon} = (\varepsilon_x, \varepsilon_y, \varepsilon_z, \gamma_{xy}, \gamma_{yz}, \gamma_{xz})^T$. Prove that $\boldsymbol{\varepsilon} = \mathbf{r}$ includes all rigid body motions in three dimensions. In fact, show that this state of constant strain corresponds to a displacement vector

$$\delta \equiv \begin{bmatrix} u \\ v \\ w \end{bmatrix} = \begin{bmatrix} a_1 \\ a_2 \\ a_3 \end{bmatrix} + \begin{bmatrix} r_1 & b_2 & b_1 \\ r_4 - b_2 & r_2 & c_1 \\ r_6 - b_1 & r_5 - c_1 & r_3 \end{bmatrix} \begin{bmatrix} x \\ y \\ z \end{bmatrix},$$

where $\mathbf{r} = (r_1, \ldots, r_6)^T$ and a_i, b_i, and c_i are arbitrary constants.

2.9. (a) Show that the momentum equation (2.5.2) may also be written in the form

$$\rho v_t + \rho v v_x = -p_x.$$

[*Hint:* Use (2.5.1).] Show that if the time-dependent position of a fluid particle is $x(t)$, and $v(x(t), t)$ denotes its velocity, then the equation above may be written as

$$\rho \frac{dv}{dt} = -p_x.$$

(b) Assume that the pressure is a function (only) of the density and let $c^2 = dp/d\rho$. Show that (2.5.1) may be written in the form

$$p_t + v p_x + c^2 \rho v_x = 0.$$

What are the units of c?

3

First-Order
Hyperbolic Systems

We begin our detailed analysis of the numerical solution of partial differential equations with a consideration of first-order hyperbolic systems. At first glance these may seem to have little to do with the notion of second-order scalar hyperbolic equations introduced in Chapter 2. However, in Section 3.2 we shall see that the two concepts are related in a simple but consistent manner. We deal with equations in the two independent variables x, t, which we assume are the coordinates[1] of a typical point in an open, simply connected set of points, $\Omega \subset R^2$.

3.1 CHARACTERISTICS AND NORMAL FORMS

Consider the system of first-order partial differential equations given by

$$\frac{\partial u_i}{\partial t} + \sum_{j=1}^{n} a_{ij} \frac{\partial u_j}{\partial x} = f_i, \qquad i = 1, \ldots, n, \tag{3.1.1}$$

---

[1] The x, t notation is used to suggest a point in a (one-dimensional) space-time continuum since this is frequently the physical interpretation of these variables for hyperbolic equations.

where

$$a_{ij}: \Omega \times R^n \to R, \qquad i, j = 1, \ldots, n,$$

and

$$f_i: \Omega \times R^n \to R, \qquad i = 1, \ldots, n,$$

possess Lipschitz continuous first derivatives with respect to their $n + 2$ arguments $(x, t, u_1, \ldots, u_n)$. System (3.1.1) is called a *quasilinear* system, and any set of n differentiable functions $u_i: \Omega \to R$ that reduce (3.1.1) to an identity in x and t is termed a *solution*. In the special case when the a_{ij} are independent of $u_1, \ldots, u_n$, we say that (3.1.1) is *semilinear*. A *linear* system results when this situation also applies to the f_i.

We wish to put (3.1.1) into a simpler form by defining curves in the xt-plane, say $x = x_i(t), i = 1, \ldots, n$, along which suitable linear combinations of the differential expressions,

$$\frac{\partial u_i}{\partial t} + \sum_{j=1}^{n} a_{ij} \frac{\partial u_j}{\partial x}, \qquad i = 1, \ldots, n,$$

reduce to total derivatives. To this end we introduce the matrix $A \equiv [a_{ij}]$ and the vectors

$$\mathbf{u} \equiv (u_1, \ldots, u_n)^T,$$

$$\mathbf{u}_t \equiv \left(\frac{\partial u_1}{\partial t}, \ldots, \frac{\partial u_n}{\partial t} \right)^T,$$

$$\mathbf{u}_x \equiv \left(\frac{\partial u_1}{\partial x}, \ldots, \frac{\partial u_n}{\partial x} \right)^T,$$

and

$$\mathbf{f} \equiv (f_1, \ldots, f_n)^T.$$

Then we may write (3.1.1) as

$$\mathbf{u}_t + A\mathbf{u}_x = \mathbf{f}. \tag{3.1.2}$$

Let $\mathbf{u}(x, t)$ be a solution of (3.1.1), and suppose that for $(x, t) \in \Omega$, $\lambda_i(x, t, \mathbf{u}(x, t))$ is a real eigenvalue of A with corresponding left eigenvector $\mathbf{v}_i = (v_{i1}, \ldots, v_{in})^T$. Then

$$\mathbf{v}_i^T A = \lambda_i \mathbf{v}_i^T,$$

and it follows that

$$\mathbf{v}_i^T \mathbf{u}_t + \mathbf{v}_i^T A \mathbf{u}_x = \mathbf{v}_i^T \mathbf{f}$$

or

$$\mathbf{v}_i^T (\mathbf{u}_t + \lambda_i \mathbf{u}_x) = \tilde{g}_i,$$

where $\tilde{g}_i = \mathbf{v}_i^T \mathbf{f}$. In terms of individual components this becomes

$$\sum_{j=1}^{n} v_{ij} \left(\frac{\partial u_j}{\partial t} + \lambda_i \frac{\partial u_j}{\partial x} \right) = \tilde{g}_i. \tag{3.1.3}$$

Now suppose that $x_i(t)$ is a solution of the *ordinary* differential equation

$$\frac{dx}{dt} = \lambda_i(x, t, \mathbf{u}(x, t)). \tag{3.1.4}$$

Then along $x = x_i(t)$ we have

$$\frac{d}{dt} u_j(x, t) = \frac{\partial u_j}{\partial x} \frac{dx}{dt} + \frac{\partial u_j}{\partial t} = \frac{\partial u_j}{\partial t} + \lambda_i \frac{\partial u_j}{\partial x},$$

so that by (3.1.3)

$$\sum_{j=1}^{n} v_{ij} \frac{du_j}{dt} = \tilde{g}_i. \tag{3.1.5}$$

If we take into account the "constant of integration," (3.1.4) actually defines a one-parameter family of solution curves. Each such curve is called a *characteristic* of (3.1.1). In view of (3.1.5) we see that along each characteristic the system (3.1.1) yields an equation in which the individual differential expressions have been replaced by total derivatives. We shall use this fact later to define several methods for the numerical integration of (3.1.1).

We have seen that each real eigenvalue of A gives rise to a characteristic. In the event that the eigenvalues of A are all real and distinct at a point $(x, t, \mathbf{u}) \in \Omega \times R^n$, we say that the system (3.1.1) is *hyperbolic* for $\mathbf{u}$ at (x, t). Throughout this chapter we assume that (3.1.1) is hyperbolic for every $\mathbf{u} \in R^n$ at all points of Ω. Thus, corresponding to any solution of (3.1.1), there are n distinct characteristics passing through each point of Ω. Moreover, the original system may be replaced by n equations of the form (3.1.3) or (3.1.5). These equations are known respectively as the *first* and *second normal forms* of (3.1.1). The tangent vectors of the characteristics through (x, t) define n distinct *characteristic directions* at (x, t). It is clear that the vector $(\lambda_i, 1)^T$ is a characteristic direction at (x, t) of the characteristic satisfying (3.1.4).

As an illustration of these ideas we consider a model describing the flow of a gas in a long thin tube. If x denotes position along the tube measured from a fixed origin, if t denotes time, and if we neglect the change in the internal energy of the gas, the relevant differential equations are[2] (see Section 2.5 and Exercise 2.9)

$$\begin{aligned} p_t + v p_x + c^2 \rho v_x &- 0, \\ \rho(v_t + v v_x) + p_x &= 0. \end{aligned} \tag{3.1.6}$$

Here p, v, and ρ are the gas pressure, axial velocity, and density, respectively, and $c^2 = dp/d\rho$ is the (local) speed of sound in the gas. To close the system, a further relation known as an *equation of state* is required. For purposes of illustration we assume an equation of state of the form

$$p = \rho K, \tag{3.1.7}$$

---

[2] These equations are sometimes referred to as the equations of *isentropic compressible* flow.

where K = constant > 0. Obviously, we can use (3.1.7) to eliminate either p or ρ from (3.1.6), but it is instructive to proceed without doing so.

The vector form (3.1.2) of (3.1.6) results by letting

$$\mathbf{u} = (p, v)^T, \qquad \mathbf{f} = (0, 0)^T,$$

and

$$A = \begin{bmatrix} v & \rho c^2 \\ \dfrac{1}{\rho} & v \end{bmatrix}.$$

An easy computation shows that the eigenvalues of A are $\lambda_1 = v + c$ and $\lambda_2 = v - c$. Thus the system is everywhere hyperbolic.

It is also not difficult to see that $(1, \rho c)^T$ and $(1, -\rho c)^T$ are left eigenvectors corresponding to λ_1 and λ_2, respectively. Hence the second normal forms (3.1.5) are

$$\frac{dp}{dt} + \rho c \frac{dv}{dt} = 0 \tag{3.1.8}$$

and

$$\frac{dp}{dt} - \rho c \frac{dv}{dt} = 0. \tag{3.1.9}$$

Note that (3.1.8) and (3.1.9) are not ordinary differential equations in the usual sense. Equation (3.1.8) holds only along a characteristic with slope $v + c$, while (3.1.9) holds on a characteristic with slope $v - c$.

Information about the physical system (in the form of the states of p, v, and ρ) is transmitted through the space-time domain along the characteristics. If the flow is *subsonic*, then $|v| < c$. Hence $v + c > 0$, $v - c < 0$, and at each point (x, t) one of the characteristics faces forward while the other faces backward (Figure 3.1.1a). This means that at a given time t the state of the fluid on *both* sides of any position x influences its future state there. In the case of *supersonic* flow, $v > c$. Now both characteristics are forward facing (Figure 3.1.1b), and the future state of the fluid at a point in the tube is influenced only by its current upstream state.

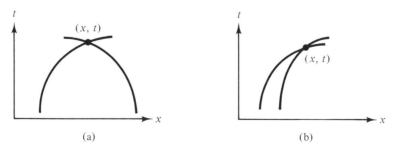

Figure 3.1.1   Forward- and backward-facing characteristics.

It has already been mentioned that characteristics and normal forms are useful in the numerical solution of hyperbolic systems. Indeed, if the system is particularly simple, such an approach can provide an exact solution.

Consider, for example, the scalar *convection* equation,

$$u_t + cu_x = 0, \tag{3.1.10}$$

where c is a constant. In this case there is a single characteristic $x = x(t)$ satisfying $dx/dt = c$. The solution of this equation is

$$x(t) - x(0) = ct \tag{3.1.11}$$

and the associated second normal form is simply $du/dt = 0$. This last equation implies that u is constant along the characteristic (3.1.11). Therefore, if we also require that $u(x, 0) = f(x)$, where f is a given differentiable function, then along the characteristic

$$u(x, t) = u(x(t), t) = u(x(0), 0) = f(x(0)) = f(x(t) - ct) = f(x - ct). \tag{3.1.12}$$

Equation (3.1.12) shows that the solution of (3.1.10) is a *traveling wave*. In other words, the solution at any time t is obtained by translating the "wave form" $f(x)$ a distance ct along the x-axis (Figure 3.1.2). The constant c may be interpreted as the wave velocity.

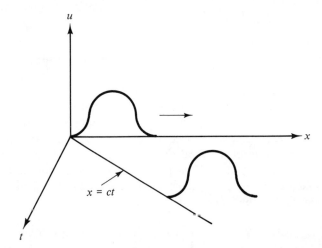

Figure 3.1.2   Traveling wave ($c > 0$).

3.2 RELATION TO SECOND-ORDER EQUATIONS

In this section we examine the scalar second-order linear equation

$$au_{tt} + 2bu_{xt} + cu_{xx} = d, \tag{3.2.1}$$

where the functions a, b, c, and d are assumed to be Lipschitz continuously differentiable in Ω and $a \neq 0$ there. According to the classification scheme presented in Section 2.1, (3.2.1) is hyperbolic at (x, t) if $ac - b^2 < 0$, and it is natural to ask how this notion of hyperbolicity is related to that of Section 3.1.

To write (3.2.1) as a system, we let $u_1 = u_t$ and $u_2 = u_x$. Then (3.2.1) is equivalent to

$$\begin{bmatrix} a & b \\ 0 & 1 \end{bmatrix} \mathbf{u}_t + \begin{bmatrix} b & c \\ -1 & 0 \end{bmatrix} \mathbf{u}_x = \mathbf{f}, \tag{3.2.2}$$

where $\mathbf{u} = (u_1, u_2)^T$ and $\mathbf{f} = (d, 0)^T$. Since $du = u_t\, dt + u_x\, dx$, the solution u is given by the formula

$$\begin{aligned} u(x, t) &= u(x^*, t^*) + \int_\gamma du \\ &= u(x^*, t^*) + \int_\gamma (u_1\, dt + u_2\, dx). \end{aligned} \tag{3.2.3}$$

Here (x^*, t^*) is a fixed point in Ω and γ is any convenient curve in Ω connecting (x, t) to (x^*, t^*).

The characteristics and normal forms of (3.2.2) are defined by the eigenvalues and left eigenvectors of the matrix

$$A = \begin{bmatrix} a & b \\ 0 & 1 \end{bmatrix}^{-1} \begin{bmatrix} b & c \\ -1 & 0 \end{bmatrix} = \begin{bmatrix} \dfrac{2b}{a} & \dfrac{c}{a} \\ -1 & 0 \end{bmatrix}.$$

Thus the eigenvalues are the roots of the quadratic

$$\lambda^2 - \frac{2b}{a}\lambda + \frac{c}{a} = 0,$$

which are $[b \pm (b^2 - ac)^{1/2}]/a$. It follows that (3.2.2) is a hyperbolic system if $ac - b^2 < 0$, that is, (3.2.1) is hyperbolic in the sense of Section 2.1.

The wave equation (cf. Section 2.2)

$$u_{tt} - u_{xx} = 0 \tag{3.2.4}$$

provides a simple example of a hyperbolic equation having the form (3.2.1). The characteristics are defined by the equations $dx/dt = \pm 1$. Thus they are given by

$$x(t) - x(0) = t \tag{3.2.5}$$

and

$$x(t) - x(0) = -t. \tag{3.2.6}$$

The corresponding second normal forms are

$$\frac{du_1}{dt} - \frac{du_2}{dt} = 0 \quad \text{and} \quad \frac{du_1}{dt} + \frac{du_2}{dt} = 0$$

or

$$\frac{d}{dt}(u_1 - u_2) = 0 \quad \text{and} \quad \frac{d}{dt}(u_1 + u_2) = 0.$$

Proceeding as in Section 3.1, we see that if $u_1(x, 0) = P(x)$ and $u_2(x, 0) = Q(x)$, then

$$u_1(x, t) - u_2(x, t) = P(x - t) - Q(x - t) \tag{3.2.7}$$

and

$$u_1(x, t) + u_2(x, t) = P(x + t) + Q(x + t). \tag{3.2.8}$$

Solving (3.2.7) and (3.2.8) for u_1 and u_2, we obtain

$$u_1(x, t) = \frac{P(x + t) + P(x - t)}{2} + \frac{Q(x + t) - Q(x - t)}{2},$$

$$u_2(x, t) = \frac{P(x + t) - P(x - t)}{2} + \frac{Q(x + t) + Q(x - t)}{2}.$$

The solution u may now be recovered from (3.2.3).

Suppose, for example, that (3.2.4) is to hold for $t > 0$, while for $t = 0$,

$$u(x, 0) = f(x) \quad \text{and} \quad u_t(x, 0) = g(x). \tag{3.2.9}$$

Setting $(x^*, t^*) = (0, 0)$ and choosing γ to be the step shown in Figure 3.2.1, we have

$$u(x, t) = f(0) + \tfrac{1}{2} \int_0^t [g(x + t) + g(x - t) + f'(x + t) - f'(x - t)] \, dt + \int_0^x f'(x) \, dx$$

$$= \tfrac{1}{2}[f(x + t) + f(x - t)] + \tfrac{1}{2} \int_{x-t}^{x+t} g(s) \, ds.$$

This is known as *d'Alembert's solution* of the wave equation. Notice that if $g(x) \equiv 0$, the solution is composed of two traveling waves moving with unit speeds in opposite directions.

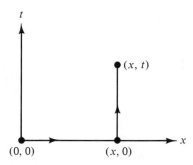

Figure 3.2.1   Step path.

3.3 INITIAL VALUE PROBLEMS FOR HYPERBOLIC SYSTEMS

The general solution of system (3.1.1) involves arbitrary functions that are the analogues of the integration constants of ordinary differential equations. To determine these functions it is necessary to append to (3.1.1) another requirement, known as an initial condition. Usually, one wishes to specify the initial condition so that the resulting initial value problem is *well posed*. Loosely speaking, this means that the problem has a unique solution for each initial condition in a sufficiently large class of such conditions and, moreover, this solution changes only slightly when the corresponding initial condition changes slightly.[3]

For a hyperbolic system of the form (3.1.1) the simplest initial condition that produces a well-posed problem consists of prescribing as initial data the functions $u_j(x, t)$ on some curve Γ which is "nowhere characteristic"; that is, no tangent direction of Γ is a characteristic direction of (3.1.1). In this case, if the initial data have Lipschitz continuous first derivatives, it can be shown (Courant and Hilbert [1962]) that the initial value problem has a unique, continuously differentiable solution in a strip adjacent to Γ.

With reference to Figure 3.3.1, we see that the solution of an initial value problem at a given point P depends only on the initial data on the arc QR of Γ cut by the two extreme characteristics of (3.1.1) that pass through P. We call QR the *analytic interval of dependence* of the point P.

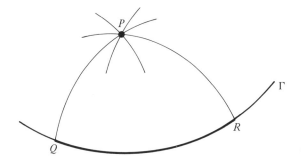

Figure 3.3.1 Analytic interval of dependence.

What happens if the initial curve Γ is part of a characteristic of (3.1.1)? In the first place, the problem cannot have a solution unless the initial data satisfy a compatibility condition of the form (3.1.5). Thus the data cannot be specified arbitrarily. Furthermore, if it is compatibly chosen, the resulting initial value problem cannot have a unique solution. To see this, observe that a point P not on the initial curve Γ can be connected to Γ by at most $n - 1$ characteristics. This follows from the uniqueness of solutions of the initial value problem (3.1.4); that is, no other characteristic in the family containing Γ can intersect Γ. Thus the initial data cannot influence the form of the solution on the "missing characteristic" and so leave its value at P indeterminate.

---

[3] We will make the notion of well-posedness more precise in Chapter 5.

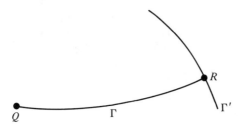

Figure 3.3.2 Nonuniqueness of solutions.

This is particularly apparent in the case of a single equation ($n = 1$). As shown in Figure 3.3.2, we assume that Γ is the characteristic arc QR and we let Γ' be a nowhere-characteristic arc through R. Since the partial differential equation reduces to an ordinary differential equation (i.e., its second normal form) on Γ, its solution is completely determined by its value at R. Thus, by varying the data everywhere on Γ' except at R, we obtain different solutions of the partial differential equation each of which assumes the *same* values on Γ. This observation can be used to give explicit constructions of multiple solutions of scalar first-order initial value problems when Γ is a characteristic (Exercise 3.5). For an example of nonuniqueness involving the wave equation (3.2.4) and a characteristic initial curve, see Smith [1978].

If (3.1.1) is linear, it can be shown (Courant and Hilbert [1962]) that a continuous solution **u** can be continued in a global manner away from Γ as long as the functions a_{ij} and f_i and the initial data retain their assumed smoothness properties. However, in the case of a genuine quasilinear hyperbolic system, it is possible for the solution of an initial value problem with *smooth* initial data to develop discontinuities away from the initial curve. (Note that this does not contradict the existence theorem cited earlier since this theorem says nothing about the size of the strip where the continuously differentiable solution exists.) These discontinuities, called *shocks*, are confined to curves (*shock lines*) in the x, t plane. The curves themselves form an additional unknown component of the problem and in principle require auxiliary conditions for their determination. The presence of shocks in an initial value problem complicates its numerical solution, and our investigations are most appropriate for solutions that are shock free. The reader is referred to the Notes and Remarks section for some references on numerical algorithms designed specifically for problems involving shocks.

3.4 NUMERICAL SOLUTION OF INITIAL VALUE PROBLEMS FOR HYPERBOLIC SYSTEMS

In this section we present two methods for the numerical solution of initial value problems involving the hyperbolic system (3.1.1). Although both methods can be formulated so as to accommodate general initial curves Γ, we assume for simplicity that Γ is an interval (possibly infinite) of the x-axis. Given that the initial value problem is well posed, we are concerned with the approximation of its solution in some region of the half-plane $t > 0$.

Each of the methods utilizes a rectangular mesh with spacings Δx and Δt. The approximate solution is then determined on a set of mesh points of the form $P_{jm} = (x_j, t_m)$, where $x_j = a + j\,\Delta x$, $a = $ constant, $j = 0, \pm 1, \ldots$, and $t_m = m\,\Delta t$, $m = 0, 1, \ldots$.

3.4.1 Integration along Characteristics

This technique is a variant of a method due to Massau [1899]. It requires that we know the characteristic slopes λ_i and the second normal forms (3.1.5).

Assuming that the approximate solution, $U_i(P_{jm})$, $i = 1, \ldots, n$, is known on the line $t = t_m$, we obtain $U_i(P_{j,m+1})$ by first numerically integrating each characteristic equation (3.1.4) backward from the point $P_{j,m+1}$ to some point $Q_i = (x(Q_i), t_m)$ using the difference formula,

$$\frac{x(P_{j,m+1}) - x(Q_i)}{\Delta t} = \lambda_i(Q_i). \qquad (3.4.1)$$

Here we have written $\lambda_i(Q_i)$ for $\lambda_i(Q_i, U_1(Q_i), \ldots, U_n(Q_i))$. If we define the values of the U_i at nonmesh points by interpolation (on the line $t = 0$, these values are given exactly by the initial data), then (3.4.1) is an equation (generally nonlinear) for the unknown abscissa $x(Q_i)$ (see Figure 3.4.1).

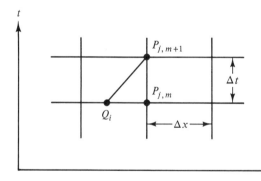

Figure 3.4.1 Mesh and approximate characteristic.

Assuming that each such equation can be solved for its unknown (in this connection see Exercise 3.8), we then numerically integrate the equations (3.1.5) along their respective approximate characteristics by means of the analogues,

$$\sum_{k=1}^{n} v_{ik}(P_{jm}) \frac{U_k(P_{j,m+1}) - U_k(Q_i)}{\Delta t} = \tilde{g}_i(Q_i), \qquad i = 1, \ldots, n. \qquad (3.4.2)$$

Here the notation $v_{ik}(P_{jm})$ and $\tilde{g}_i(Q_i)$ follows the convention established earlier for $\lambda_i(Q_i)$. Equations (3.4.2) form a linear system for the unknown approximations, $U_i(P_{j,m+1})$, $i = 1, \ldots, n$. Since the vectors $\mathbf{v}_i^T(P_{jm})$ are linearly independent, this system has a unique solution.

Sauer [1952] has considered a similar method for the case $n = 2$ and has proven that the approximations converge to the exact solution as Δx, $\Delta t \to 0$. Indeed, since the method involves only *ordinary differential equations*, a convergence analysis could presumably be fashioned along the lines of those found in the study of initial value problems for ordinary differential equations (see, e.g., Gear [1971a]). We do not follow such a course here, preferring instead to focus our attention on a method that numerically integrates the first normal forms (3.1.3) without explicitly attempting to follow the characteristics.

3.4.2 The Courant–Isaacson–Rees (CIR) Method

This method was first presented and analyzed by Courant, Isaacson, and Rees [1952]. Although there are more elaborate methods of greater accuracy for special kinds of hyperbolic equations, the CIR method is both easy to formulate and applicable to general initial value problems. Furthermore, it clearly illustrates the basic requirements of a successful numerical method for the solution of hyperbolic initial value problems.

The CIR method again utilizes normal forms of (3.1.1), this time the first normal forms (3.1.3). Using the notation of Section 3.1, we write these as

$$\mathbf{v}_i^T(\mathbf{u}_t + \lambda_i \mathbf{u}_x) = \tilde{g}_i, \qquad i = 1, \ldots, n. \tag{3.4.3}$$

We denote the approximate solution at mesh point (x_j, t_m) by the vector $\mathbf{U}_j^m$. Assuming that the $\mathbf{U}_j^m$ are known on the line $t = t_m$ (for $m = 0$, they are again given by the initial data), we obtain $\mathbf{U}_j^{m+1}$ as the solution of the linear difference equations,

$$(\mathbf{v}_{ij}^m)^T \left\{ \frac{\mathbf{U}_j^{m+1} - \mathbf{U}_j^m}{\Delta t} + \frac{\lambda_{ij}^m}{\Delta x} \begin{bmatrix} \mathbf{U}_j^m - \mathbf{U}_{j-1}^m \\ \mathbf{U}_{j+1}^m - \mathbf{U}_j^m \end{bmatrix} \right\} = \tilde{g}_{ij}^m, \qquad i = 1, \ldots, n. \tag{3.4.4}$$

The notation $(\mathbf{v}_{ij}^m)^T$, λ_{ij}^m, and $\tilde{g}_{ij}^m$ in (3.4.4) means that $\mathbf{v}_i^T$, λ_i, and $\tilde{g}_i$ are evaluated at $(x_j, t_m, \mathbf{U}_j^m)$. Furthermore, the upper or lower line within the brackets is to be used as $\lambda_{ij}^m \geq 0$ or $\lambda_{ij}^m < 0$. This idea of employing the sign of the coefficient to determine the direction in which a derivative is differenced has already been encountered in Chapter 1, where it was termed *upwind* differencing. It is a commonly employed technique in fluid dynamics calculations (Roache [1972]). Notice that (3.4.4) may be uniquely solved for $\mathbf{U}_j^{m+1}$ since the rows of its coefficient matrix are again linearly independent vectors.

Although it is possible to establish convergence of the approximate solution when (3.1.2) is genuinely quasilinear (Courant, Isaacson, and Rees [1952], Forsythe and Wasow [1960]), the proof simplifies considerably in the linear case. Therefore, to present the essential ideas of the proof without the added technical difficulties caused by the nonlinearities, we limit ourselves to systems (3.1.1) that are linear.

We begin by putting (3.4.4) in a form more suitable for analysis. Let $\lambda_i^+ = \max(\lambda_i, 0)$, $\lambda_i^- = \max(-\lambda_i, 0)$, and $r = \Delta t / \Delta x$. Then (3.4.4) becomes

$$(\mathbf{v}_{ij}^m)^T \{ \mathbf{U}_j^{m+1} - \mathbf{U}_j^m + r[\lambda_{ij}^m | \mathbf{U}_j^m - \lambda_{ij}^{+m} \mathbf{U}_{j-1}^m - \lambda_{ij}^{-m} \mathbf{U}_{j+1}^m] \} = \Delta t \, \tilde{g}_{ij}^m, \qquad i = 1, \ldots, n.$$

Defining the vector

$$\tilde{\mathbf{g}} \equiv \Delta t \, (\tilde{g}_1, \ldots, \tilde{g}_n)^T,$$

and the matrices

$$M \equiv \begin{bmatrix} \mathbf{v}_1^T \\ \cdots \\ \mathbf{v}_n^T \end{bmatrix},$$

$$\Lambda^{\pm} \equiv \text{Diag}(\lambda_i^{\pm}),$$

and

$$|\Lambda| \equiv \text{Diag}(|\lambda_i|) = \Lambda^+ + \Lambda^-,$$

we see that this in turn may be written as

$$M_j^m \mathbf{U}_j^{m+1} = (I - r|\Lambda_j^m|)M_j^m \mathbf{U}_j^m + r\Lambda_j^{+m} M_j^m \mathbf{U}_{j-1}^m + r\Lambda_j^{-m} M_j^m \mathbf{U}_{j+1}^m + \tilde{\mathbf{g}}_j^m, \qquad (3.4.5)$$

where I is the identity matrix and the subscript–superscript notation on M, Λ^+, and so on, means that these are evaluated at the point (x_j, t_m).

Next we define the *discretization errors*,

$$\mathbf{e}_j^m \equiv \mathbf{U}_j^m - \mathbf{u}(x_j, t_m),$$

and the *local truncation errors*,

$$\tau_j^m \equiv (I - r|\Lambda_j^m|)M_j^m \mathbf{u}(x_j, t_m) + r\Lambda_j^{+m} M_j^m \mathbf{u}(x_{j-1}, t_m)$$
$$+ r\Lambda_j^{-m} M_j^m \mathbf{u}(x_{j+1}, t_m) + \tilde{\mathbf{g}}_j^m - M_j^m \mathbf{u}(x_j, t_{m+1}), \qquad (3.4.6)$$

where $\mathbf{u}(x, t)$ is the exact solution of the initial value problem. Note that τ_j^m is just the residual when the exact solution is substituted into the difference equation (3.4.4). We wish, of course, to estimate the size of the $\mathbf{e}_j^m$ and in particular to show that these errors go to zero with Δx and Δt.

To carry out this plan, we need some regularity conditions on the elements of matrix M. If $\|\cdot\|_{\infty}$ denotes the usual vector (and matrix) infinity norm, we assume that there are constants K and L such that

1. $\|M(P)\|_{\infty}, \|M^{-1}(P)\|_{\infty} \leq K$,

2. $\|M(P) - M(Q)\|_{\infty} \leq L\|P - Q\|_{\infty}$ for *all* $P, Q \in \Omega$.

Finally, we require a *stability condition* on the mesh ratio r. This places a restriction on the manner in which the mesh spacings Δx and Δt are allowed to go to zero. Specifically, we assume that if

$$\lambda \equiv \sup_{P \in \Omega} \left(\max_{1 \leq i \leq n} |\lambda_i(P)| \right),$$

then $\lambda < \infty$ and

$$\lambda r \leq 1. \qquad (3.4.7)$$

In this form, (3.4.7) is known as a *C-F-L condition* after Courant, Friedrichs, and Lewy [1928], who first considered the implications of such an inequality.

We now establish an estimate of the size of the discretization errors.

Theorem 3.4.1.   *Let* Ω *be contained in the strip* $0 \le t \le T$. *Let* $\mathbf{u}(x, t)$ *be the solution of* (3.4.3), *let* $\mathbf{U}_j^{m+1}$ *be the solution of* (3.4.4), *and let* $\mathbf{e}_j^m = \mathbf{U}_j^m - \mathbf{u}(x_j, t_m)$. *If the mesh ratio* $r \ge r_0 > 0$ *and satisfies* (3.4.7), *then there is a constant* C *such that*

$$\max_j \|\mathbf{e}_j^m\|_\infty \le C \left(\max_j \|\mathbf{e}_j^0\|_\infty + \frac{1}{\Delta t} \max_{j,m} \|\boldsymbol{\tau}_j^m\|_\infty \right). \tag{3.4.8}$$

Proof.   We subtract (3.4.6) from (3.4.5) to obtain an equation for the error $\mathbf{e}_j^m$, namely

$$M_j^m \mathbf{e}_j^{m+1} = (I - r|\Lambda_j^m|)M_j^m \mathbf{e}_j^m + r\Lambda_j^{+m} M_j^m \mathbf{e}_{j-1}^m + r\Lambda_j^{-m} M_j^m \mathbf{e}_{j+1}^m + \boldsymbol{\tau}_j^m. \tag{3.4.9}$$

If we let $\mathbf{E}_j^{m+1} = M_j^m \mathbf{e}_j^{m+1}$, we may convert (3.4.9) to an equation for the transformed errors E_j^m. Thus

$$\mathbf{E}_j^{m+1} = (I - r|\Lambda_j^m|)(M_j^m - M_j^{m-1} + M_j^{m-1})\mathbf{e}_j^m + r\Lambda_j^{+m}(M_j^m - M_{j-1}^{m-1} + M_{j-1}^{m-1})\mathbf{e}_{j-1}^m$$
$$+ r\Lambda_j^{-m}(M_j^m - M_{j+1}^{m-1} + M_{j+1}^{m-1})\mathbf{e}_{j+1}^m + \boldsymbol{\tau}_j^m,$$

or

$$\mathbf{E}_j^{m+1} = (I - r|\Lambda_j^m|)\mathbf{E}_j^m + r\Lambda_j^{+m}\mathbf{E}_{j-1}^m + r\Lambda_j^{-m}\mathbf{E}_{j+1}^m + \boldsymbol{\tau}_j^m + \mathbf{R}_1 + \mathbf{R}_2 + \mathbf{R}_3, \tag{3.4.10}$$

where

$$\mathbf{R}_1 \equiv (I - r|\Lambda_j^m|)(M_j^m - M_j^{m-1})(M_j^{m-1})^{-1}\mathbf{E}_j^m,$$
$$\mathbf{R}_2 \equiv r\Lambda_j^{+m}(M_j^m - M_{j-1}^{m-1})(M_{j-1}^{m-1})^{-1}\mathbf{E}_{j-1}^m,$$

and

$$\mathbf{R}_3 \equiv r\Lambda_j^{-m}(M_j^m - M_{j+1}^{m-1})(M_{j+1}^{m-1})^{-1}\mathbf{E}_{j+1}^m.$$

Considering the ith component of (3.4.10), we find that

$$|E_{ij}^{m+1}| \le |(1 - r|\lambda_{ij}^m|)| |E_{ij}^m| + r\lambda_{ij}^{+m}|E_{i,j-1}^m| + r\lambda_{ij}^{-m}|E_{i,j+1}^m| + \|\boldsymbol{\tau}_j^m\|_\infty + \sum_{k=1}^3 \|\mathbf{R}_k\|_\infty.$$

But (3.4.7) implies that $1 - r|\lambda_{ij}^m| \ge 0$. Therefore, upon noting that $|\lambda_{ij}^m| = \lambda_{ij}^{+m} + \lambda_{ij}^{-m}$, we have

$$|E_{ij}^{m+1}| \le [1 - r(\lambda_{ij}^{+m} + \lambda_{ij}^{-m})]\|\mathbf{E}_j^m\|_\infty + r\lambda_{ij}^{+m}\|\mathbf{E}_{j-1}^m\|_\infty$$
$$+ r\lambda_{ij}^{-m}\|\mathbf{E}_{j+1}^m\|_\infty + \|\boldsymbol{\tau}_j^m\|_\infty + \sum_{k=1}^3 \|\mathbf{R}_k\|_\infty. \tag{3.4.11}$$

The regularity conditions on M yield the inequalities

$$\|\mathbf{R}_1\|_\infty \le KL\,\Delta t\,\|\mathbf{E}_j^m\|_\infty,$$
$$\|\mathbf{R}_2\|_\infty \le KL \max(\Delta x, \Delta t)\|\mathbf{E}_{j-1}^m\|_\infty,$$

and

$$\|\mathbf{R}_3\|_\infty \le KL \max(\Delta x, \Delta t)\|\mathbf{E}_{j+1}^m\|_\infty.$$

Thus if we let

$$E^m = \max_{j} \left\| \mathbf{E}_j^m \right\|_\infty \quad \text{and} \quad \tau = \max_{j,m} \left\| \boldsymbol{\tau}_j^m \right\|_\infty,$$

and observe that

$$\max (\Delta x, \Delta t) = \Delta t \max \left(\frac{1}{r}, 1 \right) \leq \Delta t \left(1 + \frac{1}{r_0} \right),$$

it follows from (3.4.11) that

$$\left| E_{ij}^{m+1} \right| \leq E^m + \tau + KL \left(3 + \frac{2}{r_0} \right) \Delta t \, E^m.$$

Letting $c_0 = KL(3 + 2/r_0)$, we write this as

$$\left| E_{ij}^{m+1} \right| \leq (1 + c_0 \, \Delta t) E^m + \tau.$$

But the right side of this inequality is independent of i and j. Hence

$$E^{m+1} \leq (1 + c_0 \, \Delta t) E^m + \tau \leq e^{c_0 \Delta t} E^m + \tau.$$

Repeated application of this inequality now gives

$$E^m \leq e^{c_0 m \, \Delta t} E^0 + \tau (1 + e^{c_0 \Delta t} + \cdots + e^{c_0 (m-1) \Delta t})$$

$$= e^{c_0 m \, \Delta t} E^0 + \frac{\tau (e^{c_0 m \, \Delta t} - 1)}{e^{c_0 \Delta t} - 1}$$

and since Ω is contained in the strip $0 \leq t \leq T$, we have

$$E^m \leq e^{c_0 T} E^0 + \frac{\tau (e^{c_0 T} - 1)}{e^{c_0 \Delta t} - 1} \leq e^{c_0 T} E^0 + \frac{\tau}{\Delta t} \frac{e^{c_0 T} - 1}{c_0}. \tag{3.4.12}$$

Finally, since

$$\max_{j} \left\| \mathbf{e}_j^m \right\|_\infty \leq K E^m \quad \text{and} \quad E^m \leq K \max_{j} \left\| \mathbf{e}_j^m \right\|_\infty,$$

(3.4.8) follows from (3.4.12) with

$$C = \max \left(K^2 e^{c_0 T}, K \frac{e^{c_0 T} - 1}{c_0} \right).$$

Q.E.D.

Theorem 3.4.1 has as an immediate corollary the following result on the convergence of the approximations.

Corollary 3.4.2. *Under the hypotheses of Theorem 3.4.1, if the solution* $\mathbf{u}(x, t)$ *of the initial value problem has bounded second partial derivatives in* Ω *and if* $\mathbf{U}_j^0 = \mathbf{u}(x_j, 0)$, *the discretization error* $\mathbf{e}_j^m = O(\Delta t)$ *as* $\Delta t \to 0$.

The proof of the corollary is left as Exercise 3.11.

The success of the CIR method depends crucially on the ability to ensure the C-F-L stability condition (3.4.7). However, it is generally difficult (or impossible) to determine the quantity λ appearing there. Thus, in practice, (3.4.7) is replaced by the less restrictive condition,

$$\Delta t_m \leq \frac{\Delta x}{\max_{i,j} |\lambda_{ij}^m|}, \tag{3.4.13}$$

and this is used to select Δt_m, the step size for the calculations on level $m + 1$. Note that if (3.4.13) is enforced, we cannot guarantee that the spacing in the t direction will be constant. Since λ_{ij}^m is usually only an estimate of λ_i at (x_j, t_m), a reasonable way to use (3.4.13) is to set

$$\Delta t_m = \min \left(\Delta t, \frac{\theta \, \Delta x}{\max_{i,j} |\lambda_{ij}^m|} \right),$$

where Δt is the desired step size and θ is a constant in the interval $(0, 1]$.

Example 3.4.1

We apply the CIR method to the gas dynamics equations (3.1.6) and (3.1.7). The data for this application are

$$K = c^2 = 1.12225 \times 10^5,$$

$$v(x, 0) = 0,$$

and

$$p(x, 0) = \begin{cases} 7200 & \text{if } |x| \leq 0.1 \\ 7000 & \text{otherwise.} \end{cases}$$

The units of v, p, and ρ are meters/second, newtons/meter^2, and kilograms/meter^3, respectively.

From the discussion following (3.1.6), it follows that the first normal forms are

$$\left(1, \frac{p}{c} \right) \begin{bmatrix} p_t + (v + c)p_x \\ v_t + (v + c)v_x \end{bmatrix} = 0,$$

and

$$\left(1, -\frac{p}{c} \right) \begin{bmatrix} p_t + (v - c)p_x \\ v_t + (v - c)v_x \end{bmatrix} = 0.$$

Therefore, the CIR difference equations become

$$\left(1, \frac{p_j^m}{c} \right) \begin{bmatrix} \dfrac{p_j^{m+1} - p_j^m}{\Delta t} + \dfrac{v_j^m + c}{\Delta x} \begin{bmatrix} p_j^m - p_{j-1}^m \\ p_{j+1}^m - p_j^m \end{bmatrix} \\ \dfrac{v_j^{m+1} - v_j^m}{\Delta t} + \dfrac{v_j^m + c}{\Delta x} \begin{bmatrix} v_j^m - v_{j-1}^m \\ v_{j+1}^m - v_j^m \end{bmatrix} \end{bmatrix} = 0$$

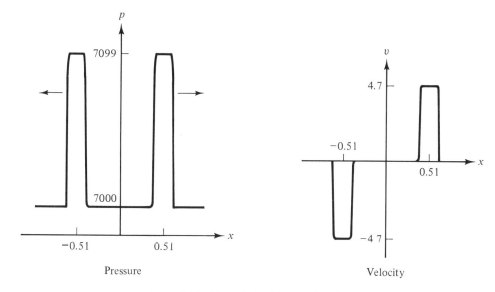

Figure 3.4.2   Numerical solution at 0.0015 sec.

and

$$
\left(1, -\frac{p_j^m}{c}\right)
\begin{bmatrix}
\dfrac{p_j^{m+1} - p_j^m}{\Delta t} + \dfrac{v_j^m - c}{\Delta x}\begin{bmatrix} p_j^m - p_{j-1}^m \\ p_{j+1}^m - p_j^m \end{bmatrix} \\[2ex]
\dfrac{v_j^{m+1} - v_j^m}{\Delta t} + \dfrac{v_j^m - c}{\Delta x}\begin{bmatrix} v_j^m - v_{j-1}^m \\ v_{j+1}^m - v_j^m \end{bmatrix}
\end{bmatrix} = 0.
$$

We present a graphical representation of the numerical solution at 0.0015 sec in Figure 3.4.2. For this solution we chose $\Delta x = 0.005$ m. From the figure we see that the initial pressure pulse has decreased in intensity by about 1.4% and is propagating in opposite directions at approximately $0.51/0.0015 \approx 337$ m/sec. This is very close to the speed of sound c (335 m/sec). Note that although the pressure pulse propagates at about the speed of sound, the velocity of the gas is, by comparison, quite small (i.e., ≈ 4.7 m/sec). Under these circumstances, we may approximate (3.1.6) by omitting the nonlinear "convection" terms, vp_x and $\rho v v_x$. The result is a linear system from which the traveling-wave nature of the solution shown in Figure 3.4.2 may be readily inferred (see Exercise 3.3).

3.5 THE NUMERICAL INTERVAL OF DEPENDENCE

The reader will recall that in Section 3.3 we introduced the analytic interval of dependence of a point P in Ω. Now consider the initial value problem of Section 3.4 and suppose that we have some numerical method (e.g., the CIR method) for its solution on a mesh having the point P as a mesh point. Let the mesh spacings be Δx and Δt. Then the smallest interval containing the mesh points on the x-axis that

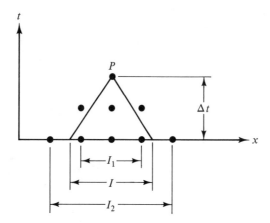

Figure 3.5.1 Numerical intervals of dependence.

enter into the determination of the approximate solution at P is called the *numerical interval of dependence* of P for the spacings Δx and Δt.

For example, assume that in order to compute the approximation at (x_j, t_{m+1}), the method requires information at (x_j, t_m) and $(x_{j\pm1}, t_m)$. Figure 3.5.1 shows I, the analytic interval of dependence of P as well I_1 and I_2, the numerical intervals of dependence for the spacings $(\Delta x, \Delta t)$ and $(\Delta x, \Delta t/2)$. Notice that $I_1 \subset I \subset I_2$. As we now show, the asymptotic inclusion of the analytic interval within the numerical interval is necessary for convergence.

Theorem 3.5.1.   *The numerical solution at P cannot in general converge to the exact solution at P unless the numerical interval of dependence includes the analytic interval of dependence as $\Delta x, \Delta t \to 0$.*

Proof. Let the numerical interval of dependence be contained in the interval I_1 for all sufficiently small Δx and Δt. If I_1 is properly contained in I, the analytic interval of dependence, and the numerical solution converges to the exact solution at P for some initial data, it cannot converge for any other initial data that agrees with the original on I_1 but not on I. This follows because a change in the data on $I - I_1$ will change the exact, but not the numerical, solution at P.

Q.E.D.

3.6 CONSERVATION LAW FORM; LAX–WENDROFF METHODS

Let $\mathbf{F}: R^n \to R^n$, $\mathbf{F} = (F_1, \ldots, F_n)^T$, be a continuously differentiable function. Then the autonomous system of first-order partial differential equations,

$$\frac{\partial}{\partial t}\mathbf{u} + \frac{\partial}{\partial x}(\mathbf{F}(\mathbf{u})) = \mathbf{0}, \tag{3.6.1}$$

is said to be in *conservation law form*. Clearly, (3.6.1) may always be written as

$$\mathbf{u}_t + A(\mathbf{u})\mathbf{u}_x = \mathbf{0}, \tag{3.6.2}$$

where $A(\mathbf{u}) = [\partial F_i / \partial u_j]$, the Jacobian matrix of $\mathbf{F}$. From this we see that (3.6.1) is equivalent to a particular type of quasilinear system (3.1.1).

Although the converse of this statement is not generally true (conditions under which (3.1.1) may be converted into (3.6.1) are implied by a result of Kerner [1933]), there are, nevertheless, important instances in which the differential equations do admit the conservation law form.

For example, since $d\rho/dp = 1/K = 1/c^2$, (3.1.6) and (3.1.7) may be written

$$\rho_t + (\rho v)_x = 0,$$

$$(\rho v)_t + [\rho vv + p]_x = 0,$$

and these assume the form (3.6.1) if we set

$$\mathbf{u} = (u_1, u_2)^T \equiv (\rho, \rho v)^T$$

and

$$\mathbf{F}(\mathbf{u}) = \left(u_2, \frac{u_2^2 + (cu_1)^2}{u_1} \right)^T.$$

Another example of the conservation law form is considered in Exercise 3.12.

Following Richtmyer and Morton [1967], we describe the "two-step" Lax–Wendroff scheme for (3.6.1). Assuming that the approximate solution is known on the mth level of the rectangular mesh of Section 3.4, intermediate values are first calculated at the mesh box centers as

$$\mathbf{U}_{j+1/2}^{m+1/2} = \frac{1}{2}(\mathbf{U}_{j+1}^m + \mathbf{U}_j^m) - \frac{r}{2}(\mathbf{F}_{j+1}^m - \mathbf{F}_j^m). \tag{3.6.3}$$

We again use the notation of Section 3.4 ($r = \Delta t/\Delta x$) and in addition let $\mathbf{F}_j^m$ denote $\mathbf{F}(\mathbf{U}_j^m)$. The values of the approximate solution at level $m+1$ are then obtained from

$$\mathbf{U}_j^{m+1} = \mathbf{U}_j^m - r(\mathbf{F}_{j+1/2}^{m+1/2} - \mathbf{F}_{j-1/2}^{m+1/2}). \tag{3.6.4}$$

Our analysis of these equations will be confined to the case in which $\mathbf{F} = A\mathbf{u}$, where A is an $n \times n$ matrix of constants. In this case we see that (3.6.3) and (3.6.4) may be combined to yield the single equation

$$\mathbf{U}_j^{m+1} = \mathbf{U}_j^m - \frac{r}{2} A(\mathbf{U}_{j+1}^m - \mathbf{U}_{j-1}^m) + \frac{r^2}{2} A^2 (\mathbf{U}_{j+1}^m - 2\mathbf{U}_j^m + \mathbf{U}_{j-1}^m). \tag{3.6.5}$$

As in Section 3.4, we define the (Lax–Wendroff) local truncation errors to be the resulting residuals when the exact solution, say $\mathbf{u}(x, t)$, is substituted into (3.6.5). Thus

$$\tau_j^m \equiv \mathbf{u}(x_j, t_m) - \frac{r}{2} A[\mathbf{u}(x_{j+1}, t_m) - \mathbf{u}(x_{j-1}, t_m)]$$

$$+ \frac{r^2}{2} A^2 [\mathbf{u}(x_{j+1}, t_m) - 2\mathbf{u}(x_j, t_m) + \mathbf{u}(x_{j-1}, t_m)] - \mathbf{u}(x_j, t_{m+1}). \tag{3.6.6}$$

If **u** has three continuous derivatives, then by Taylor's theorem,

$$\frac{\mathbf{u}(x_{j+1}, t_m) - \mathbf{u}(x_{j-1}, t_m)}{2\Delta x} = \mathbf{u}_x(x_j, t_m) + O[(\Delta x)^2]$$

and

$$\frac{\mathbf{u}(x_{j+1}, t_m) - 2\mathbf{u}(x_j, t_m) + \mathbf{u}(x_{j-1}, t_m)}{(\Delta x)^2} = \mathbf{u}_{xx}(x_j, t_m) + O(\Delta x).$$

Therefore,

$$\tau_j^m = \mathbf{u}(x_j, t_m) - \Delta t\, A\mathbf{u}_x(x_j, t_m) + \frac{(\Delta t)^2}{2} A^2\mathbf{u}_{xx}(x_j, t_m) - \mathbf{u}(x_j, t_{m+1})$$

$$+ O[\Delta t\, (\Delta x)^2] + O[(\Delta t)^2\, \Delta x]. \qquad (3.6.7)$$

Since **u** satisfies the differential equation $\mathbf{u}_t = -A\mathbf{u}_x$, we also have

$$\mathbf{u}_{tt} = -A\mathbf{u}_{xt} = -A(\mathbf{u}_t)_x = A^2\mathbf{u}_{xx}.$$

Thus

$$\mathbf{u}(x_j, t_{m+1}) = \mathbf{u}(x_j, t_m) + \Delta t\, \mathbf{u}_t(x_j, t_m) + \frac{(\Delta t)^2}{2} \mathbf{u}_{tt}(x_j, t_m) + O[(\Delta t)^3]$$

$$= \mathbf{u}(x_j, t_m) - \Delta t\, A\mathbf{u}_x(x_j, t_m) + \frac{(\Delta t)^2}{2} A^2\mathbf{u}_{xx}(x_j, t_m) + O[(\Delta t)^3].$$

Substituting this in (3.6.7), we obtain

$$\tau_j^m = O[\Delta t\, (\Delta x)^2 + (\Delta t)^2\, \Delta x + (\Delta t)^3].$$

It follows that if $r = $ constant, the Lax–Wendroff local truncation errors are $O[(\Delta t)^3]$. If this is compared with the CIR local errors (Exercise 3.11), we see that when the mesh ratio is constant, the Lax–Wendroff truncation errors are (asymptotically) a factor of Δt smaller than the CIR errors. In view of Corollary 3.4.2, we expect that the same will be true of the discretization errors, $\mathbf{U}_j^m - \mathbf{u}(x_j, t_m)$; that is, these errors are $O[(\Delta t)^2]$. If the system is hyperbolic, this is indeed the case provided that a C-F-L condition (3.4.7) holds and we measure the size of the errors in an appropriate manner. This result follows from the Lax–Richtmyer theory presented in Chapter 5 (see, in particular, Corollary 5.4.2 and Exercise 5.11). However, to set the stage for an application of this theory as we present it there, we need to show that it is sufficient to consider only the *scalar* form of (3.6.2).

If we assume that the system

$$\mathbf{u}_t + A\mathbf{u}_x = 0 \qquad (3.6.8)$$

is hyperbolic, there is a nonsingular matrix V such that $VA = \Lambda V$, where $\Lambda = \mathrm{Diag}\,(\lambda_i)$ and the λ_i are real numbers. Multiplying (3.6.5) and (3.6.6) by V and subtracting, we get

$$Ve_j^{m+1} = Ve_j^m - \frac{r}{2} \Lambda(Ve_{j+1}^m - Ve_{j-1}^m) + \frac{r^2}{2} \Lambda^2(Ve_{j+1}^m - 2Ve_j^m + Ve_{j-1}^m) + V\tau_j^m,$$

where $\mathbf{e}_j^m = \mathbf{U}_j^m - \mathbf{u}(x_j, t_m)$. If we let $\mathbf{E}_j^m = Ve_j^m$ and $\mathbf{T}_j^m = V\tau_j^m$, then

$$\mathbf{E}_j^{m+1} = \mathbf{E}_j^m - \frac{r}{2} \Lambda(\mathbf{E}_{j+1}^m - \mathbf{E}_{j-1}^m) + \frac{r^2}{2} \Lambda^2(\mathbf{E}_{j+1}^m - 2\mathbf{E}_j^m + \mathbf{E}_{j-1}^m) + \mathbf{T}_j^m. \qquad (3.6.9)$$

But (3.6.9) is equivalent to n scalar equations of the form

$$E_j^{m+1} = E_j^m - \frac{r}{2} \lambda(E_{j+1}^m - E_{j-1}^m) + \frac{r^2\lambda^2}{2}(E_{j+1}^m - 2E_j^m + E_{j-1}^m) + T_j^m, \qquad (3.6.10)$$

where λ is an eigenvalue of A and $T_j^m = O((\Delta t)^3)$. Thus (3.6.10) may be interpreted as the error equation of the Lax–Wendroff method when it is applied to the *scalar equation*

$$u_t + \lambda u_x = 0. \qquad (3.6.11)$$

NOTES AND REMARKS

3.1 For first-order hyperbolic systems in more than two independent variables, the characteristic curves are replaced by *characteristic surfaces* or *manifolds*. These are defined by the requirement that on them the solution of the system leaves its normal derivative indeterminate. More precisely, suppose that [in the notation of (3.1.2)] the system is given by

$$\mathbf{u}_t + \sum_{j=1}^m A_j \mathbf{u}_{x_j} = \mathbf{f}. \qquad (1)$$

Let the characteristic surfaces be defined implicitly by the equation

$$\phi(x_1, \ldots, x_m, t) = 0$$

and introduce a change of variables $\xi_0, \ldots, \xi_m$, where $\xi_0 = \phi$. In the ξ-system, the normal derivative to S ($\xi_0 = 0$) is just $\partial/\partial\xi_0$, and the transformed version of (1) is

$$\left[\phi_t I + \sum_{j=1}^m \phi_{x_j} A_j \right] \frac{\partial \mathbf{u}}{\partial \xi_0} + \sum_{k=1}^m \left(\frac{\partial \xi_k}{\partial t} I + \sum_{j=1}^m \frac{\partial \xi_k}{\partial x_j} A_j \right) \frac{\partial \mathbf{u}}{\partial \xi_k} = \mathbf{f}.$$

Thus S is a characteristic surface if at each point of S the matrix coefficient of $\partial \mathbf{u}/\partial\xi_0$ is singular, that is, if ϕ satisfies any of the conditions

$$\phi_t + \lambda_i(x_1, \ldots, x_m, t, \phi_{x_1}, \ldots, \phi_{x_m}) = 0, \qquad i = 1, \ldots, n, \qquad (2)$$

where λ_i is the ith eigenvalue of $\sum_j \phi_{x_j} A_j$. These quantities are real and distinct by the assumption that (1) is hyperbolic. Note that for each value of i, (2) yields a differential equation for a characteristic surface. Associated with each characteristic surface is a system of curves $x_j = x_j(t)$ known as *bicharacteristics*. These are solutions of the "canonical" system $dx_j/dt = \partial\lambda_i/\partial p_j$, $dp_j/dt = -\partial\lambda_i/\partial x_j$, $j = 1, \ldots, m$, where p_j is identified with ϕ_{x_j}. It can be shown (Courant and Hilbert [1962]) that if a bicharacteristic has a point in common with a characteristic surface S, then it remains in S. Bicharacteristics have been used (see, e.g., Butler [1960] or Johnston and Pal [1972]) to construct numerical methods for (1) that are in the spirit of the "characteristics method" given in Section 3.4. As is evident from the preceding discussion, their implementation may be quite complicated.

3.2 It is possible to obtain the characteristic equations for (3.2.1) without first reducing it to the first-order system (3.2.2). This can be done by an approach similar to the above in which a characteristic curve is defined to be one on which the solution and first derivatives of (3.2.1) leave the *second* normal derivative of u indeterminate (Courant and Hilbert [1962]). Alternatively, one may proceed as follows (Smith [1978]): Let $p = u_t$, $q = u_x$, $r = u_{tt}$, $s = u_{xt}$, and $v = u_{xx}$, and consider a curve $C: x = x(t)$. Along C,

$$r + s\frac{dx}{dt} = \frac{dp}{dt}$$

and

$$s + v\frac{dx}{dt} = \frac{dq}{dt}.$$

But if u is a solution of (3.2.1), then also

$$ar + 2bs + cv = d.$$

This gives us a system of three equations for r, s, and v along C whose coefficient matrix is

$$A = \begin{bmatrix} 1 & \dfrac{dx}{dt} & 0 \\ 0 & 1 & \dfrac{dx}{dt} \\ a & 2b & c \end{bmatrix}.$$

If A is nonsingular, this system always has a solution. However, if A is singular, a (non-unique) solution exists only if the right-hand side satisfies a compatibility condition. Since

$$\det A = a\left[\frac{dx}{dt}\right]^2 - 2b\left[\frac{dx}{dt}\right] + c,$$

we see that curves satisfying $dx/dt = \lambda$, where

$$a\lambda^2 - 2b\lambda + c = 0$$

are precisely the curves along which A is singular. These are the characteristics, and it is clear that they coincide with the curves obtained in Section 3.2. Moreover, it is not difficult to see that in this case the required compatibility condition assumes the form

$$a\frac{dp}{dt}\lambda + c\frac{dq}{dt} - d\lambda = 0.$$

3.3 It is most natural to discuss shocks in the context of the conservation law form introduced in Section 3.6, and in particular with respect to the equations of inviscid gas dynamics presented in Exercise 3.12. In this case the shock lines are mathematical idealizations of narrow regions across which the physical variables (velocity, pressure, density, and internal energy) experience continuous, but very rapid, changes. The form of the solution on each side of a shock line is connected by conditions known as the *Rankine–Hugoniot equations*. These give the relationships that must exist between finite jumps in the dependent variables, and they are derived from the principles of mass, momentum, and energy conservation (Richtmyer and Morton [1967]).

Several classes of numerical methods have been devised for the treatment of shocks. These include (but are not limited to) "shock fitting" methods (Thomas [1954], Forsythe and Wasow [1960]) in which the Rankine–Hugoniot conditions are used explicitly; "shock capturing" methods (von Neumann and Richtmyer [1950], Lax [1954], Lax and Wendroff [1960], see also the two-step Lax–Wendroff scheme of Section 3.6) which do not rely directly on the Rankine–Hugoniot equations but explicitly and/or implicitly introduce numerical dissipation into the calculations to "smear" the discontinuities produced by the shock over several mesh widths; and "cell methods" (Godunov [1959], Colella and Woodward [1984]), wherein use is made of the exact solution of a simpler problem incorporating discontinuities (the so-called Riemann shock tube problem) as part of the numerical solution procedure. The reader may also consult the review article by Woodward and Colella [1984] for additional information on shock calculations.

3.4 Earlier in these Notes and Remarks we mentioned the role played by the characteristics in the numerical solution of first-order hyperbolic systems in more than two independent variables. It is also possible to develop characteristic-like methods by employing "nebencharacteristics" (*side* characteristics) (see Sauer [1963] and Werner [1968] for details).

There are, of course, methods for first-order hyperbolic equations other than those discussed in the body of this chapter. We mention, for example, "Friedrich's method," which replaces the first-order system (3.1.2) by the difference equation

$$\frac{\mathbf{U}_j^{m+1} - \frac{1}{2}(\mathbf{U}_{j-1}^m + \mathbf{U}_{j+1}^m)}{\Delta t} + A_j^m \frac{\mathbf{U}_{j+1}^m - \mathbf{U}_{j-1}^m}{2\Delta x} = \mathbf{f}_j^m.$$

This method coincides with Lax's method (Lax [1954]) if A is a matrix of constants. Moreover, in this case the method is convergent if the C-F-L condition (3.4.7) holds (Meis and Marcowitz [1981]). Other methods may apply to specific second-order equations. Thus a natural scheme for the wave equation (3.2.4) is

$$\frac{U_j^{m+1} - 2U_j^m + U_j^{m-1}}{(\Delta t)^2} - \frac{U_{j+1}^m - 2U_j^m + U_{j-1}^m}{(\Delta x)^2} = 0.$$

This again yields convergent approximations if the C-F-L condition $\Delta t/\Delta x < 1$ holds (Forsythe and Wasow [1960]).

3.6 The body of literature treating the theory and numerical analysis of nonlinear conservation laws is sizable. This is due in no small part to the fact that the equations of inviscid gas dynamics assume this form (Exercise 3.12). Thus problems in aerodynamics (for example) may be studied and simulated within the framework of conservation laws. P. Lax has written extensively on the conservation law form and in Lax [1972] the reader will find a nice introduction to the subject. Furthermore, as we have related earlier in these Notes and

Remarks, Lax and his coworkers were among the first to utilize this form for the construction of effective numerical methods involving shocks. Other techniques for the numerical treatment of conservation laws include "TVD" methods (Harten [1984]), "hybrid" schemes (Zalesak [1979]), and "random choice methods" (Harten and Lax [1981]).

EXERCISES

3.1. Use the theory of characteristics to find a function $u(x, t)$ that satisfies the differential equation

$$u_t + (\cos t)u_x = 0, \qquad t > 0,$$

and reduces to $\cos x$ when $t = 0$.

3.2. (a) Use the theory of characteristics to show that if $u(x, t)$ satisfies

$$u_t + uu_x = g(t), \qquad t > 0,$$
$$u(x, 0) = f(x),$$

then

$$u(x, t) = G(t) + f(\phi),$$

where

$$G(t) = \int_0^t g(s)\, ds$$

and ϕ satisfies the equation

$$x = \phi + tf(\phi) + \int_0^t G(s)\, ds.$$

(b) Use the result of part (a) to find $u(x, t)$ if

$$u_t + uu_x = 1, \qquad t > 0,$$
$$u(x, 0) = x.$$

3.3. The propagation of sound waves through gas in a long thin tube is approximately described by the equations [cf. (3.1.6)]

$$p_t + c^2\rho_0 v_x = 0,$$
$$\rho_0 v_t + p_x = 0,$$

and

$$p = \rho c^2.$$

Here the sonic velocity c and the density of the gas at rest, ρ_0, are assumed to be positive constants. The remaining quantities are as in (3.1.6).

(a) Show that p and ρ each satisfy the wave equation

$$u_{tt} - c^2 u_{xx} = 0.$$

(b) Use characteristics to determine $p(x, t)$ if

$$p(x, 0) = \sin x \quad \text{and} \quad p_t(x, 0) = 0.$$

3.4. Use the theory of characteristics to solve the initial value problem

$$u_{tt} - 4u_{xx} = t, \quad t > 0,$$

$$u(x, 0) = x, \quad u_t(x, 0) = 0.$$

3.5. Let Γ be the curve $x = ct$, where c is a nonzero constant. Find (at least) two distinct solutions of the initial value problem

$$u_t + cu_x = 0, \quad (x, t) \notin \Gamma,$$

$$u\Big|_{\Gamma} = 0.$$

3.6. Find an exact expression for the error at the mesh point $P = (x, t)$ if the characteristics method (3.4.1), (3.4.2) is used to solve the initial value problem

$$u_t + 2u_x - 1,$$

$$u(x, 0) = x$$

with $\Delta x = \Delta t = t$.

3.7. Suppose that the characteristics method (3.4.1), (3.4.2) is used to approximate the solution of the initial value problem

$$u_t + u_x = t,$$

$$u(x, 0) = x,$$

at the mesh points $(j\,\Delta x, m\,\Delta t)$, where $\Delta x = \Delta t = 1/N$ and N is a positive integer. Show that at the point $(1, 1)$, the error, $u(1, 1) - U(1, 1)$, is equal to $\Delta t/2$.

3.8. Let $\rho > 0$. In order for the equation $x = \phi(x)$ to have a unique solution x^* in the interval $I = [x^{(0)} - \rho, x^{(0)} + \rho]$, it is sufficient that on I, $|\phi'| \le M$ for some $M < 1$ and $|x^{(0)} - \phi(x^{(0)})| \le (1 - M)\rho$. Furthermore, in this case if the iterates $\{x^{(k)}\}$ satisfy $x^{(k+1)} = \phi(x^{(k)})$, $k = 0, 1, \ldots$, then $x^{(k)} \to x^*$ as $k \to \infty$ (Isaacson and Keller [1966]).

(a) Show that the equation

$$x = x^{(0)} - \Delta t\,\lambda(x)$$

has a unique solution in $I = [x^{(0)} - 1, x^{(0)} + 1]$ if $\Delta t \le 1/2K$, where K is any bound for $|\lambda(x^{(0)})|$ and $\sup_{x \in I} |\lambda'(x)|$.

(b) Show that if the characteristics method is applied to

$$u_t + (1 + x^3)u_x = 0$$

at the mesh point $P = (1, 1)$ with $\Delta x = \Delta t = 1/24$, then (3.4.1) has a unique solution in $[0, 2]$. Determine this solution to four places.

3.9. Show that if c is a nonzero constant and $\Delta t/\Delta x = 1/|c|$, the CIR method is exact when applied to the initial value problem

$$u_t + cu_x = 0, \quad t > 0,$$

$$u(x, 0) = f(x).$$

3.10. Let c be a positive constant and suppose that the solution of the initial value problem

$$u_t + cu_x = 0, \qquad t > 0,$$

$$u(x, 0) = f(x),$$

is approximated at the mesh points $(j \, \Delta x, m \, \Delta t)$ by the "downwind" scheme

$$\frac{U_j^{m+1} - U_j^m}{\Delta t} + c \frac{U_{j+1}^m - U_j^m}{\Delta x} = 0.$$

(a) Show that

$$U_j^m = \sum_{k=0}^{m} U_{j+k}^0 \binom{m}{k} \left(-c \frac{\Delta t}{\Delta x} \right)^k \left(1 + c \frac{\Delta t}{\Delta x} \right)^{m-k},$$

where

$$\binom{m}{k} \quad \text{is the binomial coefficient} \quad \frac{m!}{(m-k)! \, k!}.$$

(b) In approximating the initial data $f(x) = 0$, a rounding error is made so that

$$U_j^0 = \begin{cases} 0 & \text{if } j \neq 0 \\ \varepsilon \neq 0 & \text{if } j = 0. \end{cases}$$

Let $\Delta t = 1/N$ and $\Delta x = \Delta t/r$, where r is a constant and N a positive integer. What happens to the error at the point $(0, 1)$ as $\Delta t \to 0$?

3.11. Prove Corollary 3.4.2. [*Hint:* Show that the local truncation errors are $O(\Delta t \, (\Delta t + \Delta x))$.]

3.12. The one-dimensional equations of inviscid gas dynamics may be written as

$$\rho_t + (\rho v)_x = 0,$$

$$\rho v_t + \rho v v_x = -p_x,$$

and

$$\rho E_t + \rho v E_x = -p v_x,$$

where $\rho, v,$ and p have the same meanings as in (3.1.6) and E is the internal energy per unit mass of the gas. If we assume an equation of state of the form $p = f(E, \rho)$, show that these equations may be put into the conservation law form (3.6.1).

Computer Exercises

3.13. The solution of the initial value problem

$$u_t + 3t^2 u_x = t + x,$$

$$u(x, 0) = x^2,$$

is

$$u(x, t) = \frac{t^2}{2} + \frac{t^4}{4} + (x - t^3)t + (x - t^3)^2.$$

Use the characteristics method (3.4.1), (3.4.2) to compute approximations $U_k(1, 1)$ of $u(1, 1)$ on the sequence of meshes $\Delta x = \Delta t = 2^{-k}$, $k = 1, \ldots, 5$. Assume an order relation for the error of the form

$$\left|U_k(1, 1) - u(1, 1)\right| \leq C(\Delta t)^p,$$

and use your results to estimate numerically the constant C and the integer p.

3.14. Rework Example 3.4.1.

3.15. Rework Example 3.4.1 by applying the Lax–Wendroff method to the conservation law form of (3.1.6). Note that the C-F-L condition (3.4.7) must be enforced.

4

The Parabolic
Diffusion Equation

We now turn to the study of an equation that is typical of the parabolic case. It occurs frequently in engineering applications and is used to model diffusion processes such as the flow of heat in a rod or the dispersion of dye in a quiescent liquid column. Although this equation is intrinsically different from the hyperbolic equations studied in Chapter 3, we shall see that the notion of finite differences may again be used to construct effective methods for its numerical solution. Numerical solutions using the finite element method are discussed in Chapter 9.

4.1 ONE-DIMENSIONAL DIFFUSION

We consider an equation of the form

$$\frac{\partial u}{\partial t} - \frac{\partial}{\partial x}\left(D\,\frac{\partial u}{\partial x}\right) = s, \tag{4.1.1}$$

where D and s are given functions of x and t. We also assume that $D(x, t) \geq d > 0$, for some constant d. Using the classification scheme of Section 2.1, it is easy to see that (4.1.1) is a parabolic equation.

As noted above, equations such as (4.1.1) are fundamentally different from the hyperbolic equations studied earlier. If we assume that $D \equiv 1$, $s \equiv 0$, and attempt to put (4.1.1) into the form (3.1.2) by letting $\mathbf{u} = (u_1, u_2)^T$, where $u_1 = u_x$ and $u_2 = u_t$, then we obtain the equivalent system

$$\begin{bmatrix} 0 & 0 \\ -1 & 0 \end{bmatrix}\begin{bmatrix} u_1 \\ u_2 \end{bmatrix}_t + \begin{bmatrix} 1 & 0 \\ 0 & 1 \end{bmatrix}\begin{bmatrix} u_1 \\ u_2 \end{bmatrix}_x = \begin{bmatrix} u_2 \\ 0 \end{bmatrix}. \tag{4.1.2}$$

This equation cannot be solved for $\mathbf{u}_t$, so that the direct conversion to the form (3.1.2) is not possible. Therefore, we modify (4.1.2) by writing

$$\begin{bmatrix} 0 & -\varepsilon^2 \\ -1 & 0 \end{bmatrix}\begin{bmatrix} u_1 \\ u_2 \end{bmatrix}_t + \begin{bmatrix} 1 & 0 \\ 0 & 1 \end{bmatrix}\begin{bmatrix} u_1 \\ u_2 \end{bmatrix}_x = \begin{bmatrix} u_2 \\ 0 \end{bmatrix}, \tag{4.1.3}$$

where ε is a small positive constant. Instead of the parabolic equation (4.1.1), we are now considering the perturbed equation

$$\frac{\partial u}{\partial t} = \frac{\partial^2 u}{\partial x^2} - \varepsilon^2 \frac{\partial^2 u}{\partial t^2}. \tag{4.1.4}$$

This is a *hyperbolic* equation whose characteristics (see Section 3.1) are defined in terms of the eigenvalues $\pm 1/\varepsilon$ of the matrix

$$-\frac{1}{\varepsilon^2}\begin{bmatrix} 0 & \varepsilon^2 \\ 1 & 0 \end{bmatrix} = \begin{bmatrix} 0 & -1 \\ -\dfrac{1}{\varepsilon^2} & 0 \end{bmatrix}.$$

These characteristics are seen to be straight lines with slope $\pm 1/\varepsilon$. However, as $\varepsilon \to 0$ the two characteristics coalesce into the single line $t =$ constant, and the interval of dependence (Section 3.3) becomes the entire x-axis. Thus, for $\varepsilon \neq 0$, the solution of the hyperbolic equation (4.1.4) at point P in Figure 4.1.1 is influenced by the data at points in the finite interval $[x_L, x_R]$. The parabolic equation (4.1.1) corresponds to the limiting case in which the solution at P depends on the data everywhere on the x-axis. Since $\lim_{\varepsilon \to 0} dx/dt = \infty$, interpreting dx/dt as a signal transmission speed leads to the conclusion that in the parabolic case, the signals propagate with infinite speed.

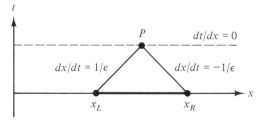

$[x_L, x_R] =$ interval of dependence

Figure 4.1.1   Characteristics for (4.1.4).

Although it is possible to consider a pure initial value problem in which (4.1.1) is supplemented by the specification of u on $t = 0$, it is more natural to study (4.1.1) in the context of an *initial–boundary value problem* which we pose in the following way. Find a function $u(x, t)$, continuous on $a \leq x \leq b$, $0 \leq t \leq T$, such that u_t and

$$\frac{\partial}{\partial x}\left(D \frac{\partial u}{\partial x} \right)$$

are continuous on $a < x < b$, $0 < t \leq T$, and satisfy there the equation

$$\frac{\partial u}{\partial t} - \frac{\partial}{\partial x}\left(D \frac{\partial u}{\partial x} \right) = s. \tag{4.1.5}$$

We assume that as a function of x, $u(x, t)$ is piecewise continuously differentiable; that is, u_x is continuous except at a finite number of points where it has jump discontinuities. These assumptions allow for the possibility that $D(x, t)$ may be only a piecewise continuous function of x. Note that the differentiability of (Du_x) implies that u_x will usually be discontinuous at any point where D is discontinuous. The function u is also required to satisfy the *initial condition*

$$u(x, 0) = f(x), \qquad a \leq x \leq b, \tag{4.1.6}$$

and the *boundary conditions*

$$u(a, t) = g(t) \quad \text{and} \quad u(b, t) = h(t), \qquad 0 \leq t \leq T, \tag{4.1.7}$$

where f, g, and h are prescribed functions.

The existence of a function u that solves this initial–boundary value problem depends strongly on the nature of the data D, s, f, g, and h. At one extreme, it can be shown (see, e.g., Friedman [1969]) that solutions possessing arbitrarily high degrees of differentiability exist, providing that we are willing to make similar assumptions about the data. At the other extreme, Ladyzhenskaya [1985] has demonstrated the existence of certain "generalized" solutions of the problem without requiring even continuity of the data. Of course, there is a price to pay for allowing this lack of smoothness in the data; in general, we do not know that these generalized solutions *literally* satisfy (4.1.5). We shall return to the notion of a generalized solution in Chapter 7 when we undertake an investigation of the finite element method.

In view of these remarks and remembering that our main subject in this book is the study of *numerical methods* for partial differential equations, we proceed under the assumption that the data of our initial–boundary value problem is smooth enough to permit the existence of a solution satisfying the continuity requirements stated above. Any such solution necessarily satisfies a *maximum principle*. If, as mentioned in the introduction to this chapter, (4.1.5) is used to model heat flow in a rod, then u represents the rod's time-dependent temperatures and the maximum principle states that at any time these must remain within the extremes of the initial temperature and boundary temperatures.

Theorem 4.1.1.   *Let u be a solution of (4.1.5)–(4.1.7) where $s \equiv 0$ and D is a positive constant function. Define*

$$b^{\min} = \min_{\substack{0 \le t \le T \\ a \le x \le b}} \{h(t), g(t), f(x)\}$$

and

$$b^{\max} = \max_{\substack{0 \le t \le T \\ a \le x \le b}} \{h(t), g(t), f(x)\}.$$

Then for $a \le x \le b$ and $0 \le t \le T$,

$$b^{\min} \le u(x, t) \le b^{\max}. \tag{4.1.8}$$

Proof. Let $v = u + \alpha e^{-t}$ for a constant $\alpha > 0$. Then for all x and t,

$$v_t - (Dv_x)_x = -\alpha e^{-t} < 0. \tag{4.1.9}$$

If v attains a maximum at a point $Q = (x^*, t^*)$ in the interior of the domain $\bar{\Omega} = \{(x, t) \mid a \le x \le b, \, 0 \le t \le T\}$, we have $v_t(x^*, t^*) = 0$ and $v_{xx}(x^*, t^*) \le 0$. But (4.1.9) implies that

$$Dv_{xx}(x^*, t^*) > 0,$$

which is a contradiction.

Thus, v attains its maximum on the boundary $\partial\Omega$ of $\bar{\Omega}$, so for $(x, t) \in \bar{\Omega}$,

$$u(x, t) < v(x, t) \le \max_{\partial\Omega} u(x, t) + \alpha.$$

Next, observe that if the maximum of v occurs at (x^*, T), then $v_t(x^*, T) \ge 0$ and $v_{xx}(x^*, T) \le 0$. But as before,

$$Dv_{xx}(x^*, T) = v_t(x^*, T) + \alpha e^{-T} > 0,$$

which leads to a contradiction, and we conclude that the maximum of v cannot occur on the boundary segment $t = T$.

Letting $\alpha \to 0$, we obtain the upper bound in (4.1.8). The lower bound is obtained by replacing α by $-\alpha$.

Q.E.D.

Note that with slight modifications of this proof we can show that if $s \ge 0$ (respectively, $s \le 0$), the left (respectively, right) inequality of (4.1.8) remains valid.

Also, if for example, $u(x)$ represents the temperature of a rod composed of one material for $a \le x \le c$ and another material for $c \le x \le b$, then D, the conductivity of the respective materials, is a piecewise constant function. For such problems, the term u_t is replaced by $\rho c u_t$ where ρ and c are both piecewise positive constant functions (see Section 2.3). However, the proof can easily be modified and the conclusion in (4.1.8) remains valid. For the latter case an appropriate smoothness assumption would be that $\rho c u_t$ is continuous on $a \le x \le b$, $0 \le t \le T$.

As a corollary of Theorem 4.1.1, we obtain a result on the uniqueness of solutions of the initial–boundary value problem (4.1.5)–(4.1.7). We give a proof for the case that D is a positive constant function. See Exercise 4.1 for the more general case.

Corollary 4.1.2.   *There is at most one solution of the initial–boundary value problem* (4.1.5)–(4.1.7).

Proof (*D a positive constant*). The difference of any two such solutions is a solution of (4.1.5)–(4.1.7) corresponding to the homogeneous data $s = f = g = h \equiv 0$. Thus it follows from Theorem 4.1.1 that this difference is identically zero.

Q.E.D.

4.2 A SEMIDISCRETE FORM

It is clear from the preceding section that we cannot exploit the notion of characteristics to formulate numerical methods for the solution of the parabolic equation (4.1.5). However, we can generate a semidiscretization of (4.1.5) as follows.

Subdivide the interval $[a, b]$ into uniform segments of length Δx as indicated in Figure 4.2.1. The jth *partition* or *mesh point* is designated by x_j and the midpoint between x_{j-1} and x_j is designated by $x_{j-1/2}$. If we formally integrate (4.1.5) from $x_{j-1/2}$ to $x_{j+1/2}$, we obtain

$$\int_{x_{j-1/2}}^{x_{j+1/2}} u_t \, dx - \left[Du_x \right]\Big|_{x_{j-1/2}}^{x_{j+1/2}} = \int_{x_{j-1/2}}^{x_{j+1/2}} s \, dx. \tag{4.2.1}$$

If u_{tx} is continuous on $[x_{j-1/2}, x_{j+1/2}]$, then by the mean value theorem,

$$u_t = u_t(x_j, t) + u_{tx}(\xi(x), t)(x - x_j)$$

for some function $\xi(x)$, $x_{j-1/2} \leq \xi(x) \leq x_{j+1/2}$. But since u_{tx} is continuous, there exists an M such that $\left| u_{tx}(\xi(x), t) \right| \leq M$ on $[x_{j-1/2}, x_{j+1/2}]$. Therefore,

$$\int_{x_{j-1/2}}^{x_{j+1/2}} u_t \, dx = \frac{du}{dt}(x_j, t) \, \Delta x + O((\Delta x)^2).$$

Similarly,

$$\int_{x_{j-1/2}}^{x_{j+1/2}} s \, dx = s(x_j, t) \, \Delta x + O((\Delta x)^2),$$

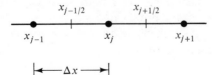

Figure 4.2.1   Partition or mesh.

provided that s_x is continuous. Finally, if we assume that u_{xxx} is continuous, then

$$u_x(x_{j+1/2}, t) = \frac{u(x_{j+1}, t) - u(x_j, t)}{\Delta x} + O((\Delta x)^2).$$

Substituting these expressions into (4.2.1) and dividing by Δx, we obtain

$$\frac{du}{dt}(x_j, t) - D(x_{j+1/2}, t)\frac{u(x_{j+1}, t) - u(x_j, t)}{(\Delta x)^2} + D(x_{j-1/2}, t)\frac{u(x_j, t) - u(x_{j-1}, t)}{(\Delta x)^2}$$
$$= s(x_j, t) + O(\Delta x). \qquad (4.2.2)$$

Now, let $\{U_j(t)\}$ denote the set of approximations to the functions $\{u(x_j, t)\}$ obtained by dropping the $O(\Delta x)$ term in (4.2.2). This means that the functions $\{U_j(t)\}$ are required to satisfy the system of ordinary differential equations

$$\frac{dU_j}{dt} - \frac{D(x_{j+1/2}, t)(U_{j+1} - U_j) + D(x_{j-1/2}, t)(U_{j-1} - U_j)}{(\Delta x)^2} = s(x_j, t). \qquad (4.2.3)$$

Note that we have discretized the dependence of u on the variable x, allowing t to vary continuously. For this reason, the approximations $\{U_j\}$ are termed *semidiscrete* approximations to $u(x, t)$.

To obtain a computational method for the solution of the initial–boundary value problem (4.1.5)–(4.1.7), it remains to impose the initial and boundary conditions and to discretize the time variable. Since the partition is of the form

$$a = x_0 < x_1 < \cdots < x_{N+1} = b,$$

where $x_j = a + j\,\Delta x$, and $\Delta x = (b - a)/(N + 1)$, the boundary conditions (4.1.7) suggest that for $t \geq 0$ we take

$$U_0(t) = u(a, t) = g(t),$$
$$U_{N+1}(t) = u(b, t) = h(t). \qquad (4.2.4)$$

Having determined $U_0(t)$ and $U_{N+1}(t)$ in this way, we seek N functions $\{U_j(t)\}_{j=1}^N$ satisfying (4.2.3). This system of N ordinary differential equations is initialized according to (4.1.6) as

$$U_j(0) = f(x_j), \qquad 1 \leq j \leq N. \qquad (4.2.5)$$

4.3 THE EXPLICIT METHOD

As a first computational method we discretize the time derivative in (4.2.3) by a *forward* difference to obtain

$$\frac{U_j^{m+1} - U_j^m}{\Delta t} - \frac{D_{j+1/2}^m(U_{j+1}^m - U_j^m) + D_{j-1/2}^m(U_{j-1}^m - U_j^m)}{(\Delta x)^2} = s_j^m, \qquad (4.3.1)$$

$1 \le j \le N$. The variable U_j^m approximates $u(x_j, t_m)$, where $t_m = m \, \Delta t$, $D_{j+1/2}^m = D(x_{j+1/2}, t_m)$, and so on. We assume that for some integer M, $M \, \Delta t = T$ and also that $\overline{\Omega} = [a, b] \times [0, T]$. Using (4.2.4) and (4.2.5), we close the system (4.3.1) by setting

$$U_j^0 = f(x_j), \qquad 1 \le j \le N$$

and

$$U_0^m = g(t_m) \quad \text{and} \quad U_{N+1}^m = h(t_m), \qquad 0 \le m \le M.$$

If we let $r = \Delta t/(\Delta x)^2$, then (4.3.1) can be written as

$$U_j^{m+1} = [1 - r(D_{j+1/2}^m + D_{j-1/2}^m)]U_j^m + [rD_{j+1/2}^m]U_{j+1}^m + [rD_{j-1/2}^m]U_{j-1}^m + \Delta t \, s_j^m \tag{4.3.2}$$

for $1 \le j \le N$ and $m = 0, 1, 2, \ldots, M - 1$. This provides a simple *explicit* recurrence formula for the approximations at the $(m + 1)$st time level in terms of the values at the mth time level.

Obviously, if the finite difference approximations are to converge to the solution of the initial–boundary value problem as Δx and Δt tend to zero in some fashion, it is necessary that they remain bounded. We now show that this "stability" property holds provided that r is suitably restricted. Note that any such restriction imposes a constraint on the manner in which Δx and Δt are allowed to approach zero.

Define the quantities

$$\Gamma = 2 \max_{(x,t) \in \overline{\Omega}} D(x, t) \quad \text{and} \quad \Sigma = \max_{(x,t) \in \overline{\Omega}} s(x, t).$$

If $r \le 1/\Gamma$, we note that the first three terms on the right side of (4.3.2) constitute a convex combination of values of u at the mth level. Hence for $1 \le j \le N$,

$$U_j^{m+1} \le \max_{0 \le i \le N+1} U_i^m + \Delta t \, s_j^m$$

$$\le \max \left[\max_{0 \le i \le N+1} U_i^{m-1}, U_0^m, U_{N+1}^m \right] + \Delta t \, (s_j^m + s_j^{m-1})$$

$$\cdots$$

$$\le \max \left[\max_{0 \le i \le N+1} U_i^0, \max_{1 \le j \le m} [U_0^j, U_{N+1}^j] \right] + (m + 1) \, \Delta t \, \Sigma \le b^{\max} + T\Sigma$$

This proves that the approximations U_j^m are bounded above by a quantity that does not depend on Δx or Δt. Since a similar argument demonstrates the existence of a lower bound that is also independent of Δx and Δt, we have the following result.

Theorem 4.3.1.   *If*

$$r \equiv \frac{\Delta t}{\Delta x^2} \le \frac{1}{\Gamma}, \tag{4.3.3}$$

where

$$\Gamma \equiv 2 \max_{(x,t)\in\bar{\Omega}} D(x, t),$$

then the explicit finite difference approximations $\{U_j^m\}$ given by (4.3.2) are bounded independent of Δx and Δt.

To get an idea of what happens when (4.3.3) does not hold, we follow Forsythe and Wasow [1960] and consider the pure initial value problem

$$u_t = u_{xx}, \qquad -\infty < x < \infty, \quad t > 0$$

$$u(x, 0) = 0, \qquad -\infty < x < \infty.$$

The solution is clearly $u(x, t) \equiv 0$, and this solution will be reproduced by (4.3.2) provided that all the computations are performed with infinite accuracy. However, suppose that we make a single rounding error of $\varepsilon > 0$ in the initial data at $x = 0$ (i.e., $U_j^0 = 0, j \neq 0$, and $U_0^0 = \varepsilon$). From (4.3.2) we have

$$U_j^{m+1} = (1 - 2r)U_j^m + rU_{j+1}^m + rU_{j-1}^m. \tag{4.3.4}$$

Now we violate (4.3.3) by assuming that $r = $ constant $> \frac{1}{2}$. Then the signs of the U_j^m will alternate in a checkerboard fashion. That is, if both U_j^m and U_{j+1}^m are nonzero, they are of opposite signs. We prove this by induction. It is obvious for $m = 0$. Assume that it holds for time level t_m. If U_j^m is positive, the right side of (4.3.4) is negative, and hence so is U_j^{m+1}. Similarly, if U_j^m is negative, U_j^{m+1} is positive and the induction argument is complete.

The alternating sign property of the set $\{U_j^m\}$ implies that the three terms on the right side of (4.3.4) have the same sign. Therefore,

$$|U_j^{m+1}| = (2r - 1)|U_j^m| + r|U_{j+1}^m| + r|U_{j-1}^m|. \tag{4.3.5}$$

Let $S^m = \sum_j |U_j^m|$, and note that S^m contains at most $(2m + 1)$ nonzero terms. By (4.3.5),

$$S^{m+1} = (4r - 1)S^m = (4r - 1)^{m+1}S^0 = (4r - 1)^{m+1}\varepsilon.$$

On the other hand, there exists an index $j(m)$ such that

$$S^m \leq (2m + 1) \max_j |U_j^m| = (2m + 1)|U_{j(m)}^m|.$$

Thus

$$|U_{j(m)}^m| \geq \frac{1}{2m + 1}(4r - 1)^m\varepsilon,$$

and in particular for $m = M$, we have

$$|U_{j(M)}^M| \geq \left(\frac{2T}{\Delta t} + 1\right)^{-1}(4r - 1)^{T/\Delta t}\varepsilon.$$

Since $4r - 1 > 1$, it follows that as $\Delta t \to 0$, $|U_{j(M)}^M| \to \infty$.

This shows that if we do not enforce (4.3.3) and commit a rounding error of *any size whatsoever* in the initial condition, then the numerical solution grows without bound as we refine the mesh, *even though we perform all subsequent computations exactly*. Clearly, we cannot expect convergence, and in fact we witness an exponential explosion of the numerical solution. Exercises 4.4 and 4.5 provide another demonstration of this phenomenon.

Condition (4.3.3) is another example of a stability condition. It should be compared with the C-F-L condition (3.4.7) for hyperbolic equations. In Chapter 5 we shall make a detailed examination of the important role that the concept of stability plays in the numerical solution of evolutionary partial differential equations by finite difference methods. However, for the present we confine our attention to the method (4.3.2) under the assumption that (4.3.3) holds.

As Δt and $\Delta x \to 0$, we investigate the behavior of the errors at the points (x_j, t_m), where $x_j = a + j\,\Delta x$ and $t_m = m\,\Delta t$. We begin by defining the *local truncation errors*,

$$\tau_j^m \equiv \left[1 - r(D_{j+1/2}^m + D_{j-1/2}^m)\right]u(x_j, t_m)$$
$$+ \left[rD_{j+1/2}^m\right]u(x_{j+1}, t_m) + \left[rD_{j-1/2}^m\right]u(x_{j-1}, t_m) + \Delta t\, s_j^m - u(x_j, t_{m+1}). \qquad (4.3.6)$$

That is, τ_j^m is the residual resulting from the substitution of the solution $u(x, t)$ into the difference formula (4.3.2). Next, we define the *discretization errors* by

$$e_j^m \equiv U_j^m - u(x_j, t_m)$$

for $1 \leq j \leq N$ and $1 \leq m \leq M$, and let

$$E^m = \max_{1 \leq j \leq N} |e_j^m|$$

and

$$\tau \equiv \max_{\substack{1 \leq j \leq N \\ 1 \leq m \leq M}} |\tau_j^m|.$$

Subtracting (4.3.6) from (4.3.2), we obtain

$$e_j^{m+1} = \left[1 - r(D_{j+1/2}^m + D_{j-1/2}^m)\right]e_j^m + \left[rD_{j+1/2}^m\right]e_{j+1}^m + \left[rD_{j-1/2}^m\right]e_{j-1}^m + \tau_j^m.$$

Since $r \leq 1/\Gamma$, we have for $1 \leq j \leq N$ that

$$\left|e_j^{m+1}\right| \leq \left[1 - r(D_{j+1/2}^m + D_{j-1/2}^m)\right]\left|e_j^m\right| + \left[rD_{j+1/2}^m\right]\left|e_{j+1}^m\right| + \left[rD_{j-1/2}^m\right]\left|e_{j-1}^m\right| + \tau.$$

Since the first three terms on the right side are a convex combination of the errors at the mth level, it follows that

$$\left|e_j^{m+1}\right| \leq E^m + \tau. \qquad (4.3.7)$$

Also, note that $e_0^m = e_{N+1}^m = 0$. Thus (4.3.7) implies that

$$E^{m+1} \leq E^m + \tau \leq \cdots \leq E^0 + (m+1)\tau.$$

But $E^0 = 0$, and $m\tau = m\,\Delta t\,(\tau/\Delta t) \leq T(\tau/\Delta t)$. Hence

$$E^m \leq T\frac{\tau}{\Delta t}. \qquad (4.3.8)$$

The following lemma gives conditions under which $\tau/\Delta t \to 0$ as Δt and $\Delta x \to 0$, and hence establishes the convergence of the approximate solution to the solution of the initial–boundary value problem.

Lemma 4.3.2.   *Let u and D have four continuous derivatives with respect to x and let u have two continuous derivatives with respect to t in $\bar{\Omega}$. Then*

$$\tau = O[\Delta t \, (\Delta t + (\Delta x)^2)].$$

Proof. From (4.1.1)

$$\frac{-\tau_j^m}{\Delta t} = \frac{u(x_j, t_{m+1}) - u(x_j, t_m)}{\Delta t}$$

$$- \frac{D_{j+1/2}^m(u(x_{j+1}, t_m) - u(x_j, t_m)) - D_{j-1/2}^m(u(x_j, t_m) - u(x_{j-1}, t_m))}{(\Delta x)^2} - s_j^m$$

$$= u_t(x_j, t_m) - \frac{D_{j+1/2}^m u_x(x_{j+1/2}, t_m) - D_{j-1/2}^m u_x(x_{j-1/2}, t_m)}{\Delta x} + O(\Delta t) + O((\Delta x)^2) - s_j^m$$

$$= \left[u_t - (Du_x)_x - s \right]\Big|_{\substack{x=x_j \\ t=t_m}} + O((\Delta x)^2 + \Delta t)$$

$$= O((\Delta x)^2 + \Delta t).$$

Q.E.D.

We summarize the implications of Lemma 4.3.2 and (4.3.8) in the following convergence theorem.

Theorem 4.3.3.   *Let u and D have four continuous derivatives with respect to x and let u have two continuous derivatives with respect to t in $\bar{\Omega}$. Let u solve the initial–boundary value problem (4.1.5)–(4.1.7). Further, let U_j^m be the explicit finite difference approximation to u given in (4.3.2). If $r \equiv \Delta t/(\Delta x)^2 \leq 1/\Gamma$, where $\Gamma \equiv 2 \max_{\bar{\Omega}} D(x,t)$, then the discretization error*

$$U_j^m - u(j\,\Delta x, m\,\Delta t) = O((\Delta x)^2 + \Delta t) \tag{4.3.9}$$

as Δt and $\Delta x \to 0$.

4.4 THE IMPLICIT METHOD

In view of the discussion in the preceding section, the applicability of the explicit method is restricted by the condition (4.3.3). For small Δx and/or large D this can require a choice of Δt that is prohibitively small. For example, if $D \equiv 10.0$ and $\Delta x = 0.01$, we must have $\Delta t < 5 \times 10^{-6}$ to ensure stability and convergence of the method, and it is not difficult to imagine situations in which this restriction on Δt would lead to unacceptably long computation times. We now consider a second method for (4.2.3) that converges without any condition on Δt.

To define this method we simply replace the time derivative in (4.2.3) by a *backward time difference.* This yields

$$\frac{U_j^{m+1} - U_j^m}{\Delta t} - \frac{D_{j+1/2}^{m+1}(U_{j+1}^{m+1} - U_j^{m+1}) - D_{j-1/2}^{m+1}(U_j^{m+1} - U_{j-1}^{m+1})}{\Delta x^2}$$

$$= s_j^{m+1}, \qquad 1 \le j \le N. \qquad (4.4.1)$$

As in Section 4.3, U_0^{m+1} and U_{N+1}^{m+1} are known from the boundary data, and U_j^0, $1 \le j \le N$, are given by the initial data. Equation (4.4.1) represents a set of N linear equations for the N unknowns U_j^{m+1}, $1 \le j \le N$, which must be solved at each time step. The approximations to u at time step $(m + 1)$ are thus given implicitly in terms of the values at time step m. For this reason we refer to this as the *implicit method.*

To analyze (4.4.1), we first rewrite it as

$$-[rD_{j-1/2}^{m+1}]U_{j-1}^{m+1} + [1 + r(D_{j-1/2}^{m+1} + D_{j+1/2}^{m+1})]U_j^{m+1} - [rD_{j+1/2}^{m+1}]U_{j+1}^{m+1}$$

$$= U_j^m + \Delta t\, s_j^{m+1}, \qquad (4.4.2)$$

where again $r \equiv \Delta t/(\Delta x)^2$.

We have the following *discrete maximum principle* (cf. Theorem 4.1.1) for this finite difference approximation.

Theorem 4.4.1.   *Let $M\, \Delta t = T$,*

$$\Sigma \equiv \max_{\substack{1 \le j \le N \\ 0 \le m \le M}} |s_j^m|, \qquad b^{\max} = \max_{\substack{0 \le t \le T \\ a \le x \le b}} \{h(t), g(t), f(x)\}$$

and

$$b^{\min} = \min_{\substack{0 \le t \le T \\ a \le x \le b}} \{h(t), g(t), f(x)\}.$$

Then for $0 \le m\, \Delta t \le T$, any solution U_j^{m+1} of (4.4.2) satisfies

$$b^{\min} - (m + 1)\, \Delta t\, \Sigma < U_j^{m+1} \le h^{\max} + (m + 1)\, \Delta t\, \Sigma. \qquad (4.4.3)$$

Proof.   Let

$$U_{\max}^m = \max_{0 \le j \le N+1} U_j^m \quad \text{and} \quad U_{\min}^m = \min_{0 \le j \le N+1} U_j^m.$$

We first consider the right inequality. The proof is by induction on the index of the time level. For time level zero, the result follows immediately. Assume that it holds for the mth time level, and consider the $(m + 1)$st time level.

If $U_{\max}^{m+1} = U_0^{m+1}$ or U_{N+1}^{m+1}, the result again is obvious. Therefore, suppose that $U_{\max}^{m+1} = U_k^{m+1}$, where $1 \le k \le N$. Then by (4.4.2),

$$U_k^{m+1} = U_k^m + \Delta t\, s_k^{m+1} - [rD_{k-1/2}^{m+1}(U_k^{m+1} - U_{k-1}^{m+1}) + rD_{k+1/2}^{m+1}(U_k^{m+1} - U_{k+1}^{m+1})].$$

But the quantity in brackets is nonnegative by the choice of the index k. So this and the induction hypothesis imply that

$$U_k^{m+1} \leq U_k^m + \Delta t\, s_k^{m+1} \leq U_{\max}^m + \Delta t\, \Sigma$$
$$\leq b^{\max} + (m+1)\,\Delta t\, \Sigma.$$

The left inequality follows in a similar manner.

Q.E.D.

Note that if $s \equiv 0$ and D is a positive function, Theorem 4.4.1 shows that the solution of the implicit finite difference model satisfies a maximum principle identical to that given in Theorem 4.1.1. In terms of the heat flow model, this means that the predicted finite difference mesh point "temperatures" cannot exceed the extremes of the initial and boundary temperatures. More important, Theorem 4.4.1 has the following corollary regarding the stability of the method.

Corollary 4.4.2.   *The implicit finite difference approximations given by* (4.4.1) *are bounded independent of* Δx *and* Δt.

Proof. From (4.4.3) we have that

$$b^{\min} - T\Sigma \leq U_j^{m+1} \leq b^{\max} + T\Sigma$$

for $0 \leq j \leq N + 1$, and these bounds are *independent* of the choice of Δt.

Q.E.D.

The solvability of (4.4.2) also follows from Theorem 4.4.1.

Corollary 4.4.3.   *The system* (4.4.2) *of finite difference equations has a unique solution.*

Proof. We use the well-known fact that either (4.4.2) has a unique solution, or the associated homogeneous system has a nonzero solution. The latter system is

$$-[rD_{j-1/2}^{m+1}]U_{j-1}^{m+1} + [1 + r(D_{j-1/2}^{m+1} + D_{j+1/2}^{m+1})]U_j^{m+1}$$
$$- [rD_{j+1/2}^{m+1}]U_{j+1}^{m+1} = 0, \qquad 1 \leq j \leq N,$$

where $U_0^{m+1} = U_{N+1}^{m+1} = 0$, and corresponds to the choice of $s \equiv f \equiv g \equiv h \equiv 0$. But then (4.4.3) implies that

$$0 \leq U_j^{m+1} \leq 0.$$

That is, the homogeneous system has only the trivial solution.

Q.E.D.

Next we develop an estimate of the *discretization errors*

$$e_j^m \equiv U_j^m - u(x_j, t_m).$$

The *local truncation errors* τ_j^m are again defined as residuals, this time by the equation

$$-[rD_{j-1/2}^{m+1}]u(x_{j-1}, t_{m+1}) + [1 + r(D_{j-1/2}^{m+1} + D_{j+1/2}^{m+1})]u(x_j, t_{m+1})$$
$$- [rD_{j+1/2}^{m+1}]u(x_{j+1}, t_{m+1}) = u(x_j, t_m) + \Delta t \, s_j^{m+1} - \tau_j^m. \qquad (4.4.4)$$

As in the analysis of the explicit method, we can show that if u is sufficiently smooth, then

$$\tau_j^m = O[\Delta t \, (\Delta t + (\Delta x)^2)].$$

Subtracting (4.4.4) from (4.4.2), we obtain

$$-[rD_{j-1/2}^{m+1}]e_{j-1}^{m+1} + [1 + r(D_{j-1/2}^{m+1} + D_{j+1/2}^{m+1})]e_j^{m+1}$$
$$- [rD_{j+1/2}^{m+1}]e_{j+1}^{m+1} = e_j^m + \tau_j^m. \qquad (4.4.5)$$

We apply Theorem 4.4.1 to this set of difference equations with $b^{\max} \equiv b^{\min} \equiv 0$ and $\Sigma \equiv \tau/\Delta t$, where $\tau \equiv \max_{\substack{1 \le j \le N \\ 1 \le m \le M}} |\tau_j^m|$. For $1 \le j \le N$ this yields

$$-(m + 1) \, \Delta t \, \Sigma \le e_j^{m+1} \le (m + 1) \, \Delta t \, \Sigma.$$

Thus, since $M \, \Delta t = T$,

$$\max_{0 \le j \le N+1} |e_j^{m+1}| \le T\Sigma = T\frac{\tau}{\Delta t}.$$

This proves the following theorem.

Theorem 4.4.4.   *Let u and D have the differentiability properties of Theorem 4.3.3. Let u solve the initial–boundary value problem (4.1.5)–(4.1.7). Further, let U_j^m be the implicit finite difference approximation to u given by (4.4.1). Then the discretization error*

$$U_j^m - u(j \, \Delta x, m \, \Delta t) = O((\Delta x)^2 + \Delta t) \qquad (4.4.6)$$

as Δt and $\Delta x \to 0$.

A class of related difference formulas involves a weighted average of the foregoing explicit and implicit schemes. These methods are obtained by replacing (4.2.3) by

$$\frac{U_j^{m+1} - U_j^m}{\Delta t} - \mu \frac{D_{j+1/2}^{m+1}(U_{j+1}^{m+1} - U_j^{m+1}) - D_{j-1/2}^{m+1}(U_j^{m+1} - U_{j-1}^{m+1})}{(\Delta x)^2}$$

$$- (1 - \mu) \frac{D_{j+1/2}^m(U_{j+1}^m - U_j^m) - D_{j-1/2}^m(U_j^m - U_{j-1}^m)}{(\Delta x)^2} = \mu s_j^{m+1} + (1 - \mu)s_j^m, \quad (4.4.7)$$

where μ is a weight, $0 \le \mu \le 1$. Note that $\mu = 1$ yields the implicit scheme (4.4.1) and $\mu = 0$ yields the explicit scheme (4.3.1). The formulas are implicit unless $\mu = 0$.

From arguments very similar to those used to prove Theorem 4.4.4, we can establish a convergence theorem for these methods. The case $\mu = \frac{1}{2}$, known as the

Crank–Nicolson scheme (Crank and Nicolson [1947]), is particularly noteworthy since for smooth solutions its discretization error is second order in both Δx and Δt. Another choice of μ is considered in Exercises 4.6 and 4.7 for the special equation $u_t = u_{xx}$. The convergence theorem for the Crank–Nicolson scheme is stated without proof.

Theorem 4.4.5.   *Let u solve the initial–boundary value problem (4.1.5)–(4.1.7) and have four continuous derivatives with respect to x and three continuous derivatives with respect to t in $\bar{\Omega}$. Assume that D has four continuous derivatives with respect to x. Further, let U_j^m be the Crank–Nicolson implicit finite difference approximation to u given by (4.4.7) with $\mu = \frac{1}{2}$. Then the approximations are bounded independent of Δx and Δt and the discretization error*

$$U_j^m - u(j\,\Delta x, m\,\Delta t) = O((\Delta x)^2 + (\Delta t)^2) \qquad (4.4.8)$$

as Δt and $\Delta x \to 0$.

To verify the implications of Theorem 4.4.5 we consider the following simple example (Cavendish [1972]).

Example 4.1

Suppose that the diffusivity $D = 1$, the source $s(x) = 0$, and the interval $[a, b]$ is $[0, 1]$. If we choose homogeneous boundary conditions and a sinusoidal initial condition, then (4.1.5) becomes

$$\frac{\partial u}{\partial t} - \frac{\partial^2 u}{\partial x^2} = 0, \qquad 0 < x < 1, \quad t > 0$$

subject to boundary conditions

$$u(0, t) = u(1, t) = 0,$$

and initial condition

$$u(x, 0) = 10 \sin \pi x, \qquad 0 \le x \le 1.$$

The solution of this problem is

$$u(x, t) = 10 e^{-\pi^2 t} \sin \pi x.$$

If we apply the Crank–Nicolson method and choose the time step $\Delta t \ll \Delta x$, we anticipate that as $\Delta x \to 0$ the discretization error will approach zero like $(\Delta x)^2$. That is, if we write

$$E(\Delta x, t_m) \equiv \max \left| U_j^m - u(x_j, t_m) \right| \approx K(\Delta x)^\alpha,$$

then as $\Delta x \to 0$ we expect $\alpha \approx 2$. For two different values of Δx, say Δx_1 and Δx_2, we can compute the left-hand sides above, take the log of their ratios, and obtain an estimate of α as

$$\alpha \approx \log \frac{E(\Delta x_1, t_m)}{E(\Delta x_2, t_m)} \bigg/ \log \frac{\Delta x_1}{\Delta x_2}.$$

Table 4.4.1 contains results for this example when the time step is taken to be $\Delta t = 0.001$ and the errors are computed for a value of time $t_m = 0.1$. It is clear that these computational results support the conclusion of Theorem 4.4.5.

TABLE 4.4.1 ORDER OF THE CRANK–NICOLSON ERROR

Δx	$\max\limits_{1 \le i \le N} \lvert U_i^m - u(x_i, t_m) \rvert$	α
0.2	0.115	—
0.10	0.0303	1.93
0.0667	0.0133	2.02
0.0500	0.00754	1.99
0.0400	0.00480	2.02

4.5 APPROXIMATIONS TO THE MATRIX EXPONENTIAL

In the event that D is independent of t, $s = 0$, and the boundary conditions are homogeneous (i.e., $g = h = 0$), we can write (4.2.3) in matrix form as

$$\frac{d\mathbf{U}}{dt} = -A\mathbf{U}, \tag{4.5.1}$$

where $\mathbf{U} = (U_1, U_2, \ldots, U_N)^T$, and

$$A = \frac{1}{(\Delta x)^2} \, \text{Tridiag} \left\{ -D_{j-1/2}, (D_{j-1/2} + D_{j+1/2}), -D_{j+1/2} \right\}. \tag{4.5.2}$$

As noted in Section 1.3, the solution of (4.5.1) may be developed in terms of the matrix exponential. In fact, one easily verifies that

$$\mathbf{U}(t) = \exp(-At)\mathbf{U}(0). \tag{4.5.3}$$

For this problem it is instructive to interpret the time discretizations given in the preceding sections as approximations to the matrix exponential appearing in (4.5.3).

Let $t_m = m\,\Delta t$ and recall from Section 1.3 that for any matrix A the matrix exponential

$$\exp(-At) \equiv I - At + \frac{1}{2!}(At)^2 - \frac{1}{3!}(At^3) + \cdots.$$

Therefore, an obvious choice of an approximation for $\exp(-At_1)$ is

$$\exp(-At_1) \approx I - At_1. \tag{4.5.4}$$

If we replace the exponential in (4.5.3) by the right side of (4.5.4), and let $\mathbf{U}^0 = \mathbf{U}(0)$, we see that the approximation $\mathbf{U}^1$ to $\mathbf{U}(t_1)$ is given by

$$\mathbf{U}^1 = (I - A\,\Delta t)\mathbf{U}^0.$$

This can be rearranged to read

$$\frac{\mathbf{U}^1 - \mathbf{U}^0}{\Delta t} = -A\mathbf{U}^0,$$

which is precisely the *explicit method* (4.3.1) for $m = 0$.

Given $\mathbf{U}^1$, one can step ahead in time and consider the problem

$$\frac{d\mathbf{U}}{dt} = -A\mathbf{U}, \qquad \mathbf{U}(0) = \mathbf{U}^1,$$

which has the solution

$$\mathbf{U}(t) = \exp(-At)\mathbf{U}^1.$$

This can be approximated at $t = t_2$ by

$$\mathbf{U}^2 = (I - A\,\Delta t)\mathbf{U}^1.$$

Repeating this process, we find in general that $\mathbf{U}(t_m)$ can be approximated by

$$\mathbf{U}^m = (I - A\,\Delta t)\mathbf{U}^{m-1}.$$

Next we compare the series

$$\frac{1}{1+t} = 1 - t + t^2 + \cdots, \qquad |t| < 1,$$

with the series for e^{-t}. From this we are lead to the choice of the approximation

$$\exp(-At_1) \approx (I + At_1)^{-1}. \tag{4.5.5}$$

The inverse in (4.5.5) exists if t_1 is sufficiently small. Letting $\mathbf{U}^0 = \mathbf{U}(0)$ and making the obvious replacement in (4.5.3), we get

$$\mathbf{U}^1 = (I + A\,\Delta t)^{-1}U^0$$

or

$$\frac{\mathbf{U}^1 - \mathbf{U}^0}{\Delta t} = -A\mathbf{U}^1,$$

which is precisely the *implicit method* (4.4.2) for $m = 0$. In a similar manner, at time step m we see that $\mathbf{U}(t_m)$ is approximated by

$$\mathbf{U}^m = (I + A\,\Delta t)^{-1}\mathbf{U}^{m-1}.$$

Finally, we note that

$$\frac{1 - \dfrac{t}{2}}{1 + \dfrac{t}{2}} = 1 - t + \frac{t^2}{2} - \cdots, \qquad |t| < 2.$$

This series agrees with $\exp(-t)$ through quadratic terms. Again, we assume that t_1 is sufficiently small and let

$$\exp(-At_1) \approx \left(I + \frac{At_1}{2}\right)^{-1}\left(I - \frac{At_1}{2}\right) \qquad (4.5.6)$$

Proceeding as before, we now find that

$$\mathbf{U}^1 = \left[\left(I + \frac{At_1}{2}\right)^{-1}\left(I - \frac{At_1}{2}\right)\right]\mathbf{U}^0.$$

Upon rearrangement, we obtain

$$\left(I + \frac{At_1}{2}\right)\mathbf{U}^1 = \left(I - \frac{At_1}{2}\right)\mathbf{U}^0$$

or

$$\frac{\mathbf{U}^1 - \mathbf{U}^0}{\Delta t} = -\left(\frac{1}{2}A\mathbf{U}^1 + \frac{1}{2}A\mathbf{U}^0\right).$$

This is the *Crank–Nicolson method* presented in Section 4.4 when $m = 0$. Stepping ahead in time, we see that in this case $\mathbf{U}(t_m)$ is approximated by

$$\mathbf{U}^m = \left[\left(I + \frac{A\,\Delta t}{2}\right)^{-1}\left(I - \frac{A\,\Delta t}{2}\right)\right]\mathbf{U}^{m-1}.$$

The three approximations to $\exp(-At)$ given above are Padé rational approximations (Section 1.2). Each of the corresponding approximations to $\mathbf{U}(t)$ is of the form

$$\mathbf{U}^m = T(\Delta t)\mathbf{U}^{m-1},$$

where $T(t)$ is the associated Padé approximation to $\exp(-At)$. It follows that

$$\mathbf{U}^m = [T(\Delta t)]^m \mathbf{U}^0, \qquad (4.5.7)$$

and if $\rho(T(\Delta t))$, the spectral radius of $T(\Delta t)$, is greater than or to equal to 1, then $\mathbf{U}^m$ will *not* in general be bounded in norm as $m \to \infty$.

Following Varga [1962], we say that a matrix $T(t)$ is *stable* for $0 \leq t \leq t_0$ if $\rho(T(t)) \leq 1$ in this interval; and *unconditionally stable* if $\rho(T(t)) < 1$ for all $t > 0$. The next theorem gives sufficient conditions for certain matrices to be stable or unconditionally stable.

Theorem 4.5.1.   *Let A be an N × N matrix whose eigenvalues $\lambda_i[A]$ satisfy*

$$0 < \alpha < \operatorname{Re}\lambda_i[A] \leq \beta, \qquad 1 \leq i \leq N.$$

Then the matrix $(I - A\,\Delta t)$ is stable for

$$0 \leq \Delta t \leq \min_i \left(\frac{2\operatorname{Re}\lambda_i}{|\lambda_i|^2}\right).$$

The matrices $(I + A \Delta t)^{-1}$ and $(I + A \Delta t/2)^{-1}(I - A \Delta t/2)$ are both unconditionally stable.

Proof. From $\lambda_i[(I - A \Delta t)] = 1 - \Delta t \, \lambda_i[A]$, we have

$$\rho(I - A \Delta t) = \max_i |1 - \Delta t \, \lambda_i[A]|.$$

Now, $\rho(I - A \Delta t) \le 1$ implies that

$$\max_i \left[(1 - \Delta t \operatorname{Re} \lambda_i[A])^2 + (\Delta t \operatorname{Im} \lambda_i[A])^2\right]^{1/2} \le 1$$

or

$$\max_i \left[\Delta t^2 |\lambda_i[A]|^2 - 2\Delta t \operatorname{Re} \lambda_i[A]\right] \le 0,$$

which is true as long as

$$\Delta t \le \frac{2 \operatorname{Re} \lambda_i[A]}{|\lambda_i[A]|^2}.$$

For the matrix $(I + \Delta t \, A)^{-1}$, we note that

$$\lambda_i[(I + \Delta t \, A)^{-1}] = \frac{1}{1 + \Delta t \, \lambda_i[A]},$$

and by hypothesis,

$$\operatorname{Re}(1 + \Delta t \, \lambda_i[A]) > 1 + \Delta t \, \alpha > 1.$$

Thus $|\lambda_i[(I + \Delta t \, A)^{-1}]| < 1$, and $(I + \Delta t \, A)^{-1}$ is unconditionally stable.

Finally, since $\operatorname{Re} \lambda_i[A] > 0$, we have

$$\left|\lambda_i\left[\left(I + \frac{A \Delta t}{2}\right)^{-1}\left(I - \frac{A \Delta t}{2}\right)\right]\right| = \left|\frac{1 - \lambda_i[A] \Delta t/2}{1 + \lambda_i[A] \Delta t/2}\right| < 1.$$

It follows that $(I + A \Delta t/2)^{-1}(I - A \Delta t/2)$ is unconditionally stable.

Q.E.D.

For the simple system (4.5.1), the matrix A is symmetric and positive definite. Hence, the first hypothesis of Theorem 4.5.1 is satisfied. Furthermore, in this case

$$\min_i \left(\frac{2 \operatorname{Re} \lambda_i}{|\lambda_i|^2}\right) \ge \frac{2}{\rho(A)} \ge \frac{\Delta x^2}{\Gamma}.$$

Hence $(I - At)$ is stable if

$$0 \le \Delta t \le \frac{\Delta x^2}{\Gamma},$$

which is precisely the stability criterion (4.3.3). From (4.5.7) we see that if $\|\cdot\|_2$ denotes the Euclidean vector norm, then $\|\mathbf{U}^m\|_2 \le \|\mathbf{U}^0\|_2$ for all $m \ge 0$ if $(I - At)$ is stable. Of course, the unconditional stability of $(I - A\,\Delta t)^{-1}$ and $(I + A\,\Delta t/2)^{-1}(I - A\,\Delta t/2)$ implies that this inequality holds for the implicit method (4.4.2) and the Crank–Nicolson method without any condition such as (4.3.3).

NOTES AND REMARKS

4.1 Diffusion processes in n-dimensions are modeled by an equation of the form

$$\phi(\mathbf{x}, t)u_t - \nabla \cdot D(\mathbf{x}, t)\nabla u + \sigma(\mathbf{x}, t)u(\mathbf{x}, t) = s(\mathbf{x}, t) \tag{1}$$

where ∇u is the gradient of u and $\nabla \cdot \mathbf{w}$ is the divergence of the vector $\mathbf{w}$. For discussions concerning the existence, uniqueness, and smoothness of solutions to such equations, see Friedman [1964, 1969]. Section 2.3 presents a derivation of a partial differential equation of the form (1) describing the transfer of heat by conduction. Reactor physics provides another source of such an equation. In the latter, $u(\mathbf{x}, t)$ is the density of neutrons of a particular average energy in a reactor, $\phi(\mathbf{x}, t)$ is the inverse of the average velocity of these neutrons, $D(\mathbf{x}, t)$ is the diffusion coefficient, $\sigma(\mathbf{x}, t)$ is the removal cross section, and $s(\mathbf{x}, t)$ is a source term. Equation (1) represents a conservation of neutrons (see Glasstone and Edlund [1952]).

4.2 The replacement of the partial differential equation (4.1.1) by the system of ordinary differential equations (4.2.3) is an example of what is sometimes referred to as the *method of lines*. This method was used by Faddeeva [1949] to approximate elliptic equations (see Kantorovich and Krylov [1958]). In this section the function $U_j(t)$ approximates $u(x_j, t)$ along the line $x = x_j, j = 1, \dots, N$.

4.4 The Crank–Nicolson scheme [1947] is second order in space *and* time. Another such finite difference scheme for the equation $u_t = u_{xx}$ is

$$\frac{3}{2}\left(\frac{U_j^{m+1} - U_j^m}{\Delta t}\right) - \frac{1}{2}\left(\frac{U_j^m - U_j^{m-1}}{\Delta t}\right) = \frac{U_{j+1}^{m+1} - 2U_j^{m+1} + U_{j-1}^{m+1}}{\Delta x^2}.$$

This scheme is unconditionally stable, involves three time levels, and is second order in space and time (see Richtmyer and Morton [1967]).

4.5 If $f(z)$ has the power series representation

$$f(z) = \sum_{m=0}^{\infty} C_m z^m, \qquad |z| < R$$

and the spectral radius, $\rho(A)$, of an $m \times m$ matrix A satisfies $\rho(A) < R$, then the value of the matrix function $f(A)$ is defined by

$$f(A) = \sum_{m=0}^{\infty} C_m A^m.$$

If $f(z) = \exp(z)$, then $R = \infty$, and

$$\exp(A) = \sum_{m=0}^{\infty} \frac{1}{m!} A^m$$

for any A. If there exists a nonsingular matrix P such that $P^{-1}AP = \text{Diag}(\lambda_1, \ldots, \lambda_N)$, then

$$\exp(-At) = P\,\text{Diag}(e^{-\lambda_1 t}, \ldots, e^{-\lambda_N t})P^{-1}.$$

If B and C commute, then

$$\exp(B)\exp(C) = \exp(C)\exp(B). \quad \cdot$$

Instead of the Pade approximations to the exponential, we could also have considered Chebyshev rational approximations as discussed, for example, in Cody, Meinardus, and Varga [1969].

EXERCISES

4.1. Construct an alternative proof of the uniqueness result of Corollary 4.1.2 using the following argument. Let v denote the difference of two solutions. Show that $dJ/dt \leq 0$, where $J(t) \equiv \int_a^b v^2(x, t)\,dx$. Next observe that $J(0) = 0$ and hence the nonincreasing function of t, $J(t)$, must be identically zero.

4.2. State and prove a maximum principle theorem for the two-dimensional parabolic initial–boundary value problem

$$u_t - \nabla \cdot (D\,\nabla u) = s, \qquad \mathbf{x} \in \Omega \subset R^2$$

$$u(\mathbf{x}, 0) = f(\mathbf{x}), \qquad \mathbf{x} \in \Omega$$

$$u(\mathbf{x}, t) = g(t), \qquad \mathbf{x} \in \partial\Omega.$$

4.3. Prove that if (4.3.3) is satisfied, then the explicit finite difference method satisfies the following discrete maximum principle:

Let U_j^m satisfy (4.3.2) where $s \equiv 0$ and D is a positive function. Then for $t \leq T$

$$b^{\min} \leq U_j^m \leq b^{\max},$$

where $b^{\min}$ and $b^{\max}$ are defined in Theorem 4.1.1.

4.4. Suppose that the explicit method (4.3.2) is used to approximate the equation $u_t = u_{xx}$, with the boundary conditions $u(a, t) = u(b, t) = 0$.
  (a) Verify that the resulting system may be written in vector form as

$$\mathbf{U}^m = (I - rB)\mathbf{U}^{m-1}, \qquad m = 1, 2, \ldots,$$

where B is the $N \times N$ tridiagonal matrix Tridiag $\{-1, 2, -1\}$, and

$$\mathbf{U}^m = (U_1^m, \ldots, U_N^m)^T.$$

  (b) Verify that for $i = 1, \ldots, N$,

$$\mathbf{y}_i = \left(\sin\frac{i\pi}{N+1}, \sin\frac{2i\pi}{N+1}, \ldots, \sin\frac{iN\pi}{N+1}\right)^T$$

is an eigenvector of B corresponding to the eigenvalue

$$\beta_i = 2\left(1 - \cos\frac{i\pi}{N+1}\right).$$

4.5. Consider the initial–boundary value problem

$$u_t = u_{xx}, \qquad 0 < x < \pi, \quad 0 < t \le T,$$

$$u(x, 0) = 0, \qquad u(0, t) = u(\pi, t) = 0.$$

Suppose that in applying the explicit method (4.3.2) to this problem, rounding errors of order ε are made in the initial condition in such a way that $U_j^0 = \varepsilon \sin(jN \Delta x), j = 1, \ldots, N$. Use the results of Exercise 4.4 to show that if $M \Delta t = T$ and $r = \text{constant} > \frac{1}{2}$, then $|U_1^M| \to \infty$ as $\Delta t \to 0$.

4.6. If the weighted implicit method (4.4.7) is used to approximate the equation $u_t = u_{xx}$, then the local truncation errors τ_j^m are defined by the expression

$$-\mu r u(x_{j-1}, t_{m+1}) + (1 + 2\mu r)u(x_j, t_{m+1}) - \mu r u(x_{j+1}, t_{m+1})$$

$$= (1 - \mu)ru(x_{j-1}, t_m) + [1 - 2(1 - \mu)r]u(x_j, t_m) + (1 - \mu)ru(x_{j+1}, t_m) - \tau_j^m,$$

where $r = \Delta t / (\Delta x)^2$ is a constant and $u(x, t)$ is a solution of the differential equation. Show that if $u(x, t)$ is sufficiently differentiable, then as $\Delta x, \Delta t \to 0$,

(a) $\dfrac{\tau_j^m}{\Delta t} = O((\Delta t)^2 + (\Delta x)^2)$ when $\mu = \dfrac{1}{2}$,

(b) $\dfrac{\tau_j^m}{\Delta t} = O((\Delta t)^2 + \Delta t(\Delta x)^2)$ when $\mu = \dfrac{1}{2}\left(1 - \dfrac{1}{6r}\right)$.

Note that since $2\Delta t(\Delta x)^2 \le (\Delta t)^2 + (\Delta x)^4$, we also have

$$\frac{\tau_j^m}{\Delta t} = O((\Delta t)^2 + (\Delta x)^4).$$

[*Hint:* Consider Taylor expansions for $\tau_j^m/\Delta t$ at the point $(x_j, t_{m+1/2})$.]

4.7. Let the weighted implicit method (4.4.7) be applied to the equation $u_t = u_{xx}$, with the boundary conditions $u(a, t) = u(b, t) = 0$.

(a) Verify that when $\mu = \frac{1}{2}(1 - 1/6r)$, where $r = \Delta t / (\Delta x)^2$, the resulting equation system may be written in matrix form as

$$[(10 + 12r)I + (1 - 6r)C]\mathbf{U}^{m+1} = [(10 - 12r)I + (1 + 6r)C]\mathbf{U}^m,$$

where $\mathbf{U}^m = (U_1^m, \ldots, U_N^m)^T$ and C is the $N \times N$ tridiagonal matrix, Tridiag $\{1, 0, 1\}$.

(b) Prove that the coefficient matrix of $\mathbf{U}^{m+1}$ appearing in part (a) is nonsingular for all $r > 0$. [*Hint:* Use the result of Exercise 4.4b to determine the eigenvalues of C.]

(c) Prove that the matrix

$$[(10 + 12r)I + (1 - 6r)C]^{-1}[(10 - 12r)I + (1 + 6r)C]$$

is unconditionally stable in the sense of Section 4.5.

4.8. Let K be a positive constant and consider the two-dimensional heat equation (cf. Section 2.3)

$$u_t = K(u_{xx} + u_{yy})$$

for (x, y) in the interior of the unit square $\Omega = [0, 1] \times [0, 1]$.

(a) By subdividing Ω into a union of mesh squares of side length h and replacing the derivatives u_{xx} and u_{yy} by their second divided differences $[u(x + h, y, t) - 2u(x, y, t) + u(x - h, y, t)]/h^2$, and so on, develop semidiscrete approximations of $u(x, y, t)$ in the manner of Section 4.2.

(b) If $u(x, y, t) = 0$ on the boundary of Ω, the semidiscrete system of part (a) again has a solution of the form (4.5.3). Show that the explicit method that results from approximating $\exp(-tA)$ by $(I - tA)$ is stable in the sense of Section 4.5 if $\Delta t < h^2/4K$.

(c) Generalize parts (a) and (b) to the n-dimensional parabolic equation

$$u_t = K \sum_{i=1}^{n} u_{x_i x_i},$$

where $(x_1, \ldots, x_n) \in \Omega \equiv [0, 1] \times \cdots \times [0, 1]$, and $u = 0$ on the boundary of Ω.

4.9. We can write (4.2.3) and (4.2.5) in matrix form as

$$\frac{d\mathbf{U}}{dt} = -A\mathbf{U} + \mathbf{S}, \qquad \mathbf{U}(0) = \mathbf{f}.$$

If D is independent of time, verify that the semidiscrete approximation $\mathbf{U}(t)$ is in fact

$$\mathbf{U}(t) = \exp(-At)\mathbf{U}(0) + \int_0^t \exp(-A(t-s))\mathbf{S}(s)\, ds.$$

Computer Exercises

4.10. The solution of the initial–boundary value problem

$$u_t = u_{xx}, \qquad 0 < x < 1, \quad t > 0,$$

$$u(0, t) = u(1, t) = 0,$$

$$u(x, 0) = \begin{cases} 2x, & 0 \le x \le \frac{1}{2} \\ 2(1 - x), & \frac{1}{2} < x \le 1, \end{cases}$$

is

$$u(x, t) = \frac{8}{\pi^2} \sum_{k=1}^{\infty} \frac{1}{k^2} \left(\sin \frac{k\pi}{2} \right) (\sin k\pi x) e^{-k^2\pi^2 t}.$$

Use the explicit method (4.3.2) with $\Delta t = \Delta x^2/10$ to determine numerical approximations of $u(x, 0.1)$. Consider the following cases: **(a)** $\Delta x = \frac{1}{10}$; **(b)** $\Delta x = \frac{1}{20}$; **(c)** $\Delta x = \frac{1}{40}$.

4.11. Rework the problem of Exercise 4.10 by the implicit method (4.4.2) and obtain a four-place numerical approximation of $u(0.3, 0.1)$.

4.12. The temperature in a hollow sphere satisfies the equation

$$u_t = u_{rr} + \frac{2}{r} u_r, \qquad 1 < r < \tfrac{3}{2}, \quad t > 0,$$

where r is the radial distance from the sphere's center. Make the change of variable $u = v/r$ and derive a transformed equation for v. Then apply the Crank–Nicolson method [(4.4.7) with $\mu = \frac{1}{2}$] to this equation to obtain a numerical approximation of $u(x, 1)$. Assume that

$$u(1, t) = 1, \, u(\tfrac{3}{2}, t) = 0, \qquad u(r, 0) = 4(\tfrac{3}{2} - r)^2.$$

Use a sequence of mesh refinements to compute an approximation for which you are convinced that the maximum error in your approximation is less than 5×10^{-4}.

5

Lax-Richtmyer Theory
for Initial Value
Problems

As we have seen in Chapters 3 and 4, the formulation of a meaningful problem involving hyperbolic or parabolic partial differential equations requires the imposition of initial (or initial–boundary) conditions. In this chapter we study such problems from an abstract point of view. This has certain advantages. For example, it allows us to assign a meaning to the solution of a problem in which the initial data do not possess sufficient smoothness to permit the existence of a solution in the classical sense. Furthermore, when the theory is supplemented by an appropriate definition of a finite difference method, it leads in principle to a simple necessary and sufficient condition for the convergence of the finite difference approximations. The body of material that constitutes what has come to be known as "Lax–Richtmyer theory" is a well-established part of the numerical analysis of partial differential equations, and although our development mainly follows that of Richtmyer and Morton [1967], related points of view may be found in Cryer [1982] and Meis and Marcowitz [1981].

5.1 BANACH SPACES

In this section we summarize some basic material on a class of abstract spaces known as Banach spaces. Such an abbreviated treatment requires the omission of many details, and in particular we do not include proofs of the theorems quoted here. The interested reader may find these proofs, for example, in Kreyszig [1978]. We assume a familiarity with the basic notions of vector spaces, fields, and norms.

Let X be a vector space over a scalar field, and let $\|\cdot\|\colon X \to R$ be a norm on X. The pairing of X with $\|\cdot\|$ defines a *normed space*.

A sequence $\{u_n\}$ in a normed space is convergent to the limit $u \in X$ if $\lim_{n \to \infty} \|u_n - u\| = 0$. In this case we write $u_n \to u$. A sequence $\{u_n\}$ in a normed space is a *Cauchy sequence* if $\lim_{m,n \to \infty} \|u_m - u_n\| = 0$. It is easy to see that if $\{u_n\}$ is convergent, it is a Cauchy sequence; however, the converse of this statement is not necessarily true. A normed space in which every Cauchy sequence is convergent is called a *complete* normed space or more simply, a *Banach space*.

If X is a normed space and $D \subset X$, then $\bar{D}$, the *closure* of D in X, is the set of limits of sequences in D. Thus $u \in \bar{D}$ if and only if there is a sequence $\{u_n\}$ in D such that $u_n \to u$. The set D is *closed* in X if $\bar{D} = D$; it is *dense* in X if $\bar{D} = X$.

A *subspace* of a Banach space, when equipped with the norm of the parent space, may not be complete. The following theorem asserts that this cannot happen if the subspace is closed.

Theorem 5.1.1.   *A subspace D of a Banach space X is complete (and therefore a Banach space) if and only if it is closed in X.*

Let X and Y be Banach spaces, and let $D \subset X$. If T is an operator whose domain is D and whose range is contained in Y, we write $T\colon D \subset X \to Y$. We say that T is *linear* if D is a subspace of X and if, in addition,

$$T(u + v) = Tu + Tv,$$

$$T(\alpha u) = \alpha Tu,$$

for all $u, v \in D$ and scalars α. A linear operator is *bounded* if there is a constant K such that

$$\|Tu\| \le K\|u\| \tag{5.1.1}$$

for all $u \in D$. Note that although the norms on X and Y may differ, we do not indicate this in (5.1.1) since there is no chance of confusion. This is a practice we will continue to follow.

If $T\colon D \subset X \to Y$ is a bounded linear operator, the infimum of the set of upper bounds is called the *norm* of T and is denoted by $\|T\|$. It is not difficult to see that

$$\|T\| = \sup_{u \ne 0} \frac{\|Tu\|}{\|u\|} = \sup_{\|u\| = 1} \|Tu\|.$$

Since this norm satisfies all the defining properties of a vector norm, the terminology is justified.

A family Γ of linear operators $T\colon X \to Y$ is said to be *uniformly bounded* if there is a constant K such that (5.1.1) holds for all $T \in \Gamma$ and $u \in X$. The next theorem, which is known as the Banach–Steinhaus theorem or the principle of uniform boundedness, provides sufficient conditions for a family Γ to be uniformly bounded.

Theorem 5.1.2.   *A family Γ of bounded linear operators mapping a Banach space X into itself is uniformly bounded if for each $u \in X$, the set of norms*

$$S = \{\|Tu\| \mid T \in \Gamma\}$$

is bounded.

A linear operator $T: D \subset X \to Y$ is *continuous* if for each $u_0 \in D$ and $\varepsilon > 0$, there is a corresponding $\delta > 0$ such that

$$\|Tu - Tu_0\| \le \varepsilon \quad \text{when} \quad \|u - u_0\| \le \delta.$$

Obviously, a bounded linear operator is continuous. The converse is also true; that is, a continuous linear operator is bounded (see Kreyszig [1978]).

Let $T: D \subset X \to Y$ and $T': D' \subset X \to Y$ be linear operators. Then T' is an *extension* of T from D to D' if $D \subset D'$ and $Tu = T'u$ for all $u \in D$. With regard to extensions we have the following theorem.

Theorem 5.1.3.   *If D is a dense subspace of a Banach space X and $T: D \subset X \to Y$ is a continuous linear operator, then T has a unique, continuous linear extension T' from D to X whose norm satisfies $\|T'\| = \|T\|$.*

5.2 INITIAL VALUE PROBLEMS

We now give a Banach space formulation of initial value problems and define the concept of a "well-posed" problem.

Let X be a Banach space with norm $\|\cdot\|$, and let $A: Y \subset X \to X$ be a linear operator. By a *genuine solution* $u(t)$ of the abstract initial value problem

$$\frac{du(t)}{dt} = Au(t), \qquad 0 \le t \le T,$$

$$u(0) = u_0,$$

(5.2.1)

we mean a one-parameter family of elements $u(t) \in Y$, such that $u(0)$ coincides with the prescribed initial condition u_0 and

$$\lim_{\Delta t \to 0} \left\| \frac{u(t + \Delta t) - u(t)}{\Delta t} - Au(t) \right\| = 0, \qquad 0 \le t \le T.$$

(5.2.2)

In this formulation it is useful to think of $u(t)$, for each t, as a member of some space of functions of the variable[1] x, and A as a linear differential operator (independent of t). In the case of an initial–boundary value problem (Chapter 4), we assume

---

[1] We again have in mind the case of two independent variables, x and t.

that the boundary conditions are linear and homogeneous. In other words, on the boundary, $Bu(t) = 0$, where B is an operator of the same nature as A. When they exist, the boundary conditions are accommodated by building them into the set Y (i.e., they are satisfied by each member of Y).

Let $D \subset Y$ be a subspace of initial conditions u_0 such that problem (5.2.1) has a unique genuine solution. For any fixed t, the operator $E_0(t)$: $D \rightarrow X$, $E_0(t)u_0 = u(t)$, is called the *genuine solution operator*. We leave as Exercise 5.3 the verification that $E_0(t)$ is a linear operator.

We can now make precise the notion of well-posedness mentioned in Chapter 3. We will say that problem (5.2.1) is *well posed*[2] (on X) if (1) there is a subspace D of initial conditions defined as above that is dense in X, and (2) the associated family of genuine solution operators $E_0(t)$, $0 \le t \le T$, is uniformly bounded. If $u(t)$ and $v(t)$ are two genuine solutions corresponding to the initial conditions u_0 and v_0, respectively, and if the problem is well posed, then (2) implies the existence of a constant K such that for all $0 \le t \le T$,

$$\|u(t) - v(t)\| = \|E_0(t)(u_0 - v_0)\| \le K\|u_0 - v_0\|.$$

Thus the solution depends continuously on the initial condition.

We will henceforth assume that (5.2.1) is well posed. With this assumption it follows from Theorem 5.1.3 that $E_0(t)$ has a continuous linear extension $E(t)$ from D to X such that $\|E(t)\| = \|E_0(t)\| \le K$. This extension is called the *generalized solution operator*.

Theorem 5.2.1.   *The generalized solution $u(t) = E(t)u_0$, $u_0 \in X$, is continuous on* $[0, T]$.

Proof. Fix $t \in [0, T]$ and choose $\{u_{0n}\}$ in D such that $u_{0n} \rightarrow u_0$. If $s \in [0, T]$, then

$$\|u(s) - u(t)\| = \|(E(s) - E(t))u_0\|$$
$$\le \|E(s)(u_0 - u_{0n})\| + \|(E(s) - E(t))u_{0n}\| + \|E(t)(u_{0n} - u_0)\|.$$

In view of the well-posed nature of (5.2.1), this implies that

$$\|u(s) - u(t)\| \le 2K\|u_0 - u_{0n}\| + \|u_n(s) - u_n(t)\|, \tag{5.2.3}$$

where K is a constant and $u_n(t) = E(t)u_{0n}$ is the genuine solution corresponding to u_{0n}. According to (5.2.2), $\eta_n \in X$ exists such that $\lim_{s \to t} \|\eta_n\| = 0$ and

$$\|u_n(s) - u_n(t)\| \le |s - t|[\|Au_n(t)\| + \|\eta_n\|].$$

Substituting this in (5.2.3), we obtain

$$\|u(s) - u(t)\| \le 2K\|u_0 - u_{0n}\| + |s - t|[\|Au_n(t)\| + \|\eta_n\|].$$

[2] This form of well-posedness is due to Hadamard.

If $\varepsilon > 0$ is given, we can choose n so large that the first term on the right does not exceed $\varepsilon/2$. We can then pick δ so that the second term is also no greater than $\varepsilon/2$ when $|s - t| \leq \delta$.

Q.E.D.

The next theorem shows that $E(t)$ has the so-called *semigroup property*.

Theorem 5.2.2.   *For all s, t, $s + t$ in $[0, T]$ we have*

$$E(s + t) = E(s)E(t). \tag{5.2.4}$$

Proof. Let $u_0 \in X$. Then there is a sequence $\{u_{0n}\}$ in D such that $u_{0n} \to u_0$. We let $u_n(t) = E(t)u_{0n}$, fix t, and set $v_n(s) = u_n(s + t)$. Obviously, $v_n(s)$ is the genuine solution in $[0, T - t]$ of (5.2.1) corresponding to the initial condition $u_n(t)$. Thus $v_n(s) = E(s)u_n(t)$. Hence

$$E(s + t)u_{0n} = u_n(s + t) = v_n(s) = E(s)u_n(t) = E(s)E(t)u_{0n}.$$

Therefore,

$$
\begin{aligned}
\left\| E(s + t)u_0 - E(s)E(t)u_0 \right\| &\leq \left\| E(s + t)(u_0 - u_{0n}) \right\| + \left\| E(s + t)u_{0n} - E(s)E(t)u_{0n} \right\| \\
&\quad + \left\| E(s)E(t)(u_{0n} - u_0) \right\| \\
&\leq \left\| E(s + t) \right\| \left\| u_0 - u_{0n} \right\| + \left\| E(s)E(t) \right\| \left\| u_{0n} - u_0 \right\| \\
&\leq (K + K^2) \left\| u_0 - u_{0n} \right\|.
\end{aligned}
$$

Letting $n \to \infty$, we get the desired conclusion.

Q.E.D.

5.3 DIFFERENCE METHODS

We will "numerically solve" the initial value problem given in Section 5.2 by a *difference method*, M_D. This is simply a one-parameter family of uniformly bounded linear operators,

$$C(\Delta t): X \to X, \qquad 0 < \Delta t \leq \Delta t_0.$$

The approximate solution of (5.2.1), which we denote by $u(\cdot, t)$, is then presumed to satisfy the *difference equation*

$$u(\cdot, t + \Delta t) = C(\Delta t)u(\cdot, t).$$

The operator $C(\Delta t)$ is supposed to approximate the generalized solution operator $E(\Delta t)$. To assess the accuracy of this approximation we introduce the concept of consistency (cf. Section 1.2). Thus we say that the difference method M_D is *consistent* [with the initial value problem (5.2.1)] if there is a dense subspace D_C of X such that for all $u_0 \in D_C$,

$$\lim_{\Delta t \to 0} \left\| \frac{[C(\Delta t) - E(\Delta t)]E(t)u_0}{\Delta t} \right\| = 0, \qquad 0 \leq t \leq T. \tag{5.3.1}$$

The quantity

$$\tau \equiv \left[C(\Delta t) - E(\Delta t)\right]E(t)u_0, \qquad u_0 \in D_C,$$

is called the *local truncation error*. If as $\Delta t \to 0$, $\|\tau\| = O((\Delta t)^{p+1})$ for some $p \geq 1$, the method M_D is said to be (at least) of *order p*. It follows from (5.3.1) that the order of any consistent method is at least unity[3].

If $u_0 \in D_C \cap D$, and I is the identity operator, then

$$\frac{\left[C(\Delta t) - E(\Delta t)\right]E(t)u_0}{\Delta t} = \frac{C(\Delta t) - I}{\Delta t}u(t) - \frac{u(t + \Delta t) - u(t)}{\Delta t}$$

$$= \left[\frac{C(\Delta t) - I}{\Delta t} - A\right]u(t) + \eta,$$

where $\lim\limits_{\Delta t \to 0} \|\eta\| = 0$. Thus, for $u_0 \in D_C \cap D$, the operator $[C(\Delta t) - I]/\Delta t$ is a convergent approximation of the operator A when M_D is consistent.

Consistency is one of the three key ingredients in the theory of abstract difference methods. The other two are convergence and stability.

The difference method M_D is *convergent* with respect to (5.2.1) if for each (fixed) $t \in [0, T]$ and $u_0 \in X$ we have

$$\lim\limits_{\Delta t_j \to 0} \left\|\left[C^{n_j}(\Delta t_j) - E(t)\right]u_0\right\| = 0,$$

where $\{n_j\}$ is a sequence of integers and $\{\Delta t_j\}$ a sequence of step sizes such that $\lim\limits_{j \to \infty} n_j \Delta t_j = t$.

Finally, the method M_D is *stable* if the family of operators

$$\Gamma = \left\{C^n(\Delta t) \mid 0 < \Delta t \leq \Delta t_0, 0 \leq n\Delta t \leq T\right\}$$

is uniformly bounded. Note that whereas consistency and convergence depend on the particular initial value problem under consideration, stability is solely a property of the difference method M_D.

5.4 THE LAX EQUIVALENCE THEOREM

We come now to the fundamental theorem relating the three concepts of consistency, convergence, and stability.

Theorem 5.4.1 (Lax).   *Given a well-posed initial value problem (5.2.1) and a consistent difference method M_D, stability is necessary and sufficient for convergence.*

---

[3] Some authors define the local truncation error as $\tau/\Delta t$. If, as in Chapter 4, the local truncation error is defined as $\tau/\Delta t$, the order of the method coincides with the order of the local error.

Proof. Suppose that M_D is convergent. Since each $C^n(\Delta t) \in \Gamma$ is bounded, the stability of M_D will follow from Theorem 5.1.2 if we can show that for each $u_0 \in X$, the set

$$S \equiv \{\|C^n(\Delta t)u_0\| \mid 0 \le \Delta t \le \Delta t_0; 0 \le n\,\Delta t \le T\}$$

is bounded. The proof of this is indirect. If S is unbounded, there are sequences $\{n_j\}$ and $\{\Delta t_j\}$ such that

$$0 \le \Delta t_j \le \Delta t_0, \qquad 0 \le n_j\,\Delta t_j \le T, \quad \text{and} \quad \|C^{n_j}(\Delta t_j)u_0\| \to \infty \text{ as } j \to \infty.$$

By selecting appropriate subsequences if necessary, we can assume without loss of generality that

$$\Delta t_j \to a \quad \text{and} \quad n_j\,\Delta t_j \to t,$$

where $0 \le a \le \Delta t_0$ and $0 \le t \le T$. If $a \ne 0$, then $n_j \to t/a$ and the sequence $\{n_j\}$ is bounded. But the inequality

$$\|[C^{n_j}(\Delta t_j)u_0\| \le \|C(\Delta t_j)\|^{n_j}\|u_0\|$$

implies that $\|C(\Delta t_j)\|^{n_j} \to \infty$. Hence $\|C(\Delta t_j)\| \to \infty$, contradicting the definition of M_D. We conclude that $\Delta t_j \to 0$. Now we apply the hypothesis that M_D is convergent to deduce the existence of a constant K such that

$$\|[C^{n_j}(\Delta t_j) - E(t)]u_0\| \le K, \qquad j = 1, 2, \ldots.$$

Then

$$\|C^{n_j}(\Delta t_j)u_0\| = \|[C^{n_j}(\Delta t_j) - E(t)]u_0\| + \|E(t)u_0\|$$
$$\le K + \|E(t)u_0\|,$$

which contradicts the assumption that $\|C^{n_j}(\Delta t_j)u_0\| \to \infty$. This proves that S is bounded and consequently, that M_D is stable.

Assume now that M_D is stable. Let $u_0 \in D_C$, and choose $\{\Delta t_j\}$, $\{n_j\}$, and $t \in [0, T]$ such that $\Delta t_j \to 0$ and $n_j\,\Delta t_j \to t$ as $j \to \infty$. Consider the quantity

$$V_j \equiv [C^{n_j}(\Delta t_j) - E(n_j\,\Delta t_j)]u_0.$$

Using the semigroup property of $E(t)$, we write this as

$$V_j \equiv [C^{n_j}(\Delta t_j) - E^{n_j}(\Delta t_j)]u_0.$$

Applying the identity

$$C^{n_j} - E^{n_j} = (C^{n_j} - C^{n_j - 1}E) + (C^{n_j - 1}E - C^{n_j - 2}E^2) + \cdots + (CE^{n_j - 1} - E^{n_j})$$
$$= C^{n_j - 1}(C - E) + C^{n_j - 2}(C - E)E + \cdots + (C - E)E^{n_j - 1},$$

we have

$$V_j = \sum_{k=0}^{n_j - 1} C^k(\Delta t_j)[C(\Delta t_j) - E(\Delta t_j)]E^{n_j - 1 - k}(\Delta t_j)u_0$$

$$= \sum_{k=0}^{n_j - 1} C^k(\Delta t_j)[C(\Delta t_j) - E(\Delta t_j)]E((n_j - 1 - k)\,\Delta t_j)u_0.$$

Therefore, since M_D is stable, there is a constant K such that

$$\|V_j\| \leq K \sum_{k=0}^{n_j-1} \left\| \frac{C(\Delta t_j) - E(\Delta t_j)}{\Delta t_j} E((n_j - 1 - k)\,\Delta t_j)u_0 \right\| \Delta t_j.$$

But M_D is also consistent. Thus if $\varepsilon > 0$, then

$$\left\| \frac{C(\Delta t_j) - E(\Delta t_j)}{\Delta t_j} E((n_j - 1 - k)\,\Delta t_j)u_0 \right\| \leq \varepsilon$$

for all j sufficiently large. It follows that for such j, $\|V_j\| \leq K\varepsilon n_j \Delta t_j \leq KT\varepsilon$; in other words, $\|V_j\| \to 0$ as $j \to \infty$.

Now we observe that

$$\|[C^{n_j}(\Delta t_j) - E(t)]u_0\| \leq \|V_j\| + \|[E(n_j \Delta t_j) - E(t)]u_0\|$$
$$= \|V_j\| + \|u(n_j \Delta t_j) - u(t)\|,$$

where $u(t) = E(t)u_0$. Recalling that $u(t)$ is continuous on $[0, T]$ (Theorem 5.2.1), this inequality shows that M_D is convergent on the set D_C.

To extend the convergence to X, we choose, for $u_0 \in X$, a sequence $\{u_{0k}\}$ in D_C such that $u_{0k} \to u_0$. Then

$$\|[C^{n_j}(\Delta t_j) - E(t)]u_0\|$$
$$\leq \|C^{n_j}(\Delta t_j)(u_0 - u_{k0})\| + \|[C^{n_j}(\Delta t_j) - E(t)]u_{k0}\| + \|E(t)(u_{k0} - u_0)\|.$$

Since M_D is stable and the problem is well posed, $\|C^{n_j}(\Delta t_j)\|$ and $\|E(t)\|$ are bounded by some constant K. Therefore, if $\varepsilon > 0$, we can choose k so large that

$$\|[C^{n_j}(\Delta t_j) - E(t)]u_0\| \leq 2K\varepsilon + \|[C^{n_j}(\Delta t_j) - E(t)]u_{k0}\|.$$

Then for all Δt_j sufficiently small, we have

$$\|[C^{n_j}(\Delta t_j) - E(t)]u_0\| \leq (2K + 1)\varepsilon.$$

Q.E.D.

By specializing the arguments used in the proof of Theorem 5.4.1, we may also establish the following corollary.

Corollary 5.4.2.   *If M_D is a stable pth-order method and $\{n_j\}$ and $\{\Delta t_j\}$ are chosen so that $n_j \Delta t_j = t$, the discretization error $C^{n_j}(\Delta t_j)u_0 - u(t)$ is $O((\Delta t_j)^p)$.*

5.5 ILLUSTRATION OF THE THEORY

As an illustration of the ideas of the previous sections, we consider an example taken from the theory of one-dimensional heat conduction (see Chapters 2 and 4). An even simpler illustration is provided by Exercise 5.4.

Let X be the vector space of real-valued functions over the real numbers that are continuous on the closed interval $[0, \pi]$ and vanish at its endpoints. The space X

becomes a Banach space when equipped with the norm $\|\cdot\|$, where

$$\|v\| \equiv \sup_{x \in [0,\pi]} |v(x)|, \qquad v \in X.$$

This follows from the fact that convergence with respect to $\|\cdot\|$ is uniform convergence. Therefore, a sequence in X is a Cauchy sequence if and only if it is uniformly convergent on $[0, \pi]$. But as each member of such a sequence is continuous, the limit function is also continuous and hence X is complete.

Let Y denote the subspace consisting of those members of X with continuous second derivatives on $[0, \pi]$. If $u: [0, \pi] \times [0, T] \to R$ and we identify $u(t)$ with the function $u(\cdot, t)$, then for $u(t) \in Y$, $0 \le t \le T$, we define $Au = u_{xx}$.

With these definitions, (5.2.1) is an abstract statement of the heat conduction initial–boundary value problem in which we seek a function $u(x, t)$ such that

$$u_t = u_{xx}, \qquad 0 \le x \le \pi, \quad 0 \le t \le T,$$

$$u(0, t) = u(\pi, t) = 0, \qquad 0 \le t \le T, \qquad \qquad (5.5.1)$$

$$u(x, 0) = u_0(x), \qquad 0 \le x \le \pi.$$

To show that this problem is well posed we let D be the set of finite linear combinations of the functions $\sin kt, k = 1, 2, \ldots$. That is, $u_0 \in D$ if for some integer n there is a set of real numbers, say $b_1, \ldots, b_n$, such that

$$u_0(x) = \sum_{k=1}^{n} b_k \sin kx.$$

Obviously, D is a subspace of Y. Furthermore, we directly verify that the function

$$u(x, t) \equiv \sum_{k=1}^{n} b_k e^{-k^2 t} \sin kx$$

is a genuine solution of the initial value problem. That this is the only genuine solution is a consequence of Corollary 4.1.2. Furthermore, Theorem 4.1.1 may be used to show that the genuine solution operators $E_0(t)$, $0 \le t \le T$, are uniformly bounded [indeed, $\|E_0(t)\| \le 1$]. A proof that does not make use of Theorem 4.1.1 is the content of Exercise 5.6.

It remains to demonstrate that D is dense in X. We can do this with the help of Fourier series. Recall that the trigonometric series

$$\frac{a_0}{2} + \sum_{k=1}^{\infty} (a_k \cos kx + b_k \sin kx)$$

is the Fourier series corresponding to $f(x)$ on the interval $[-\pi, \pi]$ if the constants a_k, b_k are given by the formulas

$$a_k = \frac{1}{\pi} \int_{-\pi}^{\pi} f(x) \cos kx \, dx,$$

$$b_k = \frac{1}{\pi} \int_{-\pi}^{\pi} f(x) \sin kx \, dx.$$

The sense in which this series converges to $f(x)$ on $[-\pi, \pi]$ depends on the nature of f. The following theorem gives sufficient conditions for this convergence to be uniform. A proof may be found, for instance, in Churchill [1941].

Theorem 5.5.1.   *Let $f(x)$ be a continuous function on the interval $[-\pi, \pi]$ such that $f(-\pi) = f(\pi)$. If $f'(x)$ is piecewise continuous*[4] *on $[-\pi, \pi]$, then the Fourier series for f converges absolutely and uniformly to f on $[-\pi, \pi]$.*

Now let F be the set of continuous, piecewise linear functions[5] on $[0, \pi]$ that vanish at 0 and π. If we extend the members of F to $[-\pi, \pi]$ as odd functions, then by Theorem 5.5.1, each such extension has a uniformly convergent Fourier series on $[-\pi, \pi]$. That is, if $f \in F$, then

$$a_k \equiv 0, \qquad b_k \equiv \frac{2}{\pi} \int_0^\pi f(x) \sin kx \, dx$$

are its kth Fourier coefficients, and the partial sums

$$\left\{ \sum_{k=1}^n b_k \sin kx \right\}$$

converge uniformly to f on $[0, \pi]$. Since D contains these partial sums, any function in F is the uniform limit of a sequence in D. But F is dense in X (Exercise 5.7), so D is also dense in X. Note that this does not prove that the Fourier series of every element of X converges uniformly to that element on $[0, \pi]$. What we *have* shown is that every function in X may be uniformly approximated to any desired degree of accuracy by a finite sum of the form $\sum b_k \sin kx$.

The genuine solution operator is given by the formula

$$E_0(t)u_0 = \sum_{k=1}^n b_k e^{-k^2 t} \sin kx, \qquad u_0 \in D, \tag{5.5.2}$$

and it is clear from this that $E_0(t)$ satisfies the semigroup property.

The action of the generalized solution operator $E(t)$ on an arbitrary element of X does not have a simple representation such as (5.5.2). However, if u_0 is restricted to a suitable subspace of X, it may be possible to give an explicit formula for $E(t)u_0$. Thus if $u_0 \in X$ has a piecewise continuous derivative in $[0, \pi]$, it can be shown that

$$E(t)u_0 = \sum_{k=1}^\infty b_k e^{-k^2 t} \sin kx, \tag{5.5.3}$$

---

[4] That is, f' is continuous on $[-\pi, \pi]$ except possibly at a finite number of points where it has (finite) jump discontinuities. Note that f' does not exist at its jump discontinuities.

[5] The graph of a piecewise linear function consists of a finite number of straight-line segments.

where

$$b_k = \frac{2}{\pi} \int_0^\pi u_0(x) \sin kx \, dx, \qquad k = 1, 2, \ldots.$$

This solution may be obtained by applying the well-known method of "separation of variables" to problem (5.5.1) (Churchill [1941]). Note that (5.5.3) admits certain initial conditions u_0 that are not in the original set D. For example, it applies when u_0 is the piecewise linear function shown in Figure 5.5.1. Clearly, this function is not a member of D.

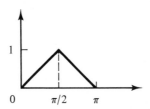

Figure 5.5.1   Piecewise linear initial condition.

As a first difference method for the initial value problem, we consider the explicit scheme given by (4.3.1). In the present context this is defined by the family of operators $C(\Delta t)$, $0 < \Delta t \leq \Delta t_0$, where for $u(\cdot, t) \in X$,

$$C(\Delta t)u(x, t) \equiv (1 - 2r)u(x, t) + ru(x - \Delta x, t) + ru(x + \Delta x, t). \qquad (5.5.4)$$

Here r is a positive constant and the spatial increment $\Delta x = (\Delta t/r)^{1/2}$ [i.e., $r = \Delta t/(\Delta x)^2$]. Furthermore, we understand that if $x \pm \Delta x$ lies outside the interval $[0, \pi]$, then $u(x \pm \Delta x, t)$ is defined by regarding $u(\cdot, t)$ as an odd function of period 2π. It is now easy to check that $C(\Delta t)$ is a linear operator that maps $X \rightarrow X$. Also, since

$$\|C(\Delta t)u\| \leq (|1 - 2r| + 2r)\|u\|, \qquad (5.5.5)$$

it follows that the family of operators $C(\Delta t)$ is uniformly bounded and so constitutes a difference method M_D. We leave as Exercise 5.8 the verification that M_D is consistent with the original initial value problem.

The stability of M_D is easy to establish *provided that* $r \leq \frac{1}{2}$. In this case we can drop the absolute-value signs appearing in (5.5.5) to obtain $\|C(\Delta t)u\| \leq \|u\|$. Hence $\|C(\Delta t)\| \leq 1$ and M_D is stable. Convergence is then assured by Theorem 5.4.1. This result is consistent with the analysis of Chapter 4. However, in that chapter we also saw that it is possible to remove the condition $r \leq \frac{1}{2}$ by making the difference equations more implicit. Accordingly, we now turn to a second difference method that is implicit in nature.

We define the operator $C(\Delta t)$ by requiring that $u(\cdot, t + \Delta t) \equiv C(\Delta t)u(\cdot, t)$ satisfy the equation

$$-ru(x - \Delta x, t + \Delta t) + (1 + 2r)u(x, t + \Delta t) - ru(x + \Delta x, t + \Delta t) = u(x, t). \qquad (5.5.6)$$

As before $r = \Delta t/(\Delta x)^2$ is a positive constant and we use oddness and 2π periodicity to extend the domains of the functions appearing in (5.5.6).

If we define the linear operator $H(\Delta t): X \to X$,

$$H(\Delta t)u(x, t) \equiv \frac{r}{1 + 2r}(u(x - \Delta x, t) + u(x + \Delta x, t)), \qquad (5.5.7)$$

(5.5.6) may be written as

$$(1 + 2r)(I - H(\Delta t))u(x, t + \Delta t) = u(x, t),$$

where I denotes the identity operator on X. It follows that $C(\Delta t)$ is the linear operator given by

$$C(\Delta t) = \frac{1}{1 + 2r}[I - H(\Delta t)]^{-1},$$

provided that the inverse exists. A sufficient condition for this is given in the next theorem.

Theorem 5.5.2.   *Let X be a Banach space with norm $\|\cdot\|$ and let $H: X \to X$ be a bounded linear operator such that $\|H\| < 1$. If I is the identity on X, then $(I - H)^{-1}: X \to X$ exists, is bounded, and*

$$\|(I - H)^{-1}\| \leq \frac{1}{1 - \|H\|}. \qquad (5.5.8)$$

Proof. Assume that $(I - H)u = 0$. If $u \neq 0$, then

$$\|u\| = \|Hu\| \leq \|H\|\,\|u\| < \|u\|,$$

which is a contradiction. Thus $u = 0$ and $I - H$ is one-to-one on X. Also, if $v \in X$ and

$$u_n = (I + H + \cdots + H^{n-1})v,$$

then for $m < n$,

$$\|u_m - u_n\| \leq \|H\|^m(1 + \|H\| + \cdots + \|H\|^{n-m-1})\|v\| \leq \|H\|^m \frac{\|v\|}{1 - \|H\|}.$$

Thus u_n is a Cauchy sequence, so $u_n \to u$ for some $u \in X$. But we also have

$$(I - H)u_n = (I - H^n)v.$$

Passing to the limit in this expression, we see that

$$(I - H)u = v;$$

that is, the range of $(I - H)$ is X. These results imply that $(I - H)^{-1}$ exists and is defined on the entire space X.

Next we show that $(I - H)^{-1}$ is bounded. If we assume that this is not the case, then there is a sequence $\{v_n\}$ such that $\|v_n\| = 1$ for all n and $\|(I - H)^{-1}v_n\| \to \infty$ as $n \to \infty$. Setting $u_n = (I - H)^{-1}v_n$, we have

$$\|v_n\| = \|(I - H)u_n\| \geq \|u_n\| - \|Hu_n\| \geq (1 - \|H\|)\|u_n\|.$$

Since $1 - \|H\| > 0$, this implies that $\|v_n\| \to \infty$, as $n \to \infty$, which is again a contradiction. It follows that $(I - H)^{-1}$ is bounded.

Now let

$$S_n = I + H + \cdots + H^{n-1}.$$

Then

$$\|S_n - (I - H)^{-1}\| \leq \|S_n(I - H) - I\| \|(I - H)^{-1}\|$$
$$= \|H^n\| \|(I - H)^{-1}\| \leq \|H\|^n \|(I - H)^{-1}\|.$$

Therefore,

$$\|(I - H)^{-1}\| \leq \|S_n\| + \|H\|^n \|(I - H)^{-1}\|$$
$$\leq 1 + \|H\| + \cdots + \|H\|^{n-1} + \|H\|^n \|(I - H)^{-1}\|$$
$$\leq \frac{1}{1 - \|H\|} + \|H\|^n \|(I - H)^{-1}\|.$$

Letting $n \to \infty$, we obtain (5.5.8).

Q.E.D.

Referring to (5.5.7), we see that $\|H(\Delta t)\| \leq 2r/(1 + 2r)$. Hence Theorem 5.5.2 implies that $C(\Delta t)$ exists. Moreover, by (5.5.8), we have

$$\|C(\Delta t)\| \leq \frac{1}{1 + 2r} \frac{1}{1 - \|H(\Delta t)\|} \leq 1,$$

so that the implicit method is stable *for any* $r > 0$. Finally, since the method is consistent (Exercise 5.8), we conclude that it is convergent, this time without any restriction on the size of r.

5.6 THE FOURIER SERIES METHOD

Usually, the most significant difficulty encountered in the application of Theorem 5.4.1 to a given difference method is the verification of the method's stability. In this respect the proper choice of norm is important and, as we have seen in Section 5.5, can greatly facilitate the task of verification.

In this section we introduce a norm that allows us to formulate a relatively simple stability criterion that is applicable to an important class of difference methods. This norm utilizes the *Lebesgue integral*, and all integrals in this section are to be interpreted as such. Although the presence of the Lebesgue integral is necessary for a rigorous statement of the general theory surrounding the stability criterion, the development of the criterion itself does not make direct use of this integral. Thus unfamiliarity with the Lebesgue theory[6] should not lead to difficulties in understanding the main results of this section.

We consider the set of complex-valued functions defined on the interval $(0, 2\pi)$ whose moduli are square integrable.[7] That is, we have in mind functions u such that $\int_0^{2\pi} |u|^2 \, dx < \infty$. It is known that these functions form a vector space over the complex numbers and we denote this vector space by $L_2(0, 2\pi)$. Moreover, if we define the function $\|\cdot\|_2 : L_2(0, 2\pi) \to R$ by

$$\|u\|_2 - \left(\frac{1}{2\pi} \int_0^{2\pi} |u|^2 \, dx \right)^{1/2},$$

then $\|\cdot\|_2$ is a norm on $L_2(0, 2\pi)$ provided that we clarify the sense in which two functions in $L_2(0, 2\pi)$ are to be regarded as being equal. A set in R has *zero length* if it can be covered by a finite or countably infinite collection of intervals the sum of whose lengths is arbitrarily small. In light of this definition, we say that two elements of $L_2(0, 2\pi)$ are equal if their function values agree everywhere on $(0, 2\pi)$ except possibly on a subset of zero length.

The pairing of $\|\cdot\|_2$ with $L_2(0, 2\pi)$ turns $L_2(0, 2\pi)$ into a Banach space.[8] Furthermore, each element of $L_2(0, 2\pi)$ has a unique Fourier series representation in terms of complex exponentials. That is, if $u \in L_2(0, 2\pi)$, then

$$u(x) = \sum_{k=-\infty}^{\infty} \hat{u}(k) e^{ikx}, \qquad (5.6.1)$$

where

$$\hat{u}(k) = \frac{1}{2\pi} \int_0^{2\pi} e^{-ikx} u(x) \, dx, \qquad k = 0, \pm 1, \dots \qquad (5.6.2)$$

is its kth Fourier coefficient. A proof of this result may be found in Yosida [1965]. As the next theorem shows, the norm of an element in $L_2(0, 2\pi)$ is related to its Fourier coefficients in a simple way.

---

[6] For a presentation of this theory, see, for example, Munroe [1953].

[7] The use of complex-valued functions considerably simplifies the theory. Furthermore, if the functions are defined on a finite interval (a, b), then the change of variable, $y = 2\pi(x - a)/(b - a)$, allows us to work on $(0, 2\pi)$.

[8] The completeness of $L_2(0, 2\pi)$ is a consequence of a famous theorem in functional analysis known as the Riesz–Fischer theorem (Riesz [1907a, 1970b], Fischer [1907]).

Theorem 5.6.1.   *If $u \in L_2(0, 2\pi)$, then*

$$\|u\|_2^2 = \sum_{k=-\infty}^{\infty} |\hat{u}(k)|^2. \tag{5.6.3}$$

Proof.   Since

$$\int_0^{2\pi} e^{imx}\, dx = \begin{cases} 0 & \text{if } m \neq 0 \\ 2\pi & \text{if } m = 0, \end{cases}$$

we find by direct computation[9] that for any positive integer n,

$$\left\| u - \sum_{k=-n}^{n} \hat{u}(k) e^{ikx} \right\|_2^2 = \|u\|_2^2 - \sum_{k=-n}^{n} |\hat{u}(k)|^2.$$

Hence (5.6.3) follows by letting $n \to \infty$.

Q.E.D.

Equation (5.6.3) is known as *Parseval's equality*.

Let J be a finite nonnegative integer and let $a_j, j = 0, \pm 1, \ldots, \pm J$, be $2J + 1$ complex constants. If $u(\cdot, t) \in L_2(0, 2\pi)$ is extended to the entire real line as a 2π periodic function and Δx and Δt are positive increments, we obtain a difference method M_D on the space $L_2(0, 2\pi)$ by defining an operator $C(\Delta t)$ such that

$$C(\Delta t)u(x, t) \equiv u(x, t + \Delta t) = \sum_{j=-J}^{J} a_j u(x + j\,\Delta x, t). \tag{5.6.4}$$

In view of (5.6.1) we can write

$$u(x, t) = \sum_{k=-\infty}^{\infty} \hat{u}(k, t) e^{ikx}$$

and

$$u(x, t + \Delta t) = \sum_{k=-\infty}^{\infty} \hat{u}(k, t + \Delta t) e^{ikx}.$$

Therefore, by (5.6.4), we have

$$\sum_{k=-\infty}^{\infty} \hat{u}(k, t + \Delta t) e^{ikx} = \sum_{j=-J}^{J} a_j \sum_{k=-\infty}^{\infty} \hat{u}(k, t) e^{ik(x + j\Delta x)}$$

$$= \sum_{k=-\infty}^{\infty} \left[\sum_{j=-J}^{J} a_j e^{ikj\Delta x} \right] \hat{u}(k, t) e^{ikx}.$$

---

[9] The Lebesgue integral shares all the elementary properties of the Riemann integral, the familiar integral of the calculus. Furthermore, every Riemann integrable function is Lebesgue integrable (but not conversely) and in this case the two integrals coincide. Since the complex exponentials are obviously Riemann integrable, the computations proceed as though the integrals involved are Riemann integrals.

Since the Fourier series representation is unique, it follows that

$$\hat{u}(k, t + \Delta t) = \left(\sum_{j=-J}^{J} a_j e^{ikj\Delta x} \right) \hat{u}(k, t), \qquad k = 0, \pm 1, \dots . \tag{5.6.5}$$

We now regard Δx as a function of Δt and define the *amplification factors*,

$$G(k, \Delta t) \equiv \sum_{j=-J}^{J} a_j e^{ikj\Delta x}, \qquad k = 0, \pm 1, \dots . \tag{5.6.6}$$

Then (5.6.5) becomes

$$\hat{u}(k, t + \Delta t) = G(k, \Delta t)\hat{u}(k, t). \tag{5.6.7}$$

The next theorem characterizes the stability of M_D in terms of powers of the amplification factors.

Theorem 5.6.2.   *The difference method M_D is stable if and only if there is a constant K such that*

$$\left| G^n(k, \Delta t) \right| \le K, \qquad 0 < n\,\Delta t \le T, \quad k = 0, \pm 1, \dots . \tag{5.6.8}$$

Proof. If $u_0 = u(\cdot, 0) \in L_2(0, 2\pi)$, we see from (5.6.3) that

$$\left\| C^n(\Delta t)u_0 \right\|_2^2 = \left\| u(x, n\,\Delta t) \right\|_2^2 = \sum_{k=-\infty}^{\infty} \left| \hat{u}(k, n\,\Delta t) \right|^2 .$$

But by repeated application of (5.6.7), we find that

$$\hat{u}(k, n\,\Delta t) = G^n(k, \Delta t)\hat{u}(k, 0).$$

Thus if (5.6.8) holds, then

$$\left\| C^n(\Delta t)u_0 \right\|_2^2 = \sum_{k=-\infty}^{\infty} \left| G^n(k, \Delta t) \right|^2 \left| \hat{u}(k, 0) \right|^2$$

$$= K^2 \sum_{k=-\infty}^{\infty} \left| \hat{u}(k, 0) \right|^2 = K^2 \|u_0\|_2^2 ,$$

and M_D is stable.

Conversely, assume that M_D is stable and for an arbitrary integer m let $u_0 = u(x, 0) = e^{imx}$. Then $\|u_0\|_2 = 1$ and $\hat{u}(k, 0) = \delta_{km}$, the Kronecker delta. Therefore, there is a constant K such that for all $n\,\Delta t \in (0, T]$,

$$K^2 = \|u_0\|_2^2 K^2 \ge \left\| C^n(\Delta t)u_0 \right\|_2^2 = \left\| u(x, n\,\Delta t) \right\|_2^2$$

$$= \sum_{k=-\infty}^{\infty} \left| \hat{u}(k, n\,\Delta t) \right|^2 = \sum_{k=-\infty}^{\infty} \left| G^n(k, \Delta t)\hat{u}(k, 0) \right|^2$$

$$= \left| G^n(m, \Delta t) \right|^2 .$$

Q.E.D.

Theorem 5.6.2 leads directly to the stability criterion alluded to at the beginning of this section.

Theorem 5.6.3.   *The difference method M_D is stable if and only if as $\Delta t \to 0$,*

$$\left| G(k, \Delta t) \right| \leq 1 + O(\Delta t), \qquad k = 0, \pm 1, \ldots. \tag{5.6.9}$$

Proof. If (5.6.9) holds, there is a constant M such that for all Δt sufficiently small,

$$\left| G(k, \Delta t) \right| \leq 1 + M \, \Delta t.$$

Then

$$\left| G^n(k, \Delta t) \right| \leq e^{Mn \, \Delta t} \leq e^{MT},$$

and M_D is stable by Theorem 5.6.2.

Suppose now that M_D is stable. Then we write (5.6.8) as

$$\left| G^n(k, \Delta t) \right| \leq 1 + \delta,$$

where $\delta \geq 0$. Hence

$$\left| G(k, \Delta t) \right| \leq (1 + \delta)^{1/n} \leq e^{\delta/n} = e^{\delta \, \Delta t/n \, \Delta t}.$$

Choosing n so that $n \, \Delta t \geq T/2$, we have

$$\left| G(k, \Delta t) \right| \leq e^{2\delta \, \Delta t/T} = 1 + O(\Delta t).$$

Q.E.D.

Inequality (5.6.9) is generally called the *von Neumann condition*.

As an example of the use of Theorem 5.6.3, we return to the explicit method defined by (5.5.4). The functions $u(\cdot, t)$ are now assumed to belong to $L_2(0, 2\pi)$. This method is clearly of the form (5.6.4) with $J = 1$, $a_0 = 1 - 2r$, and $a_{-1} = a_1 = r$. The amplification factors may be obtained directly from the definition (5.6.6). Alternatively, we can substitute $u(x, t) = e^{ikx}$ and $u(x, t + \Delta t) = G(k, \Delta t)e^{ikx}$ into the difference equation (5.6.4) and then solve the resulting expression for $G(k, \Delta t)$. If this is done for the explicit method, we obtain

$$G(k, \Delta t)e^{ikx} = \left[1 - 2r + r(e^{ik \, \Delta x} + e^{-ik \, \Delta x}) \right]e^{ikx}.$$

Hence

$$G(k, \Delta t) = 1 - 2r + r(e^{ik \, \Delta x} + e^{-ik \, \Delta x})$$
$$= 1 - 2r + 2r \cos k \, \Delta x.$$

Letting $\omega = k \, \Delta x$, we see that $\left| G(k, \Delta t) \right| \leq 1$ if $-2 \leq 2r(\cos \omega - 1) \leq 0$ for all ω. Since these last inequalities hold when $0 < r \leq \frac{1}{2}$, the latter condition is sufficient for the stability of the method in the space $L_2(0, 2\pi)$. Note that this is the same condition that we obtained in Section 5.5 for a different Banach space.

NOTES AND REMARKS

5.1 The material of this section plays a fundamental role in the mathematical discipline known as *functional analysis*. Strictly speaking, this is the study of "linear functionals" (Section 6.2), but contemporary usage of the term implies consideration of more general mappings. It has also been recognized as an indispensable tool in modern numerical analysis, and a number of texts have appeared that emphasize this connection (see, e.g., Collatz [1966], Cryer [1982], or Moore [1985]).

It is always possible to "enlarge" a normed space in such a way that the resulting space is a Banach space which has a dense subspace that is essentially indistinguishable from the original normed space (Kreyszig [1978]). This process requires the suitable definition of "ideal" elements as the limits of the Cauchy sequences that do not converge in the original space. While this is satisfying from a theoretical point of view, the intrinsic nature of the ideal elements may be difficult to discern.

Theorem 5.1.2 (the Banach–Steinhaus theorem) is one of the three "big" theorems of functional analysis. The other two are the Hahn–Banach theorem and the open mapping theorem. The Hahn–Banach theorem is an extension theorem for linear functionals, and the open mapping theorem guarantees that a bounded linear operator from a Banach space onto a Banach space maps open sets onto open sets. For an application of the open mapping theorem, see Exercise 6.14.

5.2 Richtmyer and Morton attribute the general theory of this and the next two sections to P. Lax, who developed it in a seminar at New York University in 1953. In that presentation, the operator A was allowed to depend explicitly on the parameter t.

The abstract initial value problem (5.2.1) is general enough to handle systems of first-order differential equations in several space variables. Moreover, it is not even restricted to first-order systems since higher-order systems may be reduced to equivalent first-order ones by the introduction of additional dependent variables and differential equations.

5.3 The difference methods presented in this section are called "single-step" or "two-level" methods since only the quantities $u(\cdot, t)$ and $u(\cdot, t + \Delta t)$ are involved. It is possible to modify the theory to treat "multistep" methods (see Richtmyer and Morton [1967]). Alternative definitions of stability are possible and Richtmyer and Morton [1967] discuss two of these: one weaker, the other stronger than the definition used here.

5.4 It is not difficult to see that the present theory accommodates initial value problems for ordinary differential equations (ODEs) in which the operator A in (5.2.1) is a square matrix of constants (Exercise 5.4 deals with the simplest such case). What is perhaps more surprising is that with appropriate definitions of consistency, convergence, and stability, the equivalence theorem 5.4.1 also holds for *nonlinear* initial value problems (Isaacson and Keller [1966]). In fact, under reasonable conditions on the problem data, all consistent single-step methods of the type discussed in Section 5.3 are automatically stable and hence convergent when applied to ODE initial value problems.

5.5 Theorem 5.5.2 is known as the Banach fixed point or contraction theorem for bounded linear operators. It has a generalization to nonlinear operators on metric spaces (Kreyszig [1978]). We have used it to establish the stability of the implicit method (5.5.6), but the reader should note that in Exercise 5.9 this same result may be obtained in a different norm by the Fourier series method (Section 5.6) in an almost trivial manner.

5.6 In this section we have restricted the development to *scalar* functions for simplicity. Nevertheless, the entire theory may be generalized to handle *vector* functions. In this case the amplification factors become amplification matrices and Theorem 5.6.2 holds if the modulus on the left-hand side of (5.6.8) is replaced by the Euclidean matrix norm. The von Neumann condition (5.6.9) becomes

$$\rho(G(\mathbf{k}, \Delta t)) \leq 1 + O(\Delta t),$$

where ρ denotes the spectral radius and $\mathbf{k}$ is a vector of Fourier mode numbers. This condition is in general only *necessary* for stability. However, if the amplification matrices satisfy the right additional conditions, it may also be sufficient. For example, it is enough to know that they commute with their adjoints (i.e., that they are *normal* matrices). Other sufficient conditions have been discovered by Kreiss [1962] and Buchanan [1963]; see also Richtmyer and Morton [1967] and Meis and Marcowitz [1981].

The Fourier method of this section is attributed to von Neumann by O'Brien, Hyman, and Kaplan [1951]. In this reference they state that "the partly heuristic technique of stability analysis developed by von Neumann was applied by him to a wide variety of difference and differential equation problems during World War II. This method has been very briefly mentioned in the literature ... but a detailed discussion has not yet been published. With the kind permission of Professor von Neumann, we have made such a discussion part of the present paper."

Some of the stability inequalities produced by the method had previously been discovered by Courant, Friedrichs, and Lewy [1928] for the wave and heat conduction equations. They did this, of course, without the benefit of the von Neumann condition. Indeed, in his commentary on this famous 1928 paper, Lax [1967] observes: "Then the authors turn to the centered difference scheme for the wave equation on an arbitrary grid and remark that they will not bother to write down an explicit representation of the solution because 'it is too complicated to yield a limiting value easily as the mesh-width tends to zero'; thereby they failed to discover the von Neumann stability criterion."

It is of interest to note that in her 1949 thesis, Ladyzhenskaya had also apparently developed a Fourier series method for difference equations (Ladyzhenskaya [1952]).

EXERCISES

5.1. (a) Under the familiar arithmetic operations and with the norm defined as absolute value, the rational numbers form a normed space X. Show that X is not a complete space. What is $\bar{X}$?

   (b) Show that if X is a normed space and $D \subset X$, then $\bar{D}$ is closed.

5.2. Let X be a Banach space, and $\{T_n\}$ a sequence of bounded linear operators from X into X such that $\{T_n u\}$ is a Cauchy sequence for every $u \in X$. Show that $\{T_n\}$ is uniformly bounded.

5.3. Show that the genuine solution operator $E_0(t)$ is linear.

5.4. Let α be a negative constant and consider the *ordinary differential equation* initial value problem: $du/dt = \alpha u$, $0 \leq t \leq T$, $u(0) = u_0$.

   (a) Show that the initial value problem is well posed on R (the Banach space of real numbers with absolute value as norm). [*Hint:* To show uniqueness multiply the differential equation by u and integrate.]

(b) Give an explicit formula for $E(t)$ and verify the semigroup property (5.2.4).

(c) Show that if $M_D = \{C(\Delta t), 0 < \Delta t \leq \Delta t_0\}$, where

$$C(\Delta t): R \to R, \qquad C(\Delta t)u = (1 + \alpha\,\Delta t)u,$$

then M_D ("Euler's method") is a stable, first-order method for the initial value problem.

5.5. Let $a_1, \ldots, a_n; b_1, \ldots, b_n$ be real numbers. Derive the "Cauchy–Schwarz" inequality

$$\sum_{k=1}^{n} a_k b_k \leq \left(\sum_{k=1}^{n} a_k^2\right)^{1/2} \left(\sum_{k=1}^{n} b_k^2\right)^{1/2}$$

$$\left[\textit{Hint:} \sum_{k=1}^{n} (a_k + \lambda b_k)^2 \geq 0 \text{ for all real } \lambda. \right]$$

5.6. Let $u_0(x) = \sum_{k=1}^{n} b_k \sin kx$, where $b_1, \ldots, b_n$ are real constants.

(a) Show that

$$\sum_{k=1}^{n} b_k^2 = \frac{2}{\pi} \int_0^{\pi} u_0^2(x)\, dx.$$

(b) Show that if $E_0(t)$ is the genuine solution operator of (5.5.1), then

$$\|E_0(t)u_0\| \leq \begin{cases} \|u_0\| & \text{if } t = 0, \\ \left(\dfrac{2}{e^{2t} - 1}\right)^{1/2} \|u_0\| & \text{if } 0 < t \leq T. \end{cases}$$

Thus $E_0(t)$, $0 \leq t \leq T$, is bounded. [*Hint:* Use (5.5.2), part (a), and Exercise 5.5.]

(c) Use Theorem 5.1.2 to prove that the family of genuine solution operators of (5.5.1) is uniformly bounded.

5.7. Let v be continuous on $[0, \pi]$ and assume that $v(0) = v(\pi) = 0$. Show that if $\varepsilon > 0$, then there is a continuous, piecewise linear function f such that $f(0) = f(\pi) = 0$ and $|v(x) - f(x)| \leq \varepsilon$ for all $x \in [0, \pi]$. [*Hint:* Construct f from v by linear interpolation at equally spaced abscissas. Then use the uniform continuity of $v - f$.]

5.8. Let D_C be the set of finite linear combinations of the functions $\sin kx$, $k = 1, 2, \ldots$. Show that if $u_0 \in D_C$, then the local truncation errors of the explicit method (5.5.4) and the implicit method (5.5.6) are $O((\Delta t^2))$.

5.9. Test the implicit method (5.5.6) for stability by the Fourier series method.

5.10. Test the following difference methods by the Fourier series method.

(a) *Upwind method:*

$$C(\Delta t)u(x, t) = u(x, t) - r[u(x, t) - u(x - \Delta x, t)],$$

$$r = \text{constant} = \frac{\Delta t}{\Delta x}.$$

(b) *Centered difference method:*

$$C(\Delta t)u(x, t) = u(x, t) - r[u(x + \Delta x, t) - u(x - \Delta x, t)],$$

$$r = \text{constant} = \frac{\Delta t}{2\Delta x}.$$

What is the differential equation with which these methods are consistent?

5.11. The Lax–Wendroff method (cf. Section 3.6) is given by

$$C(\Delta t)u(x, t) = u(x, t) - \frac{c}{2}\left[(u(x + \Delta x, t) - u(x - \Delta x, t)\right]$$

$$+ \frac{c^2}{2}\left[u(x + \Delta x, t) - 2u(x, t) + u(x - \Delta x, t)\right],$$

where $c = \text{constant} = \lambda \, \Delta t / \Delta x$.

(a) Show that the amplication factors satisfy

$$|G|^2 = [1 - c^2(1 - \cos \omega)]^2 + c^2 \sin^2 \omega,$$

where $\omega = k \, \Delta x$.

(b) Show that the method is stable in $L_2(0, 2\pi)$ if $|c| \leq 1$.
[*Hint:* Use the half-angle formulas from trigonometry.]

6

Sobolev Spaces

In Chapter 7 we develop a mathematical theory of the finite element method vis-à-vis boundary value problems for elliptic partial differential equations. Although the computational procedure engendered by the finite element method is conceptually straightforward, a proper analysis of the error is most easily accomplished within the framework of a class of function spaces associated with the name of the Soviet mathematician S. L. Sobolev. Comprehensive treatments of the theory of Sobolev spaces are contained in the books by Adams [1975] and Nečas [1967]. In this chapter we consider only a few of the many aspects of these spaces.

Although this material is necessary for our subsequent analysis of the finite element method, a detailed presentation is beyond the scope of this book. Consequently, we shall not include proofs of the results quoted here, preferring instead to provide suitable references where such proofs may be found. In this chapter we utilize some of the function theory introduced in Section 5.1, so the reader may wish to review that material before proceeding.

The Sobolev space concept involves the notion of a generalized derivative, which in turn depends on the behavior of certain smooth functions. Consequently, we begin with a consideration of functions that possess continuous derivatives of various orders.

6.1 SPACES OF CONTINUOUS FUNCTIONS; GENERALIZED DERIVATIVES

Let u be a real-valued function whose domain, Ω, is contained in R^2. We define the *support* of u as the closure (in R^2) of the set of points in Ω where u does not vanish. That is, if supp u denotes the support of u, then

$$\text{supp } u = \overline{\{\mathbf{x} \mid \mathbf{x} \in \Omega, \, u(\mathbf{x}) \neq 0\}}.$$

Now suppose that Ω is a *bounded region* (i.e., a bounded, open, connected set) in R^2 and let $\partial\Omega$ denote its boundary. We say that u has *compact support* in Ω if supp $u \subset \Omega$. In this case u vanishes in a boundary strip of Ω (Exercise 6.1). More precisely, there is a positive number h such that $u(\mathbf{z}) = 0$ for

$$\mathbf{z} \in \Omega_h \equiv \{\mathbf{x} \in \Omega \mid \text{dist} \, (\mathbf{x}, \partial\Omega) \leq h\},$$

where

$$\text{dist} \, (\mathbf{x}, \partial\Omega) \equiv \inf_{\mathbf{y} \in \partial\Omega} |\mathbf{x} - \mathbf{y}|.$$

If m is a nonnegative integer and Ξ is an open set, we let $C^m(\Xi)$ denote the vector space of functions that are m-times continuously differentiable on Ξ. Then the subspace $C^m(\bar{\Omega})$ consists of the restrictions to $\bar{\Omega}$ of functions in $C^m(R^2)$. Also,

$$C^\infty(\Omega) \equiv \bigcap_{m=0}^{\infty} C^m(\Omega)$$

and

$$C_0^m(\Omega) = \{\phi \in C^m(\Omega) \mid \text{supp } \phi \subset \Omega\}, \qquad 0 \leq m \leq \infty.$$

We wish to extend the notion of the classical partial derivative and we do this by way of the "integration by parts" formula. For example, let $u \in C^1(\bar{\Omega})$. If $\phi \in C_0^\infty(\Omega)$, then ϕ vanishes in a boundary strip and we can apply Green's theorem to obtain[1]

$$\int_\Omega u\phi_{x_i} \, d\mathbf{x} = \int_\Omega [(u\phi)_{x_i} - u_{x_i}\phi] \, d\mathbf{x}$$

$$= -\int_\Omega u_{x_i}\phi \, d\mathbf{x}, \qquad i - 1, 2.$$

In this light the derivative u_{x_i} may be viewed as some function, say v_i, satisfying the condition

$$\int_\Omega u\phi_{x_i} \, d\mathbf{x} = -\int_\Omega v_i\phi \, d\mathbf{x} \qquad\qquad (6.1.1)$$

for all $\phi \in C_0^\infty(\Omega)$. Conversely, if we can find a function v_i that satisfies (6.1.1) when paired with a given integrable function u, then with regard to integration against the

---

[1] The notation $d\mathbf{x}$ denotes an area element and not a vector. Furthermore, although Green's theorem requires that $\partial\Omega$ be sufficiently regular, this is not a concern here since we can, if necessary, integrate over a subregion of Ω whose boundary is a smooth curve contained in the strip where ϕ vanishes.

smooth functions ϕ, it behaves exactly like the derivative u_{x_i} *even though the latter derivative may not exist in the classical sense.*

This leads us to define generalized derivatives as follows. Let α_1 and α_2 be non-negative integers, let $\boldsymbol{\alpha} = (\alpha_1, \alpha_2)$ be a multi-index, and let $D^{\boldsymbol{\alpha}}$ be the partial differential operator of order $|\boldsymbol{\alpha}| \equiv \alpha_1 + \alpha_2$: $D^{\boldsymbol{\alpha}} = \partial^{\alpha_1 + \alpha_2}/\partial x_1^{\alpha_1}\partial x_2^{\alpha_2}$. If u is integrable on Ω and there is a function $v_{\boldsymbol{\alpha}}$ integrable[2] on Ω and satisfying the condition

$$\int_{\Omega} u D^{\boldsymbol{\alpha}}\phi \, d\mathbf{x} = (-1)^{|\boldsymbol{\alpha}|}\int_{\Omega} v_{\boldsymbol{\alpha}}\phi \, d\mathbf{x} \tag{6.1.2}$$

for all $\phi \in C_0^{\infty}(\Omega)$, then we say that $v_{\boldsymbol{\alpha}}$ is a *generalized derivative* of u.

When it exists, $v_{\boldsymbol{\alpha}}$ is unique up to its definition on sets of zero area.[3] That is, if $v_{\boldsymbol{\alpha}}$ and $w_{\boldsymbol{\alpha}}$ both satisfy (6.1.2), then they agree everywhere in Ω except possibly on a set having zero area. Functions satisfying such a condition are said to be equal *almost everywhere* (a.e.) in Ω.

If u has a generalized derivative, it is convenient to denote it by $D^{\boldsymbol{\alpha}}u$ since if the latter quantity exists in $\bar{\Omega}$ in the classical sense and is continuous, it is also the corresponding generalized derivative. There are, however, simple functions that possess generalized, but not classical, derivatives, and other equally simple functions that possess neither (see Exercises 6.2 and 6.6).

6.2 HILBERT SPACES

Let U denote a vector space over the real numbers. Then U is an *inner product space* if there is a function,

$$(\cdot, \cdot)\colon U \times U \to R,$$

such that for all $u, v, w \in U, \alpha \in R$,

$$
\begin{aligned}
&1.\ (u + v, w) = (u, w) + (v, w), \\
&2.\ (\alpha u, v) = \alpha(u, v), \\
&3.\ (u, v) = (v, u), \\
&4.\ (u, u) > 0 \text{ if } u \neq 0.
\end{aligned}
\tag{6.2.1}
$$

It is easy to verify that the function

$$\|\cdot\|\colon U \to R, \qquad \|u\| \equiv (u, u)^{1/2}$$

is a norm on U. The only part of the verification that is not obvious is the triangle inequality, but that is an easy consequence of the Cauchy–Schwarz inequality,

$$(u, v) \leq \|u\|\,\|v\| \tag{6.2.2}$$

---

[2] Integrability is again in the sense of Lebesgue (see Section 5.6).

[3] A set of zero area is defined in the same way as a set of zero length (Section 5.6) except that the covering sets are rectangles instead of intervals.

for all $u, v \in U$, and this is established in the same way as it was in Exercise 5.5. We say that $\|\cdot\|$ is the norm *induced* by the inner product $(\cdot, \cdot)$.

A *Hilbert space* U is an inner product space that is complete with respect to the norm induced by the inner product. Thus every Hilbert space is a Banach space.

In Chapter 7 we investigate the existence and uniqueness of solutions of certain equations on Hilbert spaces. Among other things, this will establish the unique solvability of the equation systems resulting from the finite element method. The main tool used in our investigation is the Riesz representation theorem. However, before we can discuss this theorem, we need to introduce the notion of a *bounded linear functional* on a Hilbert space U. This is simply a bounded linear operator (cf. Section 5.1) f mapping U into the real numbers, R. The norm on R is the absolute value.

The Riesz theorem asserts that every bounded linear functional on a Hilbert space is an inner product. The precise statement is as follows.

Theorem 6.2.1 (Riesz Representation Theorem).   *Let U be a Hilbert space with inner product $(\cdot, \cdot)$. Then f is a bounded linear functional on U if and only if there is a unique element $f^* \in U$ such that $f(u) = (f^*, u)$ for all $u \in U$.*

The proof of this fundamental theorem may be found in most textbooks on functional analysis (see, e.g., Kreyszig [1978]).

6.3 THE SPACES $H^m(\Omega)$ AND $H_0^m(\Omega)$

We are now ready to introduce the Sobolev spaces mentioned in the introduction. We let m be a nonnegative integer, and consider functions u that possess all generalized derivatives $D^{\alpha}u$ of order $|\alpha|$, $0 \leq |\alpha| \leq m$. We define

$$((u, v))_k \equiv \sum_{|\alpha|=k} \int_{\Omega} D^{\alpha}u D^{\alpha}v \, dx, \qquad k = 0, 1, \ldots,$$

provided that the right side makes sense, and then let

$$|u|_k \equiv ((u, u))_k^{1/?},$$

$$(u, v)_m \equiv \sum_{k=0}^{m} ((u, v))_k,$$

and

$$\|u\|_m \equiv (u, u)_m^{1/2} = \left(\sum_{k=0}^{m} |u|_k^2 \right)^{1/2}.$$

Next we introduce the vector space of square integrable functions on Ω,

$$L_2(\Omega) \equiv \left\{ u \mid \|u\|_0 = \left[\int_{\Omega} u^2 \, dx \right]^{1/2} < \infty \right\},$$

and note that on $L_2(\Omega)$, $(\cdot, \cdot)_0$ satisfies all the conditions of an inner product provided that we agree not to distinguish between two functions that are equal a.e. Of course, $(\cdot, \cdot)_0$ converts $L_2(\Omega)$ into an inner product space. This inner product space is also a Hilbert space thanks again to the Riesz–Fischer theorem (cf. Section 5.6).

It turns out that these same results hold for the function spaces,

$$H^m(\Omega) \equiv \{u \in L_2(\Omega) \mid D^{\alpha}u \in L_2(\Omega), \quad 0 \le |\alpha| \le m\},$$

where the inner product on $H^m(\Omega)$ is given by $(\cdot, \cdot)_m$. The proof that $H^m(\Omega)$ is a Hilbert space is surprisingly easy given the completeness of $L_2(\Omega)$. A proof may be found in Adams [1975] (see also Exercise 6.11). Although the derivatives $D^{\alpha}u$ appearing in the definition of $H^m(\Omega)$ are not necessarily classical derivatives, it can be shown (Adams [1975]) that under certain conditions on $\partial\Omega$ (e.g., it is sufficient that $\partial\Omega$ be piecewise smooth in the sense given below) $C^m(\bar{\Omega})$ is dense in $H^m(\Omega)$. The spaces $H^m(\Omega)$ are particular examples of Sobolev spaces and play a key role in the analysis of the finite element method.

It is particularly easy to give examples of functions lying in these various spaces when $\Omega \subset R^1$. (The previous definitions are obviously not restricted to R^2.) For instance, if Ω is the open interval $(-1, 1)$, and

$$u = \begin{cases} ax^m & \text{for } -1 < x < 0, \\ bx^m & \text{for } 0 \le x < 1, \end{cases}$$

then $u \in C^{\infty}(\bar{\Omega})$ when $a = b$. If $a \ne b$, then $u \in C^{m-1}(\bar{\Omega}) \cap H^m(\Omega)$, but according to Exercise 6.6, $u \notin H^{m+1}(\Omega)$.

We also consider the spaces $H_0^m(\Omega)$. These are obtained by taking the closure of $C_0^{\infty}(\Omega)$ in the spaces $H^m(\Omega)$. By Theorem 5.1.1 they are again Hilbert spaces under the inner products $(\cdot, \cdot)_m$. They are very useful in the study of problems involving "homogeneous" (i.e., zero) boundary conditions, and we shall make extensive use of the space $H_0^1(\Omega)$ in Chapter 7.

To ascertain the sense in which elements of $H_0^1(\Omega)$ satisfy homogeneous boundary conditions it is convenient to introduce the notion of a "trace operator." For this purpose we need to be more specific about the nature of the boundary $\partial\Omega$. We will say that $\partial\Omega$ is *piecewise smooth* if (1) Ω lies on one side of $\partial\Omega$ and $\partial\Omega$ can be decomposed into a finite number of arcs, each of which is the graph of an infinitely differentiable function with respect to a suitably chosen local coordinate system; and (2) the interior angles between the left and right tangents at the breakpoints of the arcs (the "corner angles") are greater than zero. In this case it makes sense to consider the Hilbert space

$$L_2(\partial\Omega) = \left\{u: \partial\Omega \to R \mid \int_{\partial\Omega} u^2(s) \, ds < \infty\right\},$$

where ds is the element of arc length along $\partial\Omega$. If we denote the norm on $L_2(\partial\Omega)$ by $\|\cdot\|_{0,\partial\Omega}$, it can be shown (cf. Nečas [1967]) that there is a constant K such that if $u \in C^1(\bar{\Omega})$, then

$$\|\gamma u\|_{0,\partial\Omega} \le K\|u\|_1, \tag{6.3.1}$$

where $\gamma u = u|_{\partial\Omega}$. Note that $\gamma: C^1(\bar{\Omega}) \subset H^1(\Omega) \to L_2(\partial\Omega)$ is a linear map.

By virtue of (6.3.1), γ is continuous on $C^1(\bar{\Omega})$. Furthermore, since $C^1(\bar{\Omega})$ is dense in $H^1(\Omega)$, it follows from Theorem 5.1.3 that γ has a continuous linear extension from $C^1(\bar{\Omega})$ to $H^1(\Omega)$. This extension, denoted by $\tilde{\gamma}$, is called a *trace operator*. It provides a means of assigning boundary values to functions for which the notion of a pointwise assignment is ambiguous ($\partial\Omega$ is a set of zero area). The following theorem gives a characterization of $H_0^1(\Omega)$ in terms of $\tilde{\gamma}$.

Theorem 6.3.1.   *Let $\partial\Omega$ be piecewise smooth and let* ker $\tilde{\gamma}$ *denote the kernel (i.e., null space) of the trace operator $\tilde{\gamma}$. Then $H_0^1(\Omega) =$ ker $\tilde{\gamma}$.*

Theorem 6.3.1 states that $u \in H_0^1(\Omega)$ if and only if $\tilde{\gamma}u = 0$ almost everywhere on $\partial\Omega$. In other words, the set of points on $\partial\Omega$ where $\tilde{\gamma}u$ is nonzero can be covered by a sequence of arcs the sum of whose lengths is arbitrarily small. If u is also in $C^1(\bar{\Omega})$, then $\tilde{\gamma}u = \gamma u = u|_{\partial\Omega}$, so $u(\mathbf{x})$, being continuous on the boundary, is zero at *all* points of $\partial\Omega$.

Theorem 6.3.1 holds for $\Omega \subset R^n$, $n > 2$, provided that the notion of a piecewise smooth boundary is suitably generalized. Furthermore, with a proper interpretation[4] of the space $L_2(\partial\Omega)$, it also holds when $n = 1$. Consider, for example, the case in which $\Omega \subset R^1$ is the open interval $(0, 1)$. If $u(x) = x - x^2$, $x \in \bar{\Omega}$, then $u \in H_0^1(\Omega)$ by Theorem 6.3.1. On the other hand, if $u(x) = 1$, $x \in \bar{\Omega}$, then $u \in H_0^0(\Omega)$ since $C_0^\infty(\Omega)$ is dense in $L_2(\Omega) = H^0(\Omega)$ (Adams [1975]). Furthermore, $u \in C^1(\bar{\Omega}) \subset H^1(\Omega)$, but $u \notin H_0^1(\Omega)$. This last assertion follows from Theorem 6.3.1 since $u(0) \neq 0$. However, for this simple example it is possible to show that $u \notin H_0^1(\Omega)$ without using the concept of a trace. Indeed, if $\phi \in C_0^\infty(\Omega)$, then by the Cauchy–Schwarz inequality,

$$\phi(x) = \int_0^x \phi' \, dx \leq x^{1/2}\left[\int_0^x (\phi')^2 \, dx\right]^{1/2} \leq x^{1/2}\left[\int_0^1 (\phi')^2 \, dx\right]^{1/2} \quad \left(' = \frac{d}{dx}\right).$$

Thus

$$\int_0^1 \phi^2 \, dx \leq \frac{1}{2}\int_0^1 (\phi')^2 \, dx. \qquad (6.3.2)$$

Then by (6.3.2),

$$\|u - \phi\|_1^2 = \int_0^1 (1 - \phi)^2 \, dx + \int_0^1 (\phi')^2 \, dx$$

$$\geq 1 - 2\int_0^1 \phi \, dx + 3\int_0^1 \phi^2 \, dx$$

$$\geq 1 - 2\left(\int_0^1 \phi^2 \, dx\right)^{1/2} + 3\int_0^1 \phi^2 \, dx.$$

If we let $y = (\int_0^1 \phi^2 \, dx)^{1/2}$, and denote the right side of the last inequality by $g(y)$, then

$$g(y) = 1 - 2y + 3y^2.$$

---

[4] In this case Ω is a bounded open interval (a, b), $\partial\Omega = \{a, b\}$, and $\|u\|_{0,\partial\Omega} = \max(|u(a)|, |u(b)|)$.

Since $g(y) \geq g(\frac{1}{3}) = \frac{2}{3}$, it follows that u cannot be the limit in $H^1(\Omega)$ of any sequence in $C_0^\infty(\Omega)$. Hence $u \notin H_0^1(\Omega)$.

6.4 APPROXIMATION BY SMOOTH FUNCTIONS

It is of interest to know how well a function in $H^m(\Omega)$ can be approximated by a smooth function. This question may be partially answered with the help of an *averaging kernel*. Let $J(\mathbf{x})$ be any nonnegative, real-valued function defined on R^2 such that $J \in C^\infty(R^2)$, $J(\mathbf{x}) = 0$ if $|\mathbf{x}| \geq 1$, and $\int_{R^2} J(\mathbf{x}) \, d\mathbf{x} = 1$. An example of such a function is developed in Exercise 6.12. Then for any $\rho > 0$ the function

$$J_\rho(\mathbf{x}) \equiv \frac{1}{\rho^2} J\left(\frac{\mathbf{x}}{\rho}\right),$$

is an averaging kernel. From the properties of $J(\mathbf{x})$ it follows that the support of $J_\rho(\mathbf{x})$ is contained in the closed disk $|\mathbf{x}| \leq \rho$. Moreover, $J_\rho(\mathbf{x}) > 0$ and $\int_{R^2} J_\rho(\mathbf{x}) \, d\mathbf{x} = 1$.

We can use an averaging kernel to obtain a smooth approximation of an integrable function. If u is integrable on Ω, we extend its definition to all of R^2 by setting it equal to zero on the complement of Ω. Then

$$J_\rho * u(\mathbf{x}) \equiv \int_{R^2} J_\rho(\mathbf{x} - \mathbf{y}) u(\mathbf{y}) \, d\mathbf{y}$$

$$= \int_{|\mathbf{x}-\mathbf{y}|<\rho} J_\rho(\mathbf{x} - \mathbf{y}) u(\mathbf{y}) \, d\mathbf{y}$$

is well defined on R^2 and is called a *regularization* of u.

Some properties of $J_\rho * u$ are contained in the next lemma (Adams [1975]).

Lemma 6.4.1. *Let u and $J_\rho * u$ be defined as above.*
(a) *If u has compact support in Ω and ρ is positive and sufficiently small, then $J_\rho * u \in C_0^\infty(\Omega)$.*
(b) *If $u \in H^m(\Omega)$, if Ω' is an open set, and if $\bar{\Omega}' \subset \Omega$, then $\lim_{\rho \to 0_+} \|u - J_\rho * u\|_{m,\Omega'} = 0$.*

In part (b) the notation $\|\cdot\|_{m,\Omega'}$ means that the integrals defining the norm $\|\cdot\|_m$ are to be carried out over Ω'.

It is a consequence of Lemma 6.4.1 that any element of $u \in H^m(\Omega)$ having compact support in Ω can be approximated to any degree of accuracy by functions in $C_0^\infty(\Omega)$. Thus $u \in H_0^m(\Omega)$.

6.5 IMBEDDINGS

Suppose that X and Y are normed spaces with norms $\|\cdot\|_X$ and $\|\cdot\|_Y$, respectively. We say that X is *imbedded* in Y if

1. X is a vector subspace of Y.
2. There is a constant K such that $\|x\|_Y \leq K\|x\|_X$ for all $x \in X$.

Our main concern with imbeddings arises in connection with the question of when, for given m and j, a function in $H^m(\Omega)$ is also a member of $C^j(\bar{\Omega})$. Since each element of $H^m(\Omega)$ is *not* a function in the strict sense of the word, but rather an *equivalence class* of functions that are equal a.e., the concept of imbedding $H^m(\Omega)$ in $C^j(\bar{\Omega})$ needs some clarification.

In the first place if we define the norm $\|\cdot\|_{j,\infty}$, where

$$\|u\|_{j,\infty} \equiv \max_{0 \le |\alpha| \le j} \sup_{x \in \bar{\Omega}} |D^\alpha u(x)|, \qquad u \in C^j(\bar{\Omega}),$$

then $C^j(\bar{\Omega})$ becomes a Banach space. Therefore, when we say that $H^m(\Omega)$ is imbedded in $C^j(\bar{\Omega})$, we mean that each $u \in H^m(\Omega)$, when considered as an ordinary function, can be redefined on a set of zero area (at most) so that the modified function (again denoted u) belongs to $C^j(\bar{\Omega})$ and satisfies $\|u\|_{j,\infty} \le K\|u\|_m$.

It is clear that the choice of j and m influences whether or not $H^m(\Omega)$ is imbedded in $C^j(\bar{\Omega})$. Other factors are the number of independent variables (in the present case this is 2) and the nature of $\partial\Omega$. Conditions under which the aforementioned imbeddings occur are part of a much more general theorem known as the Sobolev imbedding theorem. This theorem forms the cornerstone of the theory of Sobolev spaces and is proven in Adams [1975]. To apply it to our situation, we assume that $\partial\Omega$ is again piecewise smooth. The imbedding theorem is then the following.

Theorem 6.5.1. *If the bounded region $\Omega \subset R^2$, then the space $H^m(\Omega)$ is imbedded in $C^j(\bar{\Omega})$ if $m > j + 1$.*

6.6 AN EQUIVALENT NORM FOR $H_0^m(\Omega)$

For any finite-dimensional vector space X there is an important result stating that any two norms on X, say $\|\cdot\|$ and $\|\cdot\|'$, are *equivalent* in the sense that there are positive constants K_1 and K_2 such that

$$K_1\|x\| \le \|x\|' \le K_2\|x\| \tag{6.6.1}$$

for all $x \in X$. If X is not finite dimensional, then (6.6.1) may fail, a fact that significantly complicates the analysis of infinite dimensional spaces.

In this section we consider two specific norms for $H_0^m(\Omega)$ that are equivalent in the sense of (6.6.1). We have already introduced one of these, namely $\|\cdot\|_m$. The other results from the following lemma (Adams [1975]).

Lemma 6.6.1 (Poincaré's Inequality). *There is a constant K such that*

$$\|u\|_m \le K|u|_m \tag{6.6.2}$$

for all $u \in H_0^m(\Omega)$.

It is a trivial consequence of (6.6.2) that $|\cdot|_m$ is a norm on $H_0^m(\Omega)$. Furthermore, (6.6.2) and the obvious inequality, $|u|_m \le \|u\|_m$, when taken together, show that this norm is equivalent to $\|\cdot\|_m$. Note that on the larger space $H^m(\Omega)$, $|\cdot|_m$ is only a *semi-norm* for $m \geq 1$, since if u is any nonzero constant function, then $|u|_m = 0$.

NOTES AND REMARKS

6.1 The generalized derivative v_α that we have defined by (6.1.2) is also known as a *distributional derivative* (Adams [1975]). We have avoided this term to emphasize the ordinary functional nature of v_α. For any integrable function u the left side of (6.1.2) defines a *distribution*, that is, a continuous linear functional on $C_0^\infty(\Omega)$. With this distribution we can *always* associate other distributions that are interpretable as its "derivatives" of arbitrary orders. However, it is generally impossible to represent these derivatives in terms of integrals in the manner of the right side of (6.1.2). Indeed, Exercise 6.6 shows that the simple step function has no generalized first derivative. However, when identified as a distribution, its derivative exists as the celebrated *Dirac delta distribution*. For more on the theory of distributions, see the fundamental treatise of Schwartz [1966] as well as the books by Rudin [1973] and Friedlander [1982].

6.2 The axioms for an abstract Hilbert space were introduced by J. von Neumann in 1928; D. Hilbert had previously discussed the first realization of the abstract concept. Further information on Hilbert spaces is available, for example, in Halmos [1951] or Riesz and Sz-Nagy [1955].

In 1907, M. Frechet and F. Riesz independently published Theorem 6.2.1 for the spaces $L_2(\Omega)$. Although the L_p spaces described in Exercise 6.13 are not Hilbert spaces if $p \neq 2$, a kind of generalization of Theorem 6.2.1 applies to them. Specifically, if f is any bounded linear functional on $L_p(\Omega)$, $1 \leq p < \infty$, then there is an element $f^* \in L_q(\Omega)$, where q is the exponent conjugate to p, such that $f(u) = \int_\Omega f^* u \, d\mathbf{x}$ for all $u \in L_p(\Omega)$.

6.3 Under very general conditions on $\partial\Omega$, the space $H^m(\Omega)$ may also be defined as the *completion* of the space $C^m(\bar{\Omega})$ with respect to the norm $\|\cdot\|_m$. The equivalence of this definition with that given in Section 6.3 was established by Meyers and Serrin [1964]. The advantage of the definition in Section 6.3 is that it does not require one to interpret the "ideal" elements associated with the completion process (see the Notes and Remarks of Chapter 5). On the other hand, the alternative definition shows immediately that each element of $H^m(\Omega)$ is the limit of a sequence in $C^m(\bar{\Omega})$.

It is possible to prove that the range of the trace operator $\tilde{\gamma}$ is a dense subspace of $L_2(\partial\Omega)$. This subspace, denoted by $H^{1/2}(\partial\Omega)$, becomes a Hilbert space when endowed with the inner product that gives rise to the norm

$$\|u\|_{1/2,\partial\Omega} \equiv \inf \|v\|_1,$$

where the infimum is taken over all $v \in H^1(\Omega)$ such that $\tilde{\gamma}v = u$. It is also possible to define higher-order traces. These provide a characterization of $H_0^m(\Omega)$ in terms of the vanishing of u and its first $m - 1$ normal derivatives on $\partial\Omega$. All of these results hold for $\Omega \in R^n$, $n \geq 1$ (see, e.g., Adams [1975] or Nečas [1967] for more details).

6.5 As stated (and proved) in Adams [1975], the Sobolev imbedding theorem encompasses four different types of imbeddings. Theorem 6.5.1 is, of course, a special case of one of these. Its conclusion is valid when Ω is a region of R^n provided that $m > j + n/2$.

6.6 The equivalence of norms for finite-dimensional vector spaces is a standard result and may be found in most texts dealing with these spaces (see, e.g., Kreyszig [1978]).

Adams [1975] refers to (6.6.2) as "Poincaré's inequality" and we follow his terminology in Section 6.6. Other authors, for example Axelsson and Barker [1984] and Oden and Reddy [1976], call (6.6.2) "Friedrichs' inequality." Ciarlet [1978] comes down squarely on both sides of the issue by labeling (6.6.2) the "Poincaré–Friedrichs inequality."

EXERCISES

6.1. Prove that if u has compact support in a bounded region Ω, it vanishes in a boundary strip of Ω.

6.2. Find a generalized derivative on the open interval $(0, 1)$ for the function

$$u(x) = \begin{cases} x & \text{for } 0 < x \leq \frac{1}{2}, \\ 1 - x & \text{for } \frac{1}{2} < x < 1. \end{cases}$$

6.3. Let $\eta(x) = \cot \pi \left[(x^2 - a^2)/(b^2 - a^2) \right]$ where $0 \leq a < b < \infty$. Show that if Ω is any finite open interval containing $[-b, b]$, then

$$J(x) = \begin{cases} 1 & \text{for } |x| \leq a, \\ \dfrac{1}{1 + e^{-\eta(x)}} & \text{for } a < |x| < b, \\ 0 & \text{for } b \leq |x|, \end{cases}$$

is a member of $C_0^\infty(\Omega)$.

6.4. Prove that if δ is integrable on $\Omega = (-1, 1)$ and satisfies the condition

$$\int_\Omega \delta(x)\phi(x)\,dx = \phi(0) \tag{1}$$

for all $\phi \in C_0^\infty(\Omega)$, then

$$\int_{\Omega'} \delta(x)\,dx = 0,$$

where Ω' is any open subinterval of Ω. [*Hint:* Use Exercise 6.3 and the fact that when regarded as a set function, the integral is absolutely continuous; that is, $\left| \int_I \delta \, dx \right|$ is arbitrarily small provided that the length of the interval I is sufficiently small.]

6.5. Show that there is no integrable function δ satisfying condition (1).

6.6. Prove that if $a \neq b$, the step function

$$u(x) = \begin{cases} a & \text{for } -1 < x < 0 \\ b & \text{for } 0 \leq x < 1 \end{cases}$$

has no generalized derivative on $(-1, 1)$.

6.7. Show that if U is an inner product space with induced norm $\|\cdot\|$, then the *parallelogram law*,

$$\|u + v\|^2 + \|u - v\|^2 = 2(\|u\|^2 + \|v\|^2), \tag{2}$$

holds for all $u, v \in U$.

6.8. Let U be the vector space of continuous functions on the interval $[0, 1]$.

    (a) Show that $\|\cdot\|: \|u\| \equiv \max_{x \in [0,1]} |u(x)|$ is a norm on U.

    (b) Show that the norm of part (a) cannot be induced by any inner product on U. [*Hint:* Show by example that (2) does not hold for certain $u, v \in U$.]

6.9. Let U be an inner product space. Two elements, $u, v \in U$, are said to be *orthogonal* if $(u, v) = 0$. Prove that orthogonal elements u, v satisfy the "Pythagorean theorem," $\|u + v\|^2 = \|u\|^2 + \|v\|^2$.

6.10. Under the definitions of Section 5.1, the set of bounded linear functionals on a normed linear space U becomes a Banach space U' called the *dual space* of U. Let U be a Hilbert space and define the function

$$(\cdot, \cdot)': U' \times U' \rightarrow R, (f, g)' \equiv (f^*, g^*),$$

where the elements f^* and g^* of U are the respective representations of f and g (Theorem 6.2.1). Prove that U' is a Hilbert space with inner product $(\cdot, \cdot)'$.

6.11. Let Ω be a finite open interval in R. Use the completeness of $L_2(\Omega)$ to prove that $H^1(\Omega)$ is complete.

6.12. Construct an averaging kernel $J_\rho \in C^\infty(R^2)$ from the function $J(x)$ of Exercise 6.3.

6.13. For $1 \leq p < \infty$, the L_p spaces are defined by

$$L_p(\Omega) = \left\{ u \,\middle|\, \int_\Omega |u|^p \, d\mathbf{x} < \infty \right\},$$

where Ω is a bounded region in R^2. These are Banach spaces under the norm

$$\|u\|_{0,p} \equiv \left(\int_\Omega |u|^p \, d\mathbf{x} \right)^{1/p}.$$

Moreover, *Hölder's inequality*,

$$\int_\Omega uv \, d\mathbf{x} \leq \|u\|_{0,p} \|v\|_{0,q},$$

is valid for any $u \in L_p(\Omega)$, $v \in L_q(\Omega)$, providing that the "conjugate exponents" p and q satisfy the conditions $1 < p < \infty, 1 < q < \infty, 1/p + 1/q = 1$. Prove that $L_q(\Omega)$ is imbedded in $L_p(\Omega)$ if $1 \leq p \leq q < \infty$.

6.14. Let U be a vector space and let $\|\cdot\|$ and $\|\cdot\|'$ be norms on U such that $X = \{U, \|\cdot\|\}$ and $Y = \{U, \|\cdot\|'\}$ are Banach spaces. It is a consequence of the *open mapping theorem* (Kreyszig [1978]) that if T is a bounded, linear, one-to-one mapping of X onto Y, then T^{-1} is bounded. Use this to show that if there is a constant K such that $\|u\|' \leq K\|u\|$ for all $u \in U$, then the norms $\|\cdot\|$ and $\|\cdot\|'$ are equivalent.

7

Elliptic Boundary Value Problems and the Finite Element Method

In previous chapters we have dealt with partial differential equations of evolutionary type in which one of the independent variables behaves in a timelike manner. Now we turn our attention to equations where this distinguishing feature is absent. Such equations generally describe steady-state or equilibrium problems wherein the dependent variable changes over a spatial region, but is independent of time. These problems are frequently associated with elliptic equations and are usually termed "boundary value problems" since the proper auxiliary condition (to be imposed along with the partial differential equation) is the specification of the unknown function and/or its normal derivative on the boundary of the region.

In this chapter we investigate the numerical solution of a class of second-order, linear, elliptic boundary value problems by the finite element method. This proceeds more naturally from the so-called *weak* and *variational* forms of the original problem than the classical differential equation formulation. Consequently, we begin with an examination of the relationships that exist among these various versions of a given boundary value problem.

7.1 BOUNDARY VALUE PROBLEMS

We assume that Ω is a bounded region in R^2 whose boundary, $\partial\Omega$, is piecewise smooth in the sense of Section 6.3. Let a typical point in $\bar{\Omega}$ be denoted by $\mathbf{x} = (x_1, x_2)$, and let a_1, a_2, b, and f be functions defined on $\bar{\Omega}$ and satisfy there the following conditions: (1) $\partial a_i/\partial x_j$ $(i, j = 1, 2)$, b, and f are Lipschitz continuous; (2) $b \geq 0$, $a_i \geq a > 0$, $i = 1, 2$, where a is some constant. Then the *classical (differential equation) form* of the boundary value problem that we consider is given as

Problem B. *Let the operator* $L: C^2(\bar{\Omega}) \to C(\bar{\Omega})$ *be defined by*

$$Lu \equiv -(a_i u_{x_i})_{x_i} + bu.$$

Find a function $u \in C^2(\bar{\Omega})$ *such that*

$$Lu = f, \qquad \mathbf{x} \in \Omega \tag{7.1.1}$$

and

$$u = 0, \qquad \mathbf{x} \in \partial\Omega, \tag{7.1.2}$$

where a repeated index indicates summation over the integers 1, 2 *(a convention used throughout this section).*

We can write equation (7.1.1) using the "del" operator as

$$-\nabla \cdot A \, \nabla u + bu = f, \qquad \mathbf{x} \in \Omega,$$

where $A = \text{Diag} \{a_1, a_2\}$.

The functions a_i, b, and f constitute the *data* of the problem, and because of condition 2, (7.1.1) is termed a *uniformly elliptic* equation. Moreover, conditions 1 and 2 are more than enough to guarantee that Problem B has a unique solution *provided that* $\partial\Omega$ *is smooth*[1] (Courant and Hilbert [1962]).

The homogeneous boundary condition (7.1.2) is primarily one of convenience. For a treatment of more general boundary conditions, see Section 7.2, Exercise 7.4, and Chapter 8.

There are two other forms of Problem B. The first is the *weak* or *Galerkin* form and is stated as

Problem G. *Find a function* $u \in H_0^1(\Omega)$ *such that for all* $v \in H_0^1(\Omega)$,

$$\int_\Omega (a_i u_{x_i} v_{x_i} + buv - fv) \, d\mathbf{x} = 0. \tag{7.1.3}$$

[Recall that the Sobolev space $H_0^1(\Omega)$ was defined in Section 6.3.]

---

[1] That is, our piecewise smooth boundary has no breakpoints.

The second alternative form of Problem B is the *variational* form. To present it we define the (quadratic) functional on $H_0^1(\Omega)$,

$$I[v] \equiv \int_\Omega (a_i v_{x_i}^2 + bv^2 - 2fv)\, d\mathbf{x}. \tag{7.1.4}$$

Then we consider

Problem V.   *Find $u \in H_0^1(\Omega)$ such that for all $v \in H_0^1(\Omega)$,*

$$I[u] \leq I[v]. \tag{7.1.5}$$

For a discussion of the construction of functionals such as I given in (7.1.4), see Section 8.2.

Why do we work with the function space $H_0^1(\Omega)$ in Problems G and V? The answer is partly that this space has the boundary condition (7.1.2) automatically built into it; anything in $H_0^1(\Omega)$ is the limit of functions that vanish on $\partial\Omega$. Therefore, there is no need to impose such a condition on the functions in (7.1.3) and (7.1.4). Indeed, since "functions" in $H_0^1(\Omega)$ may be arbitrarily redefined at points on $\partial\Omega$, the imposition of boundary values is meaningless. Another part of the answer is that this space has just enough derivatives for the integrals in (7.1.3) and (7.1.4) to make sense. In this connection, note that the classical boundary value problem requires two continuous derivatives, whereas the weak forms need only generalized first partial derivatives. We will exploit this fact when we apply the finite element method to these problems. Of course, if Problems G and V have nothing to do with Problem B, then, whatever their merits, there is no further reason to consider them. However, it turns out that all three problems are related. The relationship between Problems G and V is simple; they are equivalent.

Theorem 7.1.1.   *The function u solves Problem G if and only if it solves Problem V.*

Proof. Suppose that u solves Problem G, and let w be any element of $H_0^1(\Omega)$. We easily verify that

$$I[u + w] = I[u] + I[w] + 2 \int_\Omega (a_i u_{x_i} w_{x_i} + buw)\, d\mathbf{x}. \tag{7.1.6}$$

Therefore, by (7.1.3),

$$I[u + w] = I[u] + I[w] + 2 \int_\Omega fw\, d\mathbf{x}$$

$$= I[u] + \int_\Omega (a_i w_{x_i}^2 + bw^2)\, d\mathbf{x} \geq I[u], \tag{7.1.7}$$

which is (7.1.5).

Conversely, let u solve Problem V. For fixed but arbitrary $v \in H_0^1(\Omega)$ and $s \in R$ define $\Phi(s) = I[u + sv]$. Then, by (7.1.6),

$$\Phi(s) = I[u] + I[sv] + 2s \int_\Omega (a_i u_{x_i} v_{x_i} + buv)\, d\mathbf{x}$$

$$= I[u] + 2s \int_\Omega (a_i u_{x_i} v_{x_i} + buv - fv)\, d\mathbf{x} + s^2 \int_\Omega (a_i v_{x_i}^2 + bv^2)\, d\mathbf{x}.$$

Since Φ has a minimum at $s = 0$, it follows that

$$\frac{d}{ds}\Phi\Big|_{s=0} = 0.$$

That is,

$$\int_\Omega (a_i u_{x_i} v_{x_i} + buv - fv)\, d\mathbf{x} = 0.$$

Q.E.D.

The connection of Problem B to Problem G (and hence also to Problem V) is more complicated. We show first that any solution of Problem B is also a solution of Problem G.

Theorem 7.1.2.   *If u solves Problem B, then u solves Problem G.*

Proof. We assume for the present that $u \in H_0^1(\Omega)$. The validity of this assumption will follow from Theorem 7.3.2. Now let $\phi \in C_0^\infty(\Omega)$. Then, since u is also in $C^2(\bar{\Omega})$,

$$-(a_i u_{x_i})_{x_i}\phi = a_i u_{x_i}\phi_{x_i} - (a_i u_{x_i}\phi)_{x_i}. \tag{7.1.8}$$

Therefore, if we multiply (7.1.1) by ϕ, use (7.1.8), and integrate, we get

$$\int_\Omega (a_i u_{x_i}\phi_{x_i} + bu\phi - f\phi)\, d\mathbf{x} = \int_\Omega (a_i u_{x_i}\phi)_{x_i}\, d\mathbf{x}. \tag{7.1.9}$$

However, the integral on the right side vanishes, as may be seen by applying Green's theorem and remembering that $\phi|_{\partial\Omega} = 0$. This proves the theorem when $v \in C_0^\infty(\Omega)$.

Next suppose that $v \in H_0^1(\Omega)$ and set

$$g(v) \equiv \int_\Omega (a_i u_{x_i} v_{x_i} + buv - fv)\, d\mathbf{x}.$$

By the Cauchy–Schwarz inequality,

$$|g(v)| \le \left[\int_\Omega (a_i u_{x_i})^2\, d\mathbf{x}\right]^{1/2}\left(\int_\Omega v_{x_i}^2\, d\mathbf{x}\right)^{1/2} + \left[\int_\Omega (bu - f)^2\, d\mathbf{x}\right]^{1/2}\left(\int_\Omega v^2\, d\mathbf{x}\right)^{1/2}$$

$$\le K\|v\|_1,$$

where K is a constant and we recall that

$$\|v\|_m \equiv \left[\int_\Omega \sum_{k=0}^{m} \sum_{|\alpha|=k} (D^\alpha u)^2\, d\mathbf{x}\right]^{1/2}$$

Thus g is a bounded, and therefore continuous, linear functional. Moreover, there is a sequence of functions $\phi_n \in C_0^\infty(\Omega)$ such that $\phi_n \to v$ in $H_0^1(\Omega)$ and $g(\phi_n) = 0$ for all n. It follows that $g(v) = \lim_{n\to\infty} g(\phi_n) = 0$.

Q.E.D.

The difficulty with the converse to Theorem 7.1.2 is the requisite smoothness of the solution of Problem G. General elements of $H_0^1(\Omega)$ simply do not have enough derivatives to qualify as classical solutions. However, if we assume that the solution of Problem G lies in a sufficiently smooth subspace of $H_0^1(\Omega)$, then, for example, we have the following converse. (See Exercise 7.5 for another result along these lines.)

Theorem 7.1.3.   *If $u \in C^2(\bar{\Omega})$ and solves Problem G, then u solves Problem B.*

Proof. Since $u \in H_0^1(\Omega) \cap C^1(\bar{\Omega})$, it follows from the discussion following Theorem 6.3.1 that $u|_{\partial\Omega} = 0$.

Next we observe that from (7.1.3) and (7.1.8) we have

$$\int_\Omega [-(a_i u_{x_i})_{x_i} + bu - f]\phi \, d\mathbf{x} = 0 \tag{7.1.10}$$

for any $\phi \in C_0^\infty(\Omega)$. Now suppose that the quantity in brackets is nonzero at some point $\mathbf{x}_0 \in \Omega$. By continuity it is of one sign in a disk of sufficiently small radius ρ centered at $\mathbf{x}_0$. But then if we choose $\phi(\mathbf{x}) = J_\rho(\mathbf{x} - \mathbf{x}_0)$, where J_ρ is an averaging kernel (Section 6.4), we contradict (7.1.10).

Q.E.D.

Having demonstrated how the three Problems B, G, and V are related, we now focus our attention on Problem G. In particular, we show that the existence and uniqueness questions for this problem are almost trivial. This is in sharp contrast to the corresponding state of affairs for Problem B, where the additional smoothness requirements make existence proofs much more difficult.

We define the function $\langle\cdot,\cdot\rangle\colon H_0^1(\Omega) \times H_0^1(\Omega) \to R$ by

$$\langle u, v \rangle \equiv \int_\Omega (a_i u_{x_i} v_{x_i} + buv) \, d\mathbf{x}. \tag{7.1.11}$$

Recall that $a_i(\mathbf{x}) \geq a > 0$ and $b(\mathbf{x}) \geq 0$ for $\mathbf{x} \in \Omega$. Hence

$$\langle u, u \rangle \geq a \int_\Omega u_{x_i} u_{x_i} \, d\mathbf{x} = a|u|_1^2$$

It follows from Lemma 6.6.1 that $\langle\cdot,\cdot\rangle$ is an inner product on $H_0^1(\Omega)$, and the associated norm is equivalent to the norms $\|u\|_1$ and

$$|u|_1 = \{\int_\Omega [(u_{x_1})^2 + (u_{x_2})^2] \, d\mathbf{x}\}^{1/2}.$$

The norm $|u|_E \equiv \langle u, u \rangle^{1/2}$ is sometimes called the *energy norm* on $H_0^1(\Omega)$.

Theorem 7.1.4.   *Problem G has a unique solution.*

Proof. Obviously, Problem G is solved if and only if there is a $u \in H_0^1(\Omega)$ such that for all $v \in H_0^1(\Omega)$, we have

$$\langle u, v \rangle = (f, v)_0. \tag{7.1.12}$$

The Cauchy–Schwarz inequality implies that

$$|(f, v)_0| \leq \|f\|_0 \|v\|_0 \leq \|f\|_0 \|v\|_1,$$

so that the right side of (7.1.12) is a bounded linear functional on $H_0^1(\Omega)$. By Theorem 6.2.1 there is a unique function $u^* \in H_0^1(\Omega)$ such that

$$(f, v)_0 = \langle u^*, v \rangle$$

for all $v \in H_0^1(\Omega)$. Hence (7.1.12) reads

$$\langle u, v \rangle = \langle u^*, v \rangle,$$

and the unique solution of this equation is certainly $u = u^*$.

Q.E.D.

Note that by Theorem 7.1.1 the function u^* is also the unique solution of Problem V.

7.2 ESSENTIAL AND NATURAL BOUNDARY CONDITIONS

So far we have considered formulations of boundary value problems involving only *homogeneous* boundary conditions. However, *nonhomogeneous* boundary conditions can be handled without major changes in the variational (or equivalently, the Galerkin) formulation. For example, suppose that (7.1.2) is replaced by

$$u = g, \qquad \mathbf{x} \in \partial\Omega. \tag{7.2.1}$$

We assume there exists a fixed element $u_1 \in C^2(\bar{\Omega})$ such that $u_1 = g$ on $\partial\Omega$. Then the function

$$u_2 = u - u_1$$

satisfies

$$Lu_2 = f - Lu_1, \qquad \mathbf{x} \in \Omega,$$

and

$$u_2 = 0, \qquad \mathbf{x} \in \partial\Omega,$$

where L is defined in (7.1.1). Equivalently, by Theorems 7.1.1 and 7.1.2,

$$I^*[u_2] = \min_{w \in H_0^1(\Omega)} I^*[w],$$

where $I^*[w] \equiv \int_\Omega [a_i w_{x_i}^2 + bw^2 - (f - Lu_1)w]\, dx$.

If we let $v = u_1 + w$ for $w \in H_0^1(\Omega)$, we have

$$I[v] = I[u_1] + I^*[w].$$

Hence

$$\begin{aligned}
I[u] &= I[u_1] + I^*[u_2] \\
&= I[u_1] + \min_{w \in H_0^1(\Omega)} I^*[w] \\
&= \min_{w \in H_0^1(\Omega)} I[u_1 + w] = \min_{v \in S} I[v],
\end{aligned}$$

where $S \equiv \{v \,|\, v = u_1 + w \text{ for } some\ w \in H_0^1(\Omega)\}$.

Note that the set S of functions that satisfy nonhomogeneous boundary conditions is *not* a linear space since the difference of two such functions does not satisfy the nonhomogeneous boundary conditions.[2] Nevertheless, one simply seeks a minimum over the *set* of functions which are admissible in the sense that the functional is defined (and bounded) and each member of the set satisfies the boundary conditions. Boundary conditions such as (7.2.1) are termed *essential boundary conditions* since the functions in S are forced to satisfy these conditions.

In contrast to essential boundary conditions there may be *natural boundary conditions* which are handled automatically by the minimization process. For example, consider the steady-state heat conduction problem discussed in Section 2.3. Let the boundary of Ω, $\partial\Omega$, be decomposed into three disjoint sets

$$\partial\Omega = \partial\Omega_1 \cup \partial\Omega_2 \cup \partial\Omega_3,$$

and let $\mathbf{n}$ be the outward unit normal to $\partial\Omega$. Further, let the set of functions S be defined by

$$S = \{w \,|\, w \in H^1(\Omega), \, w(\mathbf{x}) = g(\mathbf{x}) \text{ for } \mathbf{x} \in \partial\Omega_1\}.$$

Then we have the following theorem.

Theorem 7.2.1.   *Let $I[u]$ be the functional*

$$I[u] = \tfrac{1}{2} \int_\Omega (k|\nabla u|^2 - 2fu) \, d\mathbf{x} + \int_{\partial\Omega_3} (\tfrac{1}{2}h_0 u^2 - h_0 u_s u) \, ds. \qquad (7.2.2)$$

where k, f, h_0, and u_s are the thermal conductivity, heat source, heat transfer coefficient, and sink temperature, respectively. If u^* satisfies

$$I[u^*] = \min_{w \in S} I[w],$$

and $u^* \in C^2(\bar{\Omega})$, then u^* solves the boundary value problem

$$-\nabla \cdot k\,\nabla u = f, \qquad \mathbf{x} \in \Omega,$$
$$u = g, \qquad \mathbf{x} \in \partial\Omega_1, \qquad (7.2.3)$$
$$-\nabla u \cdot \mathbf{n} = 0, \qquad \mathbf{x} \in \partial\Omega_2,$$

and

$$-k\,\nabla u \cdot \mathbf{n} = h_0(u - u_s), \qquad \mathbf{x} \in \partial\Omega_3.$$

Proof. Let $G(\varepsilon) = I[u^* + \varepsilon v]$ for any $v = v_1 - v_2$, where $v_i \in S$. Then, by hypothesis,

$$\frac{dG}{d\varepsilon}(0) = 0,$$

---

[2] The set S is an *affine space*, that is, a translate of a linear space.

which after some manipulation leads to

$$0 = -\int_{\Omega} (\nabla \cdot k \, \nabla u^* + f) v \, d\mathbf{x} + \int_{\partial\Omega_1 \cup \partial\Omega_2} (k \, \nabla u^* \cdot \mathbf{n}) v \, ds$$

$$+ \int_{\partial\Omega_3} (h_0(u^* - u_s) + k \nabla u^* \cdot \mathbf{n}) v \, ds.$$

The result now follows since $v = 0$ on $\partial\Omega_1$, and v is arbitrary on $\partial\Omega_2$ and $\partial\Omega_3$.

Q.E.D.

Note that the boundary conditions on $\partial\Omega_2$ and $\partial\Omega_3$ were *not* used to restrict the functions in S; hence $-\nabla u \cdot \mathbf{n} = 0$ and $-k \, \nabla u \cdot \mathbf{n} = h_0(u - u_s)$ are *natural* boundary conditions for the functional I in (7.2.2).

7.3 A GENERIC DECOMPOSITION OF $\bar{\Omega}$

The utility of the finite element method stems from the fact that approximate solutions are assembled from functions whose supports are limited to relatively simple subsets of the original problem domain. This leads us to postulate that $\bar{\Omega}$ is capable of being conveniently subdivided into certain subsets called *elements*. For the applications we have in mind it is sufficient to assume that $\bar{\Omega}$ admits a decomposition of the form

$$\bar{\Omega} = \bigcup_{j=1}^{N} \bar{\Omega}_j, \tag{7.3.1}$$

where the elements, $\bar{\Omega}_j$, have pairwise disjoint interiors Ω_j whose boundaries $\partial\Omega_j$ are of the same nature as that of Ω.

Relative to the decomposition (7.3.1) we define

$$S_0(\bar{\Omega}) \equiv \left\{ u \,\middle|\, u \in C^0(\bar{\Omega}) \cap \left[\bigcap_{j=1}^{N} C^1(\bar{\Omega}_j) \right], u\big|_{\partial\Omega} = 0 \right\}. \tag{7.3.2}$$

Thus $S_0(\bar{\Omega})$ is the vector space of functions that vanish on the boundary of Ω, are continuous on $\bar{\Omega}$, and have continuous first derivatives in each $\bar{\Omega}_j$. Note that $C_0^1(\bar{\Omega}) \subset S_0(\bar{\Omega})$. But $S_0(\bar{\Omega})$ is a much larger space, since it also contains functions whose first derivatives have jump discontinuities across a common boundary of any two contiguous Ω_j.

Although there are elements of $S_0(\bar{\Omega})$ that do not have classical first derivatives on Ω, every $u \in S_0(\bar{\Omega})$ has generalized first derivatives there. To see this, observe that if $\phi \in C_0^\infty(\Omega)$, then

$$\int_{\Omega} u\phi_{x_i} \, d\mathbf{x} = \sum_j \int_{\Omega_j} u\phi_{x_i} d\mathbf{x} = \sum_j \int_{\Omega_j} [(u\phi)_{x_i} - u_{x_i}\phi] \, d\mathbf{x}$$

$$= \sum_j \int_{\Omega_j} (u\phi)_{x_i} \, d\mathbf{x} - \sum_j \int_{\Omega_j} u_{x_i}\phi \, d\mathbf{x}.$$

But $u\phi \in C^1(\bar{\Omega}_j)$, so that we may apply Green's theorem to each integral of the form $\int_{\Omega_j} (u\phi)_{x_i} \, d\mathbf{x}$. When the resulting boundary integrals are added, their contributions cancel pairwise except on $\partial\Omega$. However, $(u\phi)|_{\partial\Omega} = 0$, so that

$$\sum_j \int_{\Omega_j} (u\phi)_{x_i} \, d\mathbf{x} = \sum_j \int_{\partial\Omega_j} (u\phi) \frac{dx_i}{ds_j} \, ds_j = 0.$$

Consequently,

$$\int_\Omega u\phi_{x_i} \, d\mathbf{x} = -\sum_j \int_{\Omega_j} u_{x_i}\phi \, d\mathbf{x} = -\int_\Omega u_{x_i}\phi \, d\mathbf{x}.$$

Thus any function that agrees with u_{x_i} on the sets Ω_j and is bounded on the sets $\partial\Omega_j$ will serve as a generalized first derivative of u on Ω.

In view of the previous argument, the inclusions

$$C_0^\infty(\Omega) \subset S_0(\bar{\Omega}) \subset H^1(\Omega)$$

are obvious. It follows that if we take closures in $H^1(\Omega)$, then

$$H_0^1(\Omega) \equiv \overline{C_0^\infty(\Omega)} \subset \overline{S_0(\bar{\Omega})}. \tag{7.3.3}$$

It is plausible that this inclusion is proper. However, as we now show, these two spaces are *identical*. We begin with a preliminary lemma which establishes a Poincaré inequality (Lemma 6.6.1) for the space $S_0(\bar{\Omega})$.

Lemma 7.3.1. *There is a constant K such that*

$$\int_\Omega u^2 \, d\mathbf{x} \leq K|u|_1^2 \tag{7.3.4}$$

for all $u \in S_0(\bar{\Omega})$.

Proof. We assume without loss of generality that Ω is contained in the strip $0 \leq x_2 \leq d$ (Figure 7.3.1) and we extend $u \in S_0(\bar{\Omega})$ continuously to R^2 by setting it equal to zero on the complement of Ω. We then have by the Cauchy–Schwarz inequality,

$$u(x_1, x_2) = \int_0^{x_2} 1 \cdot u_{x_2}(x_1, t) \, dt \leq x_2^{1/2} \left[\int_0^{x_2} u_{x_2}^2(x_1, t) \, dt \right]^{1/2}$$

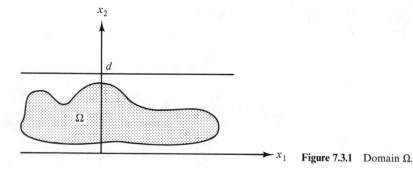

Figure 7.3.1 Domain Ω.

Therefore,

$$\int_{\Omega} u^2 \, d\mathbf{x} = \int_{-\infty}^{\infty} dx_1 \int_0^d u^2(x_1, x_2) \, dx_2$$

$$\leq \int_{-\infty}^{\infty} dx_1 \int_0^d \left[x_2 \int_0^{x_2} u_{x_2}^2(x_1, t) \, dt \right] dx_2$$

$$\leq \int_{-\infty}^{\infty} dx_1 \int_0^d x_2 \, dx_2 \int_0^d u_{x_2}^2(x_1, t) \, dt$$

$$= \frac{d^2}{2} \int_{\Omega} u_{x_2}^2(x_1, t) \, dx_1 \, dt \leq \frac{d^2}{2} |u|_1^2.$$

Q.E.D.

A second result that we need in our proof that $\overline{S_0(\bar{\Omega})} = H_0^1(\Omega)$ is the existence of a *cutoff* function $F \in C^1(\bar{\Omega})$ such that if Ω_h is a boundary strip of width h (see Figure 7.3.2), then for all sufficiently small $h > 0$:

1. $0 \leq F \leq 1$,

2. $F(\mathbf{x}) = 0$ if $\mathbf{x} \in \Omega_h$,

3. $F(\mathbf{x}) = 1$ if $\mathbf{x} \in \Omega - \Omega_{3h}$,

4. $|F_{x_i}| \leq K/h$, $i = 1, 2$,

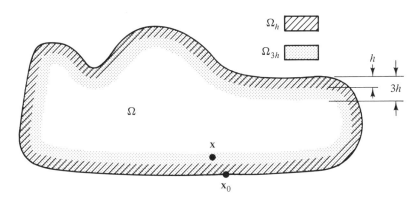

Figure 7.3.2 Domain of the cutoff function.

where K is a constant. Our assumptions about the nature of $\partial\Omega$ imply that such a function exists. In fact, its construction may be found in Mikhlin [1965].

We now state and prove the main result of this section. This theorem will be useful, for example, in convergence proofs since finite element approximations u_h will be chosen in $S_0(\bar{\Omega})$ and we will want to guarantee that $\lim_{h \to 0} u_h \in H_0^1(\Omega)$.

Theorem 7.3.2.   *The closure of the space of functions $S_0(\bar{\Omega})$ that vanish on the $\partial\Omega$, are continuous on all of $\bar{\Omega}$, and have continuous first derivatives on each $\bar{\Omega}_j$, is the Sobolev space $H_0^1(\Omega)$. That is,*

$$\overline{S_0(\bar{\Omega})} = H_0^1(\Omega).$$

Proof. Suppose we can show that if $u \in S_0(\bar{\Omega})$, then u is the limit in $H^1(\Omega)$ of a sequence of functions in $C_0^\infty(\Omega)$. Then $S_0(\bar{\Omega}) \subset \overline{C_0^\infty(\Omega)} \equiv H_0^1(\Omega)$, so $\overline{S_0(\bar{\Omega})} \subset H_0^1(\Omega)$. This inclusion and (7.3.3) then imply that the two spaces are identical.

To show that each element of $S_0(\bar{\Omega})$ is the limit of a sequence in $C_0^\infty(\Omega)$, we let $u \in S_0(\bar{\Omega})$ and choose $\varepsilon > 0$. We show first that there is a function $v \in S_0(\bar{\Omega})$, having compact support in Ω, such that

$$\|u - v\|_1 \le \frac{\varepsilon}{2}. \tag{7.3.5}$$

Then we construct a function $\phi \in C_0^\infty(\Omega)$ such that

$$\|v - \phi\|_1 \le \frac{\varepsilon}{2}.$$

Let F be a cutoff function and set

$$v(\mathbf{x}) = u(\mathbf{x})F(\mathbf{x}).$$

Then $v \in S_0(\bar{\Omega})$ and

$$v(\mathbf{x}) = \begin{cases} 0 & \text{if } \mathbf{x} \in \Omega_h \\ u(\mathbf{x}) & \text{if } \mathbf{x} \in \Omega - \Omega_{3h}. \end{cases}$$

By Lemma 7.3.1, there is a constant K such that

$$\|u - v\|_1^2 = \int_\Omega (u - v)^2 \, d\mathbf{x} + |u - v|_1^2 \le (1 + K)|u - v|_1^2$$

$$= (1 + K) \sum_{i=1}^2 \left[\int_{\Omega_h} u_{x_i}^2 \, d\mathbf{x} + \int_{\Omega_{3h} - \Omega_h} (u_{x_i} - v_{x_i})^2 \, d\mathbf{x} \right]. \tag{7.3.6}$$

If $u_{x_i}^2 \le K_1$, $i = 1, 2$, then

$$\sum_{i=1}^2 \int_{\Omega_h} u_{x_i}^2 \, d\mathbf{x} \le 2K_1 \, \text{Area} \, (\Omega_h). \tag{7.3.7}$$

Furthermore, the elementary inequality $(a + b)^2 \le 2(a^2 + b^2)$ and the properties of F imply that

$$|u_{x_i} - v_{x_i}|^2 \le 2(u_{x_i}^2 + v_{x_i}^2) \le 2u_{x_i}^2 + 2(uF_{x_i} + u_{x_i}F)^2$$

$$\le 2u_{x_i}^2 + 4(u^2 F_{x_i}^2 + u_{x_i}^2) \le 6u_{x_i}^2 + \frac{K_2 u^2}{h^2}$$

for some constant K_2. Hence

$$\sum_{i=1}^{2} \int_{\Omega_{3h} - \Omega_h} (u_{x_i} - v_{x_i})^2 \, d\mathbf{x} \le 6 \sum_{i=1}^{2} \int_{\Omega_{3h} - \Omega_h} u_{x_i}^2 \, d\mathbf{x} + \frac{2K_2}{h^2} \int_{\Omega_{3h} - \Omega_h} u^2 \, d\mathbf{x}.$$

Since u is Lipschitz continuous, if $\mathbf{x} \in \Omega_{3h} - \Omega_h$, there is a point $\mathbf{x}_0 \in \partial\Omega$ and a constant L such that

$$|u(\mathbf{x})| = |u(\mathbf{x}) - u(\mathbf{x}_0)| \le L|\mathbf{x} - \mathbf{x}_0| \le 3Lh.$$

Therefore,

$$\sum_{i=1}^{2} \int_{\Omega_{3h} - \Omega_h} (u_{x_i} - v_{x_i})^2 \, d\mathbf{x} \le (12K_1 + 18K_2 L^2) \, \text{Area} \, (\Omega_{3h} - \Omega_h). \qquad (7.3.8)$$

Combining (7.3.7) and (7.3.8) with (7.3.6), we obtain

$$\|u - v\|_1^2 \le (1 + K)[2K_1 \, \text{Area} \, (\Omega_h) + (12K_1 + 18K_2 L^2) \, \text{Area} \, (\Omega_{3h} - \Omega_h)].$$

Therefore, (7.3.5) holds for $h > 0$ and sufficiently small.

Now let $\Omega' = \Omega - \Omega_{h/2}$ and choose $0 < \rho < h/2$, where h is such that (7.3.5) is valid. Then $\phi \equiv J_\rho * v \equiv \int_{R^2} J_\rho(\mathbf{x} - \mathbf{y}) v(\mathbf{y}) \, d\mathbf{y} \in C_0^\infty(\Omega)$, and by Lemma 6.4.1,

$$\|v - \phi\|_1 = \|v - \phi\|_{1,\Omega'} \le \frac{\varepsilon}{2} \qquad (7.3.9)$$

if ρ is small enough. Consequently, by (7.3.5) and (7.3.9),

$$\|u - \phi\|_1 \le \|u - v\|_1 + \|v - \phi\|_1 \le \varepsilon.$$

Q.E.D.

Theorem 7.3.2 characterizes the Sobolev space $H_0^1(\Omega)$ as the closure of the space $S_0(\bar{\Omega})$, with respect to the H^1 norm.

7.4 FINITE ELEMENT SPACES

In the finite element method, the solution of Problem G is approximated by functions that are drawn from *finite-dimensional* subspaces of $S_0(\bar{\Omega})$. In view of what was proven in Section 7.3, we know that all these subspaces are contained in $H_0^1(\Omega)$.

The procedure defining a finite element approximation is straightforward. First we choose a finite-dimensional subspace, $S_0^h(\bar{\Omega})$, of $S_0(\bar{\Omega})$. (The significance of the superscript h will be made clear in Section 7.6.) Then we determine a finite element approximation $u^h \in S_0^h(\bar{\Omega})$ such that

$$\langle u^h, v \rangle = (f, v)_0 \qquad (7.4.1)$$

for all $v \in S_0^h(\bar{\Omega})$ [cf. (7.1.12)]. Recalling the definitions of these inner products, we see that (7.4.1) is in fact

$$\int_\Omega (a_i u_{x_i}^h v_{x_i} + b u^h v) \, d\mathbf{x} = \int_\Omega f v \, d\mathbf{x}.$$

It is natural to ask under what circumstances the approximate solution u^h is well defined. First, we observe that u^h is simply the solution of Problem G on $S_0^h(\bar{\Omega})$ instead of $H_0^1(\Omega)$. Since $S_0^h(\bar{\Omega}) \subset H_0^1(\Omega)$, the bilinear form $\langle \cdot, \cdot \rangle$ is an inner product on $S_0^h(\bar{\Omega})$. But every finite-dimensional inner product space is complete (see Exercise 7.7) so that $S_0^h(\bar{\Omega})$ is a Hilbert space under $\langle \cdot, \cdot \rangle$. Therefore, we can repeat the proof of Theorem 7.1.4 with $S_0^h(\bar{\Omega})$ in place of $H_0^1(\Omega)$ to establish the following result.

Theorem 7.4.1.   *There is a unique function $u^h \in S_0^h(\bar{\Omega})$ satisfying (7.4.1).*

For the actual determination of u^h we choose a basis for $S_0^h(\bar{\Omega})$, say $\{\phi_1, \ldots, \phi_n\}$. Then

$$u^h \equiv \sum_{j=1}^n c_j \phi_j \tag{7.4.2}$$

for some unknown coefficients $\{c_j\}$, and (7.4.1) is equivalent to the n scalar equations,

$$\sum_{j=1}^n \langle \phi_i, \phi_j \rangle c_j = (f, \phi_i)_0, \qquad i = 1, \ldots, n. \tag{7.4.3}$$

This is a linear system for the c_i which may be written in matrix form as

$$A\mathbf{c} = \mathbf{b}, \tag{7.4.4}$$

where A is an $n \times n$ matrix and $\mathbf{c}, \mathbf{b}$ are n-vectors,

$$A = [a_{ij}], \qquad a_{ij} \equiv \langle \phi_i, \phi_j \rangle,$$

$$\mathbf{c}^T = (c_1, \ldots, c_n),$$

$$\mathbf{b}^T = (b_1, \ldots, b_n), \qquad b_i \equiv (f, \phi_i)_0.$$

Theorem 7.4.1 asserts, in effect, that the coefficient matrix A of (7.4.4) is nonsingular. By utilizing the specific form of the entries of A, it is possible to give another proof of this theorem (Exercise 7.8); the matrix A is actually positive definite. A brief survey of solution procedures for linear systems of the type (7.4.4) is presented in Section 10.3. The frontal method is commonly used to solve finite element systems and is discussed in Section 8.6.

The following example illustrates the geometric flexibility inherent in the finite element method.

Example 7.4.1

Let $u(x, y)$ be the electrostatic potential at a point $(x, y) \in \Omega$. In the absence of charges, u satisfies

$$\nabla^2 u = 0.$$

The domain Ω is a circular enclosure with the condensers deleted (Figure 7.4.1). The outer boundary Γ_1 of the enclosure is assumed to be an equipotential line with value

A: $(-21, 0)$
B: $(-7, 0)$
C: $(-4, 0)$
D: $(2, 0)$
E: $(5, 0)$
F: $(21, 0)$

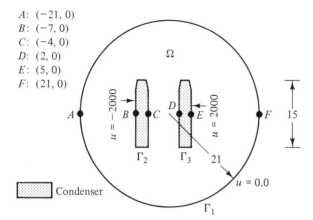

Condenser

Figure 7.4.1 Domain for the potential problem.

0, while the values of the potential on the condenser faces Γ_2 and Γ_3 are ± 2000, respectively, as indicated.

The weak or Galerkin form for this problem is: Find $u \in S \subset H^1(\Omega)$ such that for all $v \in H_0^1(\Omega)$

$$\int_\Omega \nabla u \cdot \nabla v \, d\mathbf{x} = 0,$$

where $S = \{w \in H^1(\Omega) \, | \, w = 0 \text{ on } \Gamma_1, \; w = -2000 \text{ on } \Gamma_2, \text{ and } w = 2000 \text{ on } \Gamma_3\}$. We subdivide $\bar{\Omega}$ by a triangular mesh as illustrated in Figure 7.4.2. There are 95 triangles

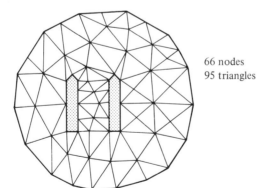

66 nodes
95 triangles

Figure 7.4.2 Finite element mesh.

and we choose $S^h(\bar{\Omega})$ as the space of functions which are linear on each triangular element and continuous on $\bar{\Omega}$. This space is studied in detail in Section 7.6. Figure 7.4.3 illustrates the electrostatic potential field for the mesh in Figure 7.4.2. Each triangle in Figure 7.4.2 is then subdivided into four triangles by adding nodes at the midpoints of the three

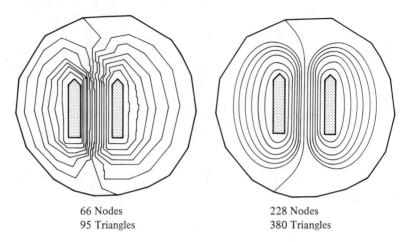

66 Nodes
95 Triangles

228 Nodes
380 Triangles

Figure 7.4.3   Electrostatic potential contours.

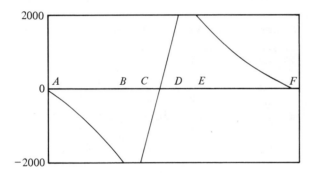

Figure 7.4.4   Plot of u along the equator.

sides. This refined mesh contains 380 triangles and the finite element solution for the elec-
static potential is considerably smoother. Figure 7.4.4 shows a plot of $u(x, y)$ along the
line $\overline{AF}$.

7.5 THE FINITE ELEMENT ERROR

Now that we know that a unique finite element approximation u^h is defined by (7.4.1),
we wish to assess the size of the error $e^h = u^* - u^h$, where u^* is the solution of Problem
G guaranteed by Theorem 7.1.4. As a first step in this direction, we show that if the
metric is properly chosen, this error is the smallest possible for approximations lying
in $S_0^h(\bar{\Omega})$.

As defined by (7.1.11), $\langle \cdot, \cdot \rangle$ is an inner product on $H_0^1(\Omega)$. Therefore, we can
use the vanishing of this expression to assign a meaning to the notion of orthogonality
in $H_0^1(\Omega)$ (see Exercise 6.9). With this in mind we note that if u^* and u^h satisfy (7.1.12)
and (7.4.1), respectively, then by subtraction $\langle u^* - u^h, v \rangle = 0$ for all $v \in S_0^h(\bar{\Omega})$. That

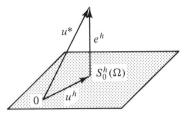

Figure 7.5.1   Orthogonality of the finite element error.

is, the error e^h is orthogonal to the subspace $S_0^h(\bar{\Omega})$. Figure 7.5.1 illustrates this and suggests that e^h is the smallest possible error, or equivalently that u^h is the best approximation to u^* in terms of the norm $\langle \cdot, \cdot \rangle^{1/2}$. As we now prove, this is precisely the case.

Theorem 7.5.1.   *If v is any element of $S_0^h(\bar{\Omega})$, and $e = u^* - v$, then the error $e^h = u^* - u^h$ satisfies*

$$\langle e^h, e^h \rangle \le \langle e, e \rangle. \tag{7.5.1}$$

Proof. Since $u^h - v \in S_0^h(\bar{\Omega})$ and e^h is orthogonal to $S_0^h(\bar{\Omega})$, it follows that

$$
\begin{aligned}
\langle e, e \rangle &= \langle (u^* - u^h) + (u^h - v), (u^* - u^h) + (u^h - v) \rangle \\
&= \langle e^h, e^h \rangle + 2\langle e^h, u^h - v \rangle + \langle u^h - v, u^h - v \rangle \\
&= \langle e^h, e^h \rangle + \langle u^h - v, u^h - v \rangle \ge \langle e^h, e^h \rangle.
\end{aligned}
$$

Q.E.D.

In terms of the norm $\|\cdot\|_1$ we have

Corollary 7.5.2.   *If v is any element of $S_0^h(\bar{\Omega})$, then there is a constant K such that*

$$\|u^* - u^h\|_1 \le K \|u^* - v\|_1. \tag{7.5.2}$$

Proof. Inequality (7.5.1) and the equivalence of the norms $\|\cdot\|_1$ and $\langle \cdot, \cdot \rangle^{1/2}$ combine to imply that

$$\|e^h\|_1 \le K_1 \langle e^h, e^h \rangle^{1/2} \le K_1 \langle e, e \rangle^{1/2} \le K \|e\|_1.$$

Q.E.D.

This corollary establishes that the *discretization error* is bounded by an *approximation error* in the sense that

$$\|u^* - u^h\|_1 \le K \inf_{v \in S_0^h(\bar{\Omega})} \|u^* - v\|_1.$$

The next step in our analysis of the finite element error is an appraisal of the size of $u^* - v$ when the function v is chosen to interpolate u^* on certain points of the sets $\bar{\Omega}_j$. However, to take this step we need to be more precise about the nature of the Ω_j and the associated finite element subspaces $S_0^h(\bar{\Omega})$. Although it is possible to develop a unified error analysis for a comprehensive collection of elements and subspaces (see, e.g., Oden and Reddy [1976] and Ciarlet [1978]), such a course would take us too far afield. What we shall do instead is complete the error analysis for two simple, but widely used, element–subspace pairs, the *linear isoparametric triangles* and the *bilinear isoparametric quadrilaterals*.

7.6 LINEAR ISOPARAMETRIC TRIANGLES

In this section we assume that Ω is the interior of a polygon which has been triangulated to obtain the decomposition (7.3.1). That is, each Ω_j is the interior of a non-degenerate triangle. As the context demands, we will use geometric terms such as "triangle," "quadrilateral," and so on, to denote either the element or its boundary. We restrict the triangulations to those in which any side of a triangle in the decomposition is either a part of $\partial\Omega$ or is the side of another triangle in the decomposition. The collection of triangular elements $\{\bar{\Omega}_j\}_{j=1}^{N}$ has a vertex or *node* set which we denote by $Z = \{z_i\}_{i=1}^{m}$. Although the actual triangulation of $\bar{\Omega}$ may be carried out in a variety of ways, it is important for the subsequent analysis to regard it as being effected by a collection of mappings of a fixed or *master* element[3] $\bar{M}$ onto the individual elements $\bar{\Omega}_j$.

Such mappings are easy to construct. For example, let M be the interior of the triangle whose nodes have coordinates $(0, 0)$, $(1, 0)$, and $(0, 1)$ with respect to the Cartesian coordinates $\zeta = (\xi, \eta)$, and let $\bar{\Omega}_j$ have nodes $z_{00} = (x_{00}, y_{00})$, $z_{10} = (x_{10}, y_{10})$, and $z_{01} = (x_{01}, y_{01})$ relative to the $z = (x, y)$ coordinates.[4] Then the mapping, $F: \bar{M} \rightarrow \bar{\Omega}_j$, defined by

$$z = F(\zeta) \equiv z_{00}(1 - \xi - \eta) + z_{10}\xi + z_{01}\eta, \tag{7.6.1}$$

is an affine transformation such that $\partial\Omega_j = F(\partial M)$. Its constant Jacobian matrix is

$$DF = \begin{bmatrix} x_\xi & x_\eta \\ y_\xi & y_\eta \end{bmatrix} = \begin{bmatrix} x_{10} - x_{00} & x_{01} - x_{00} \\ y_{10} - y_{00} & y_{01} - y_{00} \end{bmatrix}$$

with associated determinant

$$\det DF = (x_{10} - x_{00})(y_{01} - y_{00}) - (x_{01} - x_{00})(y_{10} - y_{00}).$$

If we regard z_{00}, z_{10}, and z_{01} as vectors in the xy-plane of a three-dimensional Cartesian coordinate system, then

$$|\det DF| = |(z_{10} - z_{00}) \times (z_{01} - z_{00})|$$
$$= |z_{10} - z_{00}||z_{01} - z_{00}| \sin\theta,$$

---

[3] We again assume that M is a region with a piecewise smooth boundary.

[4] To simplify the notation, we supress the obvious dependence on j.

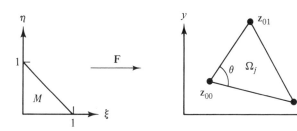

Figure 7.6.1 Affine map (7.6.1).

where θ is the angle shown in Figure 7.6.1. Since $\theta \neq 0$ or π, det $DF \neq 0$, and therefore, $\mathbf{F}$ is a one-to-one map of $\bar{M}$ onto $\bar{\Omega}_j$.

To determine the subspace $S_0^h(\bar{\Omega})$ associated with these triangular elements, we define for each $\mathbf{z}_i \in Z$ a support set

$$\bar{E}_i \equiv \left\{ \bigcup \bar{\Omega}_j \,\middle|\, \mathbf{z}_i \text{ is a node of } \bar{\Omega}_j \right\}.$$

A typical set $\bar{E}_i$ is shown as the shaded portion of Figure 7.6.2.

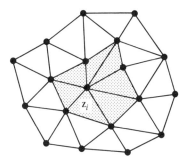

Figure 7.6.2 Set $\bar{E}_i$.

For each $\mathbf{z}_i \in Z$ we construct a *basis* function $\phi_i \colon \bar{\Omega} \to R$ such that

1. supp $\phi_i = \bar{E}_i$,
2. $\phi_i \in C^0(\bar{\Omega})$ and is a linear function of x and y in each $\bar{\Omega}_j$, and
3. $\phi_i(\mathbf{z}_j) = \delta_{ij}$ (Kronecker's delta).

This is done as follows. On the complement of $\bar{E}_i$ we define ϕ_i to be zero. If $\mathbf{z} \in \bar{E}_i$, then $\mathbf{z}$ belongs to some $\bar{\Omega}_j$, where one of the nodes of $\bar{\Omega}_j$ is $\mathbf{z}_i$. Therefore, let $\bar{\Omega}_j$ have nodes $\mathbf{z}_i$ (which we identify with node $\mathbf{z}_{00}$ in Figure 7.6.1), $\mathbf{z}_{01}$, and $\mathbf{z}_{10}$. Then with reference to the transformation (7.6.1), we set

$$\phi_i(\mathbf{z}) = 1 - \xi - \eta, \tag{7.6.2}$$

where $(\xi, \eta) = \zeta = \mathbf{F}^{-1}(\mathbf{z})$.

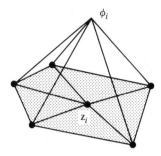

Figure 7.6.3   Basis function ϕ_i.

Since $\mathbf{F}$ is affine on $\bar{M}$, its inverse is affine on $\bar{\Omega}_j$, so ϕ_i is linear there. Moreover, it is clear that under $\mathbf{F}^{-1}$, $\mathbf{z}_i \to (0, 0)$, $\mathbf{z}_{10} \to (1, 0)$, and $\mathbf{z}_{01} \to (0, 1)$. Therefore, $\phi_i(\mathbf{z}_i) = 1$ and $\phi_i(\mathbf{z}_{10}) = \phi_i(\mathbf{z}_{01}) = 0$. Finally, since ϕ_i is linear on the sides of each $\bar{\Omega}_j$, and since it is single valued at the nodes, its global continuity on $\bar{\Omega}$ is assured.

Although the technical definition of ϕ_i is somewhat complicated, it is very easy to visualize the "shape" of such a function. We simply erect a pyramid over $\bar{E}_i$ with unit altitude at $\mathbf{z}_i$. Then on $\bar{E}_i$, ϕ_i is the surface of this pyramid (Figure 7.6.3).

It is clear that the functions $\phi_1, \ldots, \phi_m$ form a basis for the m-dimensional space

$$S^h(\bar{\Omega}) = \text{span} \ (\phi_1, \ldots, \phi_m).$$

Furthermore, if we assume without loss of generality that $\mathbf{z}_i \in \Omega$ for $i = 1, \ldots, n < m$, and we set

$$S^h_0(\bar{\Omega}) = \text{span} \ (\phi_1, \ldots, \phi_n), \tag{7.6.3}$$

then $S^h_0(\bar{\Omega})$ is a subspace of $S_0(\bar{\Omega})$. Thus, in the case of triangular elements the subspace $S^h_0(\bar{\Omega})$ is just the set of linear combinations of the basis functions ϕ_i associated with the interior nodes of Ω.

If $v \in S^h(\bar{\Omega})$, then obviously

$$v(\mathbf{z}) = \sum_{i=1}^{m} c_i \phi_i(\mathbf{z})$$

for some constants $c_1, \ldots, c_m$. For $\mathbf{z} \in \bar{\Omega}_j$, this sum reduces to three terms, say

$$v(\mathbf{z}) = c_{00}\phi_{00}(\mathbf{z}) + c_{10}\phi_{10}(\mathbf{z}) + c_{01}\phi_{01}(\mathbf{z}), \tag{7.6.4}$$

where ϕ_{00}, ϕ_{10}, and ϕ_{01} are the basis functions associated, respectively, with the nodes $\mathbf{z}_{00}$, $\mathbf{z}_{10}$, and $\mathbf{z}_{01}$ of $\bar{\Omega}_j$. Now, according to (7.6.2), this may be written as

$$v(\mathbf{z}) = c_{00}(1 - \xi - \eta) + c_{10}(1 - \xi' - \eta') + c_{01}(1 - \xi'' - \eta''), \tag{7.6.5}$$

$\zeta' = (\xi', \eta')$ and $\zeta'' = (\xi'', \eta'')$ being copies of the coordinates (ξ, η) that are used to define the functions ϕ_{10} and ϕ_{01}. But ζ and ζ' are related by the condition that for any $\mathbf{z} \in \bar{\Omega}_j$,

$$\mathbf{F}(\zeta) = \mathbf{z} = \mathbf{F}'(\zeta'),$$

where in analogy to (7.6.1),

$$\mathbf{F}'(\zeta') = \mathbf{z}_{10}(1 - \xi' - \eta') + \mathbf{z}_{01}\xi' + \mathbf{z}_{00}\eta'. \tag{7.6.6}$$

Hence, by subtracting (7.6.6) from (7.6.1), we have

$$\mathbf{z}_{00}(1 - \xi - \eta - \eta') + \mathbf{z}_{10}(\xi - 1 + \xi' + \eta') + \mathbf{z}_{01}(\eta - \xi') = 0.$$

Since the points $\mathbf{z}_{00}$, $\mathbf{z}_{10}$, and $\mathbf{z}_{01}$ are not collinear, this equation, along with the identity

$$(1 - \xi - \eta - \eta') + (\xi - 1 + \xi' + \eta') + (\eta - \xi') \equiv 0,$$

implies that the three expressions in parentheses vanish. Thus $1 - \xi' - \eta' = \xi$. In the same way we find that $1 - \xi'' - \eta'' = \eta$. It follows that (7.6.5) may be written solely in terms of ξ and η as

$$v(\mathbf{z}) = c_{00}(1 - \xi - \eta) + c_{10}\xi + c_{01}\eta. \tag{7.6.7}$$

The form (7.6.7) shows that on each $\bar{\Omega}_j$ the function v has precisely the same form as the original transformation (7.6.1). This is the reason that the term *isoparametric* is used to describe these elements. In fact, we may write

$$\begin{bmatrix} x(\xi, \eta) \\ y(\xi, \eta) \\ v(x(\xi, \eta), y(\xi, \eta)) \end{bmatrix} = \begin{bmatrix} x_{00} \\ y_{00} \\ c_{00} \end{bmatrix} (1 - \xi - \eta) + \begin{bmatrix} x_{10} \\ y_{10} \\ c_{10} \end{bmatrix} \xi + \begin{bmatrix} x_{01} \\ y_{01} \\ c_{01} \end{bmatrix} \eta, \quad (\xi, \eta) \in M. \tag{7.6.8}$$

As mentioned at the end of Section 7.5, the final step in estimating the finite element error requires consideration of an interpolation error, where the interpolating functions are taken from the finite element subspace.

Therefore, given a function $v \in C^0(\bar{\Omega})$, we define its *interpolant* at the nodes of $\bar{\Omega}$ as $v_I \in S^h(\bar{\Omega})$:

$$v_I(\mathbf{z}) = \sum_{i=1}^{m} v(\mathbf{z}_i)\phi_i(\mathbf{z}). \tag{7.6.9}$$

(see Figure 7.6.4). On each element $\bar{\Omega}_j$, we also introduce the functions

$$\hat{v}: \bar{M} \to R, \qquad \hat{v} = v \circ \mathbf{F},$$

and

$$\hat{v}_I: \bar{M} \to R, \qquad \hat{v}_I = v_I \circ \mathbf{F},$$

where $\mathbf{F}$ is given by (7.6.1). Note that with a suitable ordering of the nodes of $\bar{\Omega}_j$, $\hat{v}_I$ has the form (7.6.7). That is,

$$\hat{v}_I(\xi, \eta) = v(\mathbf{z}_{00})(1 - \xi - \eta) + v(\mathbf{z}_{10})\xi + v(\mathbf{z}_{01})\eta.$$

Now let $v \in H^2(\Omega)$. According to Theorem 6.5.1, $v \in C^0(\bar{\Omega})$, so its interpolant (7.6.9) is well defined. Furthermore, it is clear that if v is a linear function of x and y, then $v_I = v$. This property is sufficient for the next lemma, whose proof we omit.

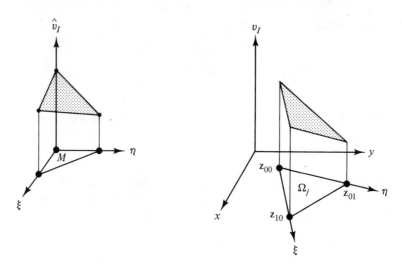

Figure 7.6.4 Interpolant.

It is a technical result that bounds the interpolation error on the master element $\bar{M}$. The interested reader may find a proof in Ciarlet [1978].

Lemma 7.6.1.   *Let $v \in H^2(\Omega)$ and let $v_I \in S^h(\bar{\Omega})$ be its interpolant. If $S^h(\bar{\Omega})$ contains the linear functions, then there is a constant K such that for $m = 0, 1, 2$,*

$$|\hat{v} - \hat{v}_I|_{m,M} \le K|\hat{v}|_{2,M}, \tag{7.6.10}$$

where

$$|\hat{v}|_{m,M} \equiv \left[\sum_{|\alpha|=m} \int_M (D^\alpha \hat{v})^2 \, d\zeta \right]^{1/2}$$

We can regard (7.6.10) as an extension of the familiar Taylor series estimates to the Sobolev space $H^2(\Omega)$. In fact, if $\hat{v} \in C^2(\bar{M})$, and we define

$$|\hat{v}|_{m,M,\infty} = \max_{|\alpha|=m} \sup_{\zeta \in \bar{M}} |D^\alpha \hat{v}(\zeta)|, \tag{7.6.11}$$

then (7.6.10) is a direct consequence of Taylor's theorem. For example, suppose that M is the triangle of Figure 7.6.1 and let $\hat{v}_I$ interpolate $\hat{v}$ at the vertices of M. If $\zeta = (\xi, \eta) \in \bar{M}$ and $\mathbf{e}_i$, $i = 1, 2$, are unit coordinate vectors, then Taylor's theorem yields

$$\hat{v}(\zeta) = \hat{v}(0) + \hat{v}_\xi(0)\xi + \hat{v}_\eta(0)\eta + \tfrac{1}{2}(\hat{v}_{\xi\xi}(\theta_1\zeta)\xi^2 + 2\hat{v}_{\xi\eta}(\theta_1\zeta)\xi\eta + \hat{v}_{\eta\eta}(\theta_1\zeta)\eta^2)$$

and

$$\begin{aligned}
\hat{v}_I(\zeta) &= \hat{v}(0)(1 - \xi - \eta) + \hat{v}(\mathbf{e}_1)\xi + \hat{v}(\mathbf{e}_2)\eta \\
&= \hat{v}(0) + \hat{v}_\xi(\theta_2\mathbf{e}_1)\xi + \hat{v}_\eta(\theta_3\mathbf{e}_2)\eta,
\end{aligned}$$

where $0 < \theta_i < 1$, $i = 1, 2, 3$. Therefore,

$$|\hat{v}(\zeta) - \hat{v}_I(\zeta)| \leq 4|\hat{v}|_{2,M,\infty},$$

which is (7.6.10) when $m = 0$. The case when $m = 1$ is left as Exercise 7.9.

To put Lemma 7.6.1 to use we need to obtain inequalities between the semi-norms of functions defined on Ω_j and their preimages on M.

Theorem 7.6.2.   Let $\mathbf{F}: \bar{M} \to \bar{\Omega}_j$ be defined by (7.6.1). If $v \in H^m(\Omega)$, $m = 0, 1,$ or 2, then there is a constant K such that

$$|\hat{v}|_{m,M} \leq K\|DF\|^m|\det DF|^{-1/2}|v|_{m,\Omega_j} \tag{7.6.12}$$

and

$$|v|_{m,\Omega_j} \leq K\|(DF)^{-1}\|^m|\det DF|^{1/2}|\hat{v}|_{m,M}, \tag{7.6.13}$$

where DF is the Jacobian matrix of $\mathbf{F}$ and $\|\cdot\|$ is the Euclidean matrix norm.

Proof. We will prove (7.6.12) for $m = 2$, leaving the remaining inequalities as an exercise for the reader. In the first place, since $C^2(\bar{\Omega})$ is dense in $H^2(\Omega)$ (Section 6.3), it suffices to prove the result for $v \in C^2(\bar{\Omega})$. By definition,

$$|\hat{v}|^2_{2,M} = \int_M (\hat{v}^2_{\xi\xi} + \hat{v}^2_{\xi\eta} + \hat{v}^2_{\eta\eta})\, d\zeta.$$

Furthermore, the chain rule gives

$$\hat{v}_{\xi\xi} = v_{xx}x^2_\xi + 2v_{xy}x_\xi y_\xi + v_{yy}y^2_\xi.$$

Applying the change of variables formula for double integrals, we have

$$\int_M \hat{v}^2_{\xi\xi}\, d\zeta = |\det DF|^{-1} \int_{\Omega_j} (v_{xx}x^2_\xi + 2v_{xy}x_\xi y_\xi + v_{yy}y^2_\xi)^2\, d\mathbf{z}.$$

But $|x_\xi|$ and $|y_\xi|$ are bounded by $\|DF\|$. Therefore,

$$\int_M \hat{v}^2_{\xi\xi}\, d\zeta \leq \|DF\|^4|\det DF|^{-1} \int_{\Omega_j} (|v_{xx}| + 2|v_{xy}| + |v_{yy}|)^2\, d\mathbf{z}$$

$$\leq 6\|DF\|^4|\det DF|^{-1}|v|^2_{2,\Omega_j},$$

the last inequality being a consequence of the Cauchy-Schwarz inequality for sums.

Since entirely similar inequalities hold for the integrals $\int_M \hat{v}^2_{\xi\eta}\, d\zeta$ and $\int_M \hat{v}^2_{\eta\eta}\, d\zeta$, we see that

$$|\hat{v}|_{2,M} \leq K\|DF\|^2|\det DF|^{-1/2}|v|_{2,\Omega_j}.$$

Q.E.D.

It is natural to expect that the finite element approximation u^h of the solution u^* will improve as the triangulation of $\bar{\Omega}$ is refined. This suggests that the error should be a function of some measure of the fineness of the triangulation. On each element we can define such a measure in terms of the largest side length h_j of the elements. More generally, for any decomposition of $\bar{\Omega}$ (not necessarily in terms of triangular

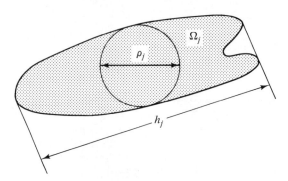

Figure 7.6.5   Geometric quantities h_j and ρ_j.

elements) let h_j denote the *diameter* of the element $\bar{\Omega}_j$; that is, let

$$h_j = \sup_{\mathbf{x},\mathbf{y} \in \bar{\Omega}_j} |\mathbf{x} - \mathbf{y}|.$$

Also, let ρ_j denote the largest diameter of any disk contained in $\bar{\Omega}_j$ (Figure 7.6.5).

The connection of the error with the size of the elements is established in the next theorem.

Theorem 7.6.3.   *Let $\mathbf{F}_j$ be the affine mapping given by (7.6.1). If $\hat{h}$ and $\hat{\rho}$ are the analogues of h_j and ρ_j for the master element $\bar{M}$, then*

$$\|D\mathbf{F}\| \le \frac{h_j}{\hat{\rho}} \quad and \quad \|D\mathbf{F}^{-1}\| \le \frac{\hat{h}}{\rho_j}. \tag{7.6.14}$$

Proof.   By definition

$$\|D\mathbf{F}\| = \max_{|\zeta|=1} |D\mathbf{F}\,\zeta|.$$

If $|\zeta| = 1$, let $\alpha = \hat{\rho}\zeta$. Then

$$\|D\mathbf{F}\| = \hat{\rho}^{-1} \max_{|\rho\zeta|=\hat{\rho}} |D\mathbf{F}\,\hat{\rho}\zeta| = \hat{\rho}^{-1} \max_{|\alpha|=\hat{\rho}} |D\mathbf{F}\,\alpha|.$$

But from the definition of $\hat{\rho}$ we see that any vector α for which $|\alpha| = \hat{\rho}$ may be represented as $\alpha = \beta - \gamma$, where β and γ are points in $\bar{M}$. Since F is an affine map, we have

$$D\mathbf{F}\,\alpha = D\mathbf{F}\,\beta - D\mathbf{F}\,\gamma = \mathbf{F}(\beta) - \mathbf{F}(\gamma).$$

Hence

$$|D\mathbf{F}\,\alpha| = |\mathbf{F}(\beta) - \mathbf{F}(\gamma)| \le h_j.$$

This proves the first of the inequalities (7.6.14), and the second follows in the same way by considering the affine map $\mathbf{F}^{-1}$.

Q.E.D.

Note that since $\bar{M}$ is a fixed element, the quantities $\hat{h}$ and $\hat{\rho}$ are constants. In fact, for the master triangle used in the mapping (7.6.1), $\hat{h} = \sqrt{2}$, $\hat{\rho} = (2 - \sqrt{2})$.

We now assemble the results of Lemma 7.6.1 and Theorems 7.6.2 and 7.6.3 to produce elementwise interpolation error estimates.

Theorem 7.6.4.   *If $v \in H^2(\Omega)$ and $\mathbf{F}$ is the map (7.6.1), there is a constant K such that*

$$\left|v - v_I\right|_{m,\Omega_j} \leq K \frac{h_j^2}{\rho_j^m} \left|v\right|_{2,\Omega_j}, \qquad m = 0, 1. \tag{7.6.15}$$

Proof. Since $S^h(\bar{\Omega})$ obviously contains the linear functions, Lemma 7.6.1 holds. Then (7.6.13) and (7.6.10) imply that

$$\left|v - v_I\right|_{m,\Omega_j} \leq K_1 \|D\mathbf{F}^{-1}\|^m \left|\det D\mathbf{F}\right|^{1/2} \left|\hat{v} - \hat{v}_I\right|_{m,M}$$
$$\leq K_2 \|D\mathbf{F}^{-1}\|^m \left|\det D\mathbf{F}\right|^{1/2} \left|\hat{v}\right|_{2,M},$$

where K_1 and K_2 are constants. We continue this string of inequalities by applying (7.6.12) with $m = 2$. Thus

$$\left|v - v_1\right|_{m,\Omega_j} \leq K_3 \|D\mathbf{F}^{-1}\|^m \|D\mathbf{F}\|^2 \left|v\right|_{2,\Omega_j}.$$

Finally, (7.6.15) results by using (7.6.14).

Q.E.D.

To complete the error analysis it remains to relate the finite element error to the *global* interpolation error over Ω. For this purpose it is convenient to introduce a single quantity to measure the size of all the elements in the decomposition. This is the *mesh gauge*,

$$h \equiv \max_{1 \leq j \leq N} h_j.$$

Obviously, the mesh gauge induces a parametrization on the family of element decompositions of Ω.

Since we are ultimately interested in the behavior of the finite element error as $h \to 0$, we are led to a uniformity assumption about the element shapes. Specifically, we assume that there is a constant $\rho > 0$ such that for all h sufficiently small,

$$\rho_j \geq \rho h. \tag{7.6.16}$$

A family of element decompositions satisfying (7.6.16) is said to be *regular*. For example, the family of triangular element decompositions is regular if in any triangulation of $\bar{\Omega}$, the ratio of the largest to the smallest side lengths is uniformly bounded above and all angles are uniformly bounded below (Exercise 7.13).

The following theorem shows that in the norm of $H_0^1(\Omega)$ the finite element error for classical solutions is $O(h)$.

Theorem 7.6.5.   *Let u^* solve Problem B and let u^h be the solution of (7.4.1), where $S_0^h(\bar{\Omega})$ is given by (7.6.3). If the family of triangulations is regular, there is a constant K such that for $h \leq h_0$,*

$$\left\|u^* - u^h\right\|_1 \leq K h \left|u^*\right|_2. \tag{7.6.17}$$

Proof. We know from Section 7.3 that $u^* \in H_0^1(\Omega)$. Then Theorem 7.1.2 implies that u^* solves Problem G. Consequently, from Corollary 7.5.2 we have for any element $v \in S_0^h(\bar{\Omega})$,

$$\|u^* - u^h\|_1^2 \leq K_1^2 \sum_{m=0}^{1} |u^* - v|_{m,\Omega}^2 = K_1^2 \sum_{m=0}^{1} \sum_{j=1}^{N} |u^* - v|_{m,\Omega_j}^2.$$

Since $u^*|_{\partial\Omega} = 0$, its interpolant on the node set Z belongs to $S_0^h(\bar{\Omega})$. Therefore, if we choose v to be this interpolant, apply Theorem 7.6.4, and use the hypothesis that we have a regular family of triangulations, we see that

$$\|u^* - u^h\|_1^2 \leq K_1^2 K_2^2 \sum_{j=1}^{N} \left(h_j^4 + \frac{h_j^4}{\rho_j^2}\right) |u^*|_{2,\Omega_j}^2$$

$$\leq (K_1 K_2)^2 \left(h^4 + \frac{h^2}{\rho^2}\right) \sum_{j=1}^{N} |u^*|_{2,\Omega_j}^2$$

$$\leq (K_1 K_2)^2 (h_0^2 + \rho^{-2}) h^2 |u^*|_2^2.$$

The conclusion (7.6.17) follows by setting

$$K \equiv (K_1 K_2)(h_0^2 + \rho^{-2})^{1/2}.$$

$$\text{Q.E.D.}$$

What happens to the error when u^* is only the weak solution of Problem G? In this case there is a function ϕ belonging to $C_0^\infty(\bar{\Omega})$ such that if $\varepsilon > 0$, then $\|u^* - \phi\|_1 \leq \varepsilon/(2K)$, where K is the constant of Corollary 7.5.2. Hence

$$\|u^* - u^h\|_1 \leq K \left(\|u^* - \phi\|_1 + \|\phi - v\|_1\right) \leq \frac{\varepsilon}{2} + K \|\phi - v\|_1,$$

where v is any element of $S_0^h(\bar{\Omega})$. Since $\phi|_{\partial\Omega} = 0$, we may choose v to be the interpolant of ϕ on Z. As in the proof of Theorem 7.6.4, we find that $\|\phi - v\|_1 \leq K_1 h |\phi|_2$ for some constant K_1. Therefore,

$$\|u^* - u^h\|_1 \leq \frac{\varepsilon}{2} + K K_1 h |\phi|_2,$$

and for all h sufficiently small, $\|u^* - u^h\|_1 \leq \varepsilon$. This shows that the finite element errors again converge to zero with h, but convergence may proceed at a rate that is less than that guaranteed by (7.6.17).

Example 7.6.1

Find $u(x, y)$ such that

$$-\nabla^2 u + \pi^2 u = 2[1 - \pi^2(x - 2)^2] \sin \pi y$$

for $(x, y) \in \Omega \equiv (0, 2) \times (0, 2)$ subject to the boundary conditions

$$u(x, 0) = u(x, 2) = u(2, y) = 0,$$
$$u(0, y) = -4 \sin \pi y. \tag{7.6.18}$$

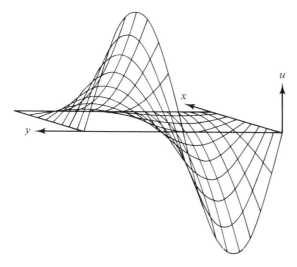

Figure 7.6.6   Exact solution.

The solution of this problem is

$$u(x, y) = -(x - 2)^2 \sin \pi y$$

and is illustrated in Figure 7.6.6.

The weak formulation is: Find $u \in S \subset H^1(\Omega)$ such that for all $v \in H_0^1(\Omega)$,

$$\int_\Omega [\nabla u \cdot \nabla v + \pi^2 uv - 2[[1 - \pi^2(x - 2)^2] \sin \pi y]v] \, d\mathbf{x} = 0,$$

where $S \equiv \{w \in H^1(\Omega) | w$ satisfies (7.6.18)$\}$. The finite element space S^h is chosen in turn as the space of linear triangles on a uniform mesh with $h = \frac{2}{3}, \frac{1}{3}$, and $\frac{1}{6}$ (Figure 7.6.7).

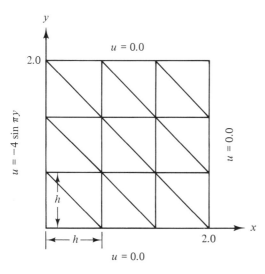

Figure 7.6.7   Finite element mesh of triangles.

TABLE 7.6.1 RESULTS FOR EXAMPLE 7.6.1

h	Dim S_0^h	Number of elements	$\|u^* - u^h\|_0$	$\|u^* - u^h\|_1$	Maximum nodal error
2/3	4	18	1.000	4.34	0.352
1/3	25	72	0.251	2.86	0.086
1/6	121	288	0.062	1.53	0.024

Table 7.6.1 contains a summary of results. Note that the rate of convergence in the norm $\|\cdot\|_0$ is greater than the rate of convergence in the norm $\|\cdot\|_1$; that is, halving the mesh reduces the error in $\|\cdot\|_1$ by about a factor of 2, while it reduces the error in $\|\cdot\|_0$ by about a factor of 4. We provide a theoretical basis for this phenomenon in Section 7.8.

7.7 BILINEAR ISOPARAMETRIC QUADRILATERALS

The notation of this section follows that of Section 7.6 whenever possible. We again assume that Ω is the interior of a polygon, but now the elements of the decomposition (7.3.1) are quadrilateral in nature. As before, the node set Z is the set of vertices of the elements.

We take the master element $\bar{M}$ to be the unit square in the ξ, η plane with vertices (0, 0), (0, 1), (1, 1), and (1, 0). The mapping $\mathbf{F}$ of $\bar{M}$ onto a quadrilateral $\bar{\Omega}_j$ in the xy-plane with vertices $\mathbf{z}_{pq} = (x_{pq}, y_{pq})$, p, $q = 0, 1$, is given by

$$\mathbf{z} = \mathbf{F}(\zeta) \equiv \mathbf{z}_{00}(1 - \xi)(1 - \eta) + \mathbf{z}_{10}\xi(1 - \eta) + \mathbf{z}_{11}\xi\eta + \mathbf{z}_{01}(1 - \xi)\eta. \qquad (7.7.1)$$

As in the case of (7.6.1), $\mathbf{F}$ takes the vertices of $\bar{M}$ onto those of $\bar{\Omega}_j$ (Figure 7.7.1). However, unlike the affine transformation (7.6.1), the mapping (7.7.1) is *nonlinear*. Consequently, the nonvanishing of its Jacobian does not necessarily imply its invertibility.

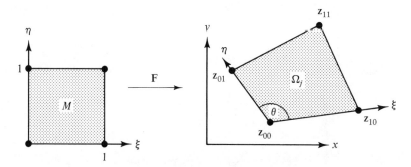

Figure 7.7.1 Bilinear map (7.7.1).

Notice, however, that **F** is affine on each side of $\bar{M}$. For instance, for $\eta = 0$, $0 \le \xi \le 1$, we have

$$x = x_{00} + (x_{10} - x_{00})\xi$$

and

$$y = y_{00} + (y_{10} - y_{00})\xi.$$

Therefore, the sides of $\bar{M}$ are mapped onto the sides of $\bar{\Omega}_j$ in a one-to-one manner. If the sides of $\bar{\Omega}_j$ do not intersect except at the vertices, it follows that **F** is a one-to-one map of ∂M onto $\partial\Omega_j$. There is a theorem of de la Vallee Poussin [1926] which states that *if a continuously differentiable transformation has this boundary property, then the nonvanishing of its Jacobian is sufficient to guarantee its invertibility.*

By direct calculation we see that the Jacobian matrix of **F** is

$$\mathbf{DF} = \begin{bmatrix} X_{10} + X_{11}\eta & X_{01} + X_{11}\xi \\ Y_{10} + Y_{11}\eta & Y_{01} + Y_{11}\xi \end{bmatrix},$$

where

$$X_{10} = x_{10} - x_{00},$$

$$X_{01} = x_{01} - x_{00},$$

$$X_{11} = x_{00} - x_{10} + x_{11} - x_{01},$$

and similar definitions apply to Y_{10}, Y_{01}, and Y_{11}. Thus the Jacobian, det **DF**, is a *linear* function of ξ and η since the coefficient of $\xi\eta$ vanishes.

Clearly, the minimum value of such a function defined over a quadrilateral element occurs at some vertex of the element. At each vertex det $\mathbf{DF} = \pm pq \sin \theta$, where p and q are the lengths of the sides sharing the vertex and θ is the vertex angle (cf. Section 7.6). It can be checked that the sign choice $\pm$ is the same for all vertices. *Hence* det **DF** *is of one sign on* $\bar{\Omega}_j$ *if* (*and only if*) *all corner angles are strictly between zero and* π (i.e., $\bar{\Omega}_j$ *is a convex set*). This is an assumption that we will make from here on.

We construct a set of basis functions as before. If $\mathbf{z}_i$ is a node and $\bar{E}_i$ its support set, we set $\phi_i \equiv 0$ on the complement of $\bar{E}_i$. For $\mathbf{z} \in \bar{\Omega}_j \subset \bar{E}_i$, we define

$$\phi_i(\mathbf{z}) \equiv (1 - \xi)(1 - \eta),$$

where $(\xi, \eta)^T = \mathbf{F}^{-1}(\mathbf{z})$, and **F** is given by (7.7.1) with the understanding that $\mathbf{z}_i = \mathbf{z}_{00}$. Obviously, ϕ_i is continuously differentiable on Ω_j and satisfies $\phi_i(\mathbf{z}_j) = \delta_{ij}$. Although ϕ_i is nonlinear on $\bar{\Omega}_j$, it is *linear* on $\partial\Omega_j$. Therefore, since it is single-valued at the nodes, it is continuous across the sides of the elements. Defining the subspaces $S^h(\bar{\Omega})$ and $S_0^h(\bar{\Omega})$ as in Section 7.6, we again have the inclusion $S_0^h(\bar{\Omega}) \subset S_0(\bar{\Omega})$.

By an argument similar to that used in Section 7.6, it can be shown that if $v \in S^h(\bar{\Omega})$, then on $\bar{\Omega}_j$, v has the representation

$$v(\mathbf{z}) = c_{00}(1 - \xi)(1 - \eta) + c_{10}\xi(1 - \eta) + c_{11}\xi\eta + c_{01}(1 - \xi)\eta. \tag{7.7.2}$$

The combination of (7.7.1) and (7.7.2) once more justifies the term *isoparametric*.

The error analysis is carried out along the same lines as for triangular elements. For any $v \in C^0(\bar{\Omega})$ we define the interpolant, $v_I \in S^h(\bar{\Omega})$:

$$v_I(\mathbf{z}) = \sum_{i=1}^{m} v(\mathbf{z}_i)\phi_i(\mathbf{z}). \tag{7.7.3}$$

To see that $S^h(\bar{\Omega})$ again contains the linear functions, we show that it contains the functions 1, x, and y. Then, since any linear function is a linear combination of these special functions, it too is a member of $S^h(\bar{\Omega})$.

Suppose, for example, that $u(\mathbf{z}) \equiv x$. Then its interpolant, u_I, has the form (7.7.2) on $\bar{\Omega}_j$. But by definition, $u_I(\mathbf{z}_{pq}) = x_{pq}$, $p, q = 0, 1$, and hence the coefficients in (7.7.2) satisfy $c_{pq} = x_{pq}$. Thus

$$u_I(\mathbf{z}) = x_{00}(1 - \xi)(1 - \eta) + x_{10}\xi(1 - \eta) + x_{11}\xi\eta + x_{01}(1 - \xi)\eta,$$

and by (7.7.1) the right side of this equality is precisely x. This same argument also works for the functions 1 and y.

In view of this, Lemma 7.6.1 again holds. However, the conclusions of Theorems 7.6.2 and 7.6.3 must be modified to accommodate the nonlinear nature of $\mathbf{F}$. One way to do this is to regard $\mathbf{F}$ as a perturbation of some affine map $\tilde{\mathbf{F}}$. By Taylor's theorem we can write

$$\mathbf{F}(\zeta) = \mathbf{F}(0) + D\mathbf{F}(0)\zeta + \mathbf{Q}(\zeta),$$

where

$$\mathbf{Q}(\zeta) = (X_{11}, Y_{11})^T \xi\eta. \tag{7.7.4}$$

Therefore, if we define the affine transformation

$$\tilde{\mathbf{F}}(\zeta) \equiv \mathbf{F}(0) + D\mathbf{F}(0)\zeta$$

$$= \begin{bmatrix} x_{00} \\ y_{00} \end{bmatrix} + \begin{bmatrix} x_{10} - x_{00} & x_{01} - x_{00} \\ y_{10} - y_{00} & y_{01} - y_{00} \end{bmatrix} \begin{bmatrix} \xi \\ \eta \end{bmatrix}, \tag{7.7.5}$$

then $\mathbf{F}$ results by perturbing $\tilde{\mathbf{F}}$ by an amount $\mathbf{Q}$.

The four vertices of M, $\{(0, 0), (1, 0), (0, 1), \text{and } (1, 1)\}$, are mapped, respectively, by $\tilde{\mathbf{F}}$ onto the points $\mathbf{z}_{00}$, $\mathbf{z}_{10}$, $\mathbf{z}_{01}$, and

$$\tilde{\mathbf{z}}_{11} = (x_{10} + x_{01} - x_{00}, y_{10} + y_{01} - y_{00}).$$

Since $\tilde{\mathbf{z}}_{11} - \mathbf{z}_{01} = \mathbf{z}_{10} - \mathbf{z}_{00}$, it follows that $\tilde{\mathbf{F}}$ maps $\bar{M}$ onto a *parallelogram*, $\bar{P}_j$. The original quadrilateral, $\bar{\Omega}_j$, is then obtained from $\bar{P}_j$ by perturbing the position of the fourth vertex from $\tilde{\mathbf{z}}_{11}$ to $\mathbf{z}_{11}$, as illustrated in Figure 7.7.2. Notice that the x and y components of the perturbation are just X_{11} and Y_{11}, respectively.

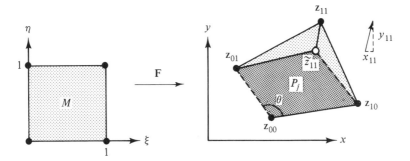

Figure 7.7.2 $\bar{\Omega}_j$ as a perturbation of parallelogram $\bar{P}_j$.

In Section 7.6 we defined, for the element $\bar{\Omega}_j$, the geometric quantities $h_j \equiv \sup_{\mathbf{x},\mathbf{y} \in \bar{\Omega}_j} |\mathbf{x} - \mathbf{y}|$ and ρ_j, the largest diameter of any disk contained in Ω_j. Let $\tilde{h}_j$ and $\tilde{\rho}_j$ denote the same quantities for the parallelogram $\bar{P}_j$. (We again use $\hat{h}$ and $\hat{\rho}$ for the master element $\bar{M}$.) To complete the error analysis we assume that the perturbation $\mathbf{z}_{11} - \tilde{\mathbf{z}}_{11}$ is of order $\tilde{h}_j^2$. In other words, we assume that there is a constant c such that

$$|X_{11}|, |Y_{11}| \le c\tilde{h}_j^2. \tag{7.7.6}$$

We also assume that there is a constant $\tilde{\rho}$ such that

$$\tilde{\rho}_j \ge \tilde{\rho}\tilde{h}_j. \tag{7.7.7}$$

For a geometric condition on parallelograms that is sufficient to produce the inequality (7.7.7), see Exercise 7.17.

The theorem that replaces Theorems 7.6.2 and 7.6.3 is as follows.

Theorem 7.7.1.   *If* $\mathbf{F}$ *is given by* (7.7.1) *and if* (7.7.6) *and* (7.7.7) *hold, then there are constants* K_0, K_1, *and* K_2 *such that for all* $v \in H^2(\Omega)$ *and all* $\tilde{h}_j$ *sufficiently small,*

$$|v|_{0,\Omega_j} \le K_0|\hat{v}|_{0,M}, \tag{7.7.8}$$

$$|v|_{1,\Omega_j} \le K_1\tilde{h}_j^{-1}|\hat{v}|_{1,M}, \tag{7.7.9}$$

and

$$|\hat{v}|_{2,M} \le K_2\tilde{h}_j^2\|v\|_{2,\Omega_j}. \tag{7.7.10}$$

Proof. As in the proof of Theorem 7.6.2 it is sufficient to prove the inequalities for $v \in C^2(\bar{\Omega})$. With regard to (7.7.8) we have

$$|v|_{0,\Omega_j}^2 = \int_{\Omega_j} v^2 \, d\mathbf{x}$$

$$= \int_M \hat{v}^2 \, |\det D\mathbf{F}| \, d\zeta$$

$$\le \sup_{\zeta \in \bar{M}} |\det D\mathbf{F}| \, |\hat{v}|_{0,M}^2.$$

Next we prove (7.7.10). Applying the chain rule, we see that

$$\hat{v}_{\xi\xi} = v_{xx}x_\xi^2 + 2v_{xy}x_\xi y_\xi + v_{yy}y_\xi^2,$$

$$\hat{v}_{\eta\eta} = v_{xx}x_\eta^2 + 2v_{xy}x_\eta y_\eta + v_{yy}y_\eta^2,$$

and

$$\hat{v}_{\xi\eta} = v_{xx}x_\xi x_\eta + v_{xy}(x_\xi y_\eta + y_\xi x_\eta) + v_{yy}y_\xi y_\eta + v_x X_{11} + v_y Y_{11}.$$

[Note that unlike the case of the affine mapping (7.6.1), the expression for $\hat{v}_{\xi\eta}$ contains the *first* derivatives v_x and v_y.]

From (7.7.4) and (7.7.5) we have

$$\mathbf{F} = \tilde{\mathbf{F}} + \mathbf{Q},$$

so that

$$D\mathbf{F} = D\tilde{\mathbf{F}} + D\mathbf{Q},$$

where

$$D\mathbf{Q} = \begin{bmatrix} X_{11}\eta & X_{11}\xi \\ Y_{11}\eta & Y_{11}\xi \end{bmatrix}.$$

Now we have

$$\|D\mathbf{Q}\| \equiv \sup_{\|\mathbf{x}\|_2 = 1} \|D\mathbf{Q}\mathbf{x}\|_2$$

$$= \sup_{\|\mathbf{x}\|_2 = 1} [(X_{11}\eta x_1 + X_{11}\xi x_2)^2 + (Y_{11}\eta x_1 + Y_{11}\xi x_2)^2]^{1/2}$$

$$\leq \sqrt{2} \max (|X_{11}|, |Y_{11}|) |\eta x_1 + \xi x_2|.$$

This, the Cauchy–Schwarz inequality, and (7.7.6) yield

$$\|D\mathbf{Q}\| \leq \sqrt{2} \max (|X_{11}|, |Y_{11}|)(\xi^2 + \eta^2)^{1/2}$$

$$\leq 2c\tilde{h}_j^2.$$

Furthermore, since Theorem 7.6.3 applies to the affine map $\tilde{F}$, for $\tilde{h}_j \leq \tilde{h}_0$ we obtain

$$\|D\mathbf{F}\| \leq \|D\tilde{\mathbf{F}}\| + \|D\mathbf{Q}\|$$

$$\leq \tilde{h}_j\hat{\rho}^{-1} + 2c\tilde{h}_j^2$$

$$\leq [\hat{\rho}^{-1} + 2c\tilde{h}_0]\tilde{h}_j \equiv c_1\tilde{h}_j.$$

This shows that $|x_\xi|$, $|x_\eta|$, $|y_\xi|$, and $|y_\eta|$ are all bounded by $c_1\tilde{h}_j$. Hence

$$\max (|\hat{v}_{\xi\xi}|, |\hat{v}_{\eta\eta}|) \leq (c_1\tilde{h}_j)^2(|v_{xx}| + 2|v_{xy}| + |v_{yy}|)$$

and

$$|\hat{v}_{\xi\eta}| \leq (c_1\tilde{h}_j)^2(|v_{xx}| + 2|v_{xy}| + |v_{yy}| + |v_x| + |v_y|).$$

Then, for example,

$$\int_M \hat{v}_{\xi\eta}^2 \, d\zeta \le (c_1 \tilde{h}_j)^4 \int_{\Omega_j} (|v_{xx}| + 2|v_{xy}| + |v_{yy}| + |v_x| + |v_y|)^2 \, |\det DF^{-1}| \, dx$$

$$\le \frac{8(c_1 \tilde{h}_j)^4}{\inf_{\zeta \in \bar{M}} |\det DF|} (|v|_{1,\Omega_j}^2 + |v|_{2,\Omega_j}^2) \qquad (7.7.11)$$

$$\le c_2 \, \tilde{h}_j^4 \, \|v\|_{2,\Omega_j}^2,$$

where

$$c_2 = \frac{8c_1^4}{\inf_{\zeta \in \bar{M}} |\det DF|}.$$

Clearly, similar bounds hold for the integrals $\int_M \hat{v}_{\xi\xi}^2 \, d\zeta$ and $\int_M \hat{v}_{\eta\eta}^2 \, d\zeta$, and upon combining these with (7.7.11), we get (7.7.10).

Finally, we consider (7.7.9). In this case we must bound the derivatives,

$$v_x = v_\xi \xi_x + v_\eta \eta_x$$

and

$$v_y = v_\xi \xi_y + v_\eta \eta_y.$$

This in turn requires bounds for ξ_x, ξ_y, η_x, and η_y. However, according to the inverse function theorem,

$$\begin{bmatrix} \xi_x & \xi_y \\ \eta_x & \eta_y \end{bmatrix} = DF^{-1} = [DF]^{-1}.$$

Thus this problem reduces to finding a bound for $\|[DF]^{-1}\|$. For this purpose we use the result of Exercise 7.14.

We observe that Theorem 7.6.3 again shows that

$$\|[D\tilde{F}]^{-1}\| \le \frac{\tilde{h}}{\tilde{\rho}_j} \equiv \alpha.$$

Also,

$$\|D\tilde{F} - DF\| = \|-DQ\| \le 2 \, c\tilde{h}_j^2 \equiv \beta.$$

Therefore, since $\tilde{\rho}_j \ge \tilde{\rho}\tilde{h}_j$, we have $\alpha\beta \le 1/2$, provided that $\tilde{h}_j \le \tilde{\rho}/(4c\hat{h})$. Applying the conclusion of Exercise 7.14, we deduce the estimate,

$$\|[DF]^{-1}\| \le 2\alpha \le 2\hat{h} \, (\tilde{\rho}\tilde{h}_j)^{-1},$$

and the rest of the proof follows the preceding cases.

Q.E.D.

Elementwise interpolation error bounds for the quadrilaterals are obtained by combining the results of Lemma 7.6.1 with those of Theorem 7.7.1.

Theorem 7.7.2.   *Let* $v \in H^2(\Omega)$ *and let* v_I *denote its interpolant* (7.7.3). *If* **F** *is the map* (7.7.1), *and if* (7.7.6) *and* (7.7.7) *hold, then there are constants* K_0 *and* K_1 *such that*

$$|v - v_I|_{0,\Omega_j} \le K_0 \,\tilde{h}_j^2 \,\|v\|_{2,\Omega_j} \tag{7.7.12}$$

and

$$|v - v_I|_{1,\Omega_j} \le K_1 \,\tilde{h}_j \,\|v\|_{2,\Omega_j}. \tag{7.7.13}$$

Proof. Employing (7.7.8), (7.6.10), and (7.7.10), we have for some constants c_0, c_2, and K, that

$$
\begin{aligned}
|v - v_I|_{0,\Omega_j} &\le c_0 \,|\hat{v} - \hat{v}_I|_{0,M} \le c_0 \, K \,|\hat{v}|_{2,M} \\
&\le c_0 \, K c_2 \,\tilde{h}_j^2 \,\|v\|_{2,\Omega_j} \equiv K_0 \,\tilde{h}_j^2 \,\|v\|_{2,\Omega_j}.
\end{aligned}
$$

Inequality (7.7.13) follows in a similar manner.

Q.E.D.

The convergence results are identical to those for the linear triangles and they are established by the same arguments that concluded Section 7.6. *If we have a regular family of quadrilateral decompositions satisfying the perturbation hypothesis* (7.7.6), *and if* u* *is the solution of Problem B, then the finite element error is of order h in the norm of* $H^1(\Omega)$. *If* u* *only solves Problem G, then the error goes to zero with the mesh gauge, but the rate of convergence may be less than* $O(h)$.

Example 7.7.1

This is the same problem as in Example 7.6.1. Now the finite element space S^h is chosen to be the space of four-node bilinear quadrilaterals on a uniform mesh with $h = \frac{2}{3}, \frac{1}{3}$, and $\frac{1}{6}$ (Figure 7.7.3). Table 7.7.1 contains a summary of the results. Again we note that

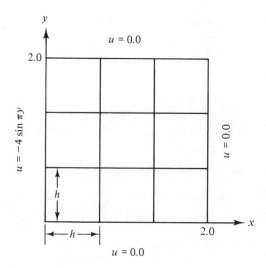

Figure 7.7.3   Finite element mesh of quadrilaterals.

TABLE 7.7.1 RESULTS FOR EXAMPLE 7.7.1

h	Dim S_0^h	Number of elements	$\|u^* - u^h\|_0$	$\|u^* - u^h\|_1$	Maximum nodal error
2/3	4	9	0.842	4.27	0.186
1/3	25	36	0.203	2.34	0.063
1/6	121	144	0.050	1.20	0.017

the convergence in $\|\cdot\|_1$ is apparently linear, but the convergence in $\|\cdot\|_0$ seems to be quadratic. To explain this behavior we need to study the error in the L_2 norm. This subject is taken up in the next section.

7.8 THE L_2 FINITE ELEMENT ERROR

We have seen that, under the conditions of Sections 7.6 and 7.7, the finite element error is $O(h)$. An examination of the proof of Theorem 7.6.5 reveals that this is so because the norm $\|\cdot\|_1$ employed to measure the error involves both function values and *first derivatives*, and the order of interpolation of the latter quantities is only $O(h)$. At the same time we know (Theorems 7.6.4 and 7.7.2) that interpolation of the function values is an $O(h^2)$ process. Therefore, it is not unreasonable to conjecture that in terms of the L_2 norm $\|\cdot\|_0$, the finite element error is $O(h^2)$. In fact, as we have seen, Examples 7.6.1 and 7.7.1 illustrate quadratic convergence of the error in the L_2 norm. To see under what conditions this is true, we use an ingenious method due to Aubin [1967] and Nitsche [1968].

As in previous sections we denote the solutions of (7.1.12) and (7.4.1) by u^* and u^h, respectively. The idea now is to introduce the solutions w^* and w^h of related equations in which the data f have been replaced by the difference $u^* - u^h$. That is, for all $v \in H_0^1(\Omega)$,

$$\langle w^*, v \rangle = (u^* - u^h, v)_0, \tag{7.8.1}$$

and for all $v \in S_0^h(\bar{\Omega})$,

$$\langle w^h, v \rangle = (u^* - u^h, v)_0. \tag{7.8.2}$$

In terms of a boundary value problem, we are associating the function w^* with the solution of the equation (7.1.1), where the right-hand side is now the function $u^* - u^h$.

Since $u^* - u^h \in H_0^1(\Omega)$, it follows from (7.8.1) that

$$\|u^* - u^h\|_0^2 = (u^* - u^h, u^* - u^h)_0 = \langle w^*, u^* - u^h \rangle. \tag{7.8.3}$$

Moreover, since $w^h \in S_0^h(\bar{\Omega})$, we have seen in Section 7.5 that $\langle u^* - u^h, w^h \rangle = 0$. Subtracting this equation from (7.8.3) then yields

$$\|u^* - u^h\|_0^2 = \langle u^* - u^h, w^* - w^h \rangle,$$

and by applying the Cauchy–Schwarz inequality, we deduce that

$$\|u^* - u^h\|_0^2 \leq \langle u^* - u^h, u^* - u^h \rangle^{1/2} \langle w^* - w^h, w^* - w^h \rangle^{1/2}. \tag{7.8.4}$$

If u^* and w^* are also members of $H^2(\Omega)$, then by Theorem 7.6.5 and the equivalence of the norms $\langle \cdot, \cdot \rangle^{1/2}$ and $\|\cdot\|_1$ there is a constant K such that

$$\langle u^* - u^h, u^* - u^h \rangle^{1/2} \leq Kh \, |u^*|_2$$

and

$$\langle w^* - w^h, w^* - w^h \rangle^{1/2} \leq Kh \, |w^*|_2.$$

Therefore, by (7.8.4),

$$\|u^* - u^h\|_0^2 \leq K^2 h^2 \, |u^*|_2 \, |w^*|_2. \tag{7.8.5}$$

Now we need to invoke the assumption that the solution w^* of (7.8.1) is "two derivatives smoother" than the data $u^* - u^h$. In particular, we suppose that

$$|w^*|_2 \leq c \, \|u^* - u^h\|_0. \tag{7.8.6}$$

This *regularity* condition on the solution usually is not too restrictive. For example, it is satisfied by the solution of Problem G if Ω is convex and the data are sufficiently smooth (Ciarlet [1978]). Further results concerning the regularity of solutions of elliptic boundary value problems can be found in Nečas [1967], Grisvard [1985], or Ladyzhenskaya [1985].

By combining (7.8.5) and (7.8.6) and canceling the common factor $\|u^* - u^h\|_0$, we finally obtain

$$\|u^* - u^h\|_0 \leq K^2 c h^2 \, |u^*|_2,$$

which provides the desired order of convergence.

Theorem 7.8.1.   *Let u^* solve Problem G [i.e., satisfy (7.1.12)], and let u^h be its finite element approximation satisfying (7.4.1). If (7.8.6) holds and if $S_0^h(\bar{\Omega})$ is the finite element space of linear triangles or bilinear quadrilaterals, then we have*

$$\|u^* - u^h\|_0 = O(h^2)$$

as $h \to 0$.

NOTES AND REMARKS

7.1 The Galerkin form of Problem B takes its name from a Russian engineer, B. G. Galerkin, who in 1915 developed a version of this idea. It is a particular instance of the method of "weighted residuals" (Finlayson [1972]).

The variational approach to boundary value problems goes back to Lord Rayleigh [1870] and W. Ritz [1908]. Consequently, early attempts to exploit the variational form in the numerical solution of boundary value problems are known as "Rayleigh–Ritz" methods.

In the terminology of the variational calculus, the differential equation (7.1.1) is the "Euler equation" corresponding to the functional (7.1.4) (cf. Courant and Hilbert [1953] and Exercise 7.2). The solution of (7.1.1) is termed an "extremal." In the present case, the extremal actually minimizes (7.1.4), but in general this need not be so. For this reason a solution of the Euler equation is sometimes called a "stationary point" rather than an extremal.

Existence and uniqueness of the solution of Problem G can also be deduced from a general result on abstract variational problems known as the "Lax–Milgram lemma." This lemma and its proof may be found, for example, in Ciarlet [1978].

7.3 It is clearly possible to define smoother analogues of the space $S_0(\bar{\Omega})$. These would provide, in the presence of a smoother solution of Problem G, more accurate approximations of that solution. This leads to the construction of finite element spaces of various orders of accuracy, a subject that occupies a prominent place in the engineering literature (see Zienkiewicz [1977] and the references contained therein). The value of the rather technical Theorem 7.3.2 is that it assures us that subspaces drawn from $S_0(\bar{\Omega})$ are "conforming" in the sense that they are also subspaces of the parent space $H_0^1(\Omega)$. This is essential for the subsequent error analysis.

7.4 The mathematical theory of the finite element method appears to have been launched by Courant [1943]. In this paper he proposed the simple but powerful idea of using approximating functions defined in a *piecewise* manner over $\bar{\Omega}$ rather than the global manner of the earlier Rayleigh–Ritz methods (cf. the notes for Section 7.1). The name of the method is attributed to Clough [1960]. Zlamal [1968] gave what is thought to be the first mathematical error analysis of the finite element method in its present general form. More specialized versions had been studied by (among others) Varga [1966] and Birkhoff, Schultz, and Varga [1968].

Paralleling, and in many instances predating, the mathematicians' contributions to the method were those of the engineering community. In this respect the work of Argyris [1954–1955] and Turner et al. [1956] should be mentioned.

Formation of the finite element linear system (7.4.3) requires the evaluation of integrals whose integrands involve products of basis functions and problem data. Except in the most special cases, these cannot be evaluated exactly, and in practice quadrature formulas are employed. This adds another contribution to the error, and the interested reader is referred to Strang and Fix [1973] or Ciarlet [1978] for accounts of the effects of numerical integration errors on the total error.

7.5 Corollary 7.5.2 is a special case of an abstract error estimate known as "Cea's lemma" (Cea [1964]). It provides the basic link between the finite element error and the more familiar approximation errors of interpolation theory.

7.6 What we have termed the linear isoparametric triangle is also known as "Courant's triangle" (Courant [1943]), the "constant strain triangle," the "linear triangle" (Zienkiewicz [1977]), and the "triangle of type (1)" (Ciarlet [1978]). It is unquestionably the most basic two-dimensional element. The isoparametric concept was introduced by Argyris and Fried [1968] and Ergatoudis, Irons, and Zienkiewicz [1968]. For discussions and algorithms concerning the generation of triangulations of two- and three-dimensional domains, see Cavendish [1974], Thacker [1980], and Cavendish, Field, and Frey [1984].

The full power of the isoparametric approach only becomes apparent when we consider elements having *curvilinear* sides. For example, the quadratic isoparametric triangle is a curvilinear triangle whose sides are parabolic segments. It is defined by the coordinates of its vertices and those of three other distinct points, each of which lies on one of the curved sides. Obviously, this is a valuable element for domains with curved boundaries. For a discussion of isoparametric quadrilateral elements, see Section 8.4.

The basis functions of this section correspond to what are known in the finite element literature as "global basis (or shape) functions." The restriction of a global basis function to an element where it is nontrivial produces a "local basis (or shape) function."

In developing our interpolation error analysis we have followed Ciarlet [1978], who derives the equivalent of Lemma 7.6.1 from a theorem due to Deny and Lions [1953–1954] on equivalent norms on "quotient spaces." For another approach, using the so-called "Bramble–Hilbert lemma," see Oden and Reddy [1976].

7.7 The proof of the one-to-one nature of the mapping (7.7.1) is taken from Frey, Hall, and Porsching [1978] (see also Strang and Fix [1973]).

Regarding (7.7.1) as a perturbation of the affine transformation (7.7.5) leads to a simple, albeit restrictive treatment of the nonlinear case. For an analysis that avoids the perturbation assumption (7.7.6), see Ciarlet [1978] and Ciarlet and Raviart [1972].

7.8 The idea of using the smoothness of the solution of the auxiliary equation (7.8.1) to increase the order of convergence in the L_2 norm is (or was) known in the numerical analysis literature as "Nitsche's trick." The technique is also referred to as "L_2 lifting" (Axelsson and Barker [1984]).

EXERCISES

7.1. Let $\Omega = (0, 1)$. Find the function $u \in H_0^1(\Omega)$ that minimizes the functional

$$I[v] = \int_\Omega \left[\left(\frac{dv}{dx} \right)^2 + v^2 - 2xv \right] dx$$

over $H_0^1(\Omega)$.

7.2. According to Courant and Hilbert [1953], the "simplest" problem" of the variational calculus is the following. Given $\Omega = (x_0, x_1)$, a twice continuously differentiable function $F: \Omega \times R \times R \to R$, and the vector space $U = \{u \mid u \in C^2(\bar{\Omega}), u(x_0) = u(x_1) = 0\}$, find $u \in U$ such that the functional

$$J[v] = \int_\Omega F(x, v, v') \, dx \qquad \left(' = \frac{d}{dx} \right)$$

is a minimum over U.

(a) Show that if u solves this problem, then it satisfies *Euler's equation*

$$F_u - (F_{u'})' = 0.$$

(b) Solve the Euler equation corresponding to the functional $J[v] = \int_\Omega [1 + (v')^2]^{1/2} \, dx$. What common observation is "proven" by this solution?

(c) Show that if F is independent of x, then a solution of the Euler equation is also a solution of

$$(F - u'F_{u'})' = 0.$$

7.3. The uniqueness of a solution of the boundary value problem (7.1.1), (7.1.2) follows from Theorems 7.1.2 and 7.1.4. Give another *uniqueness* proof for this problem that does not use Hilbert space theory. [*Hint:* Apply (7.1.8) and Green's theorem to the difference of two solutions.]

7.4. Consider the following problem: Find $u \in C^2(\bar{\Omega})$ such that (7.1.1) holds along with the *inhomogeneous* boundary condition $u(x) = g(x)$, for $x \in \partial\Omega$, where $g \colon \partial\Omega \to R$ is some given continuous function.

    (a) Show that if $v \in C^2(\bar{\Omega})$ is any function such that $v|_{\partial\Omega} = g$, then $w \equiv u - v$ satisfies

$$-(a_i w_{x_i})_{x_i} + bw = F, \qquad \mathbf{x} \in \Omega$$

and

$$w\Big|_{\partial\Omega} = 0,$$

where F is completely determined by v and the original data.

    (b) If $\bar{\Omega}$ is the unit square of Figure 7.E.1, and g is defined on its boundary, verify that

$$v(x, y) \equiv (1 - x)g(0, y) + xg(1, y) + (1 - y)g(x, 0) + yg(x, 1)$$
$$-(1 - x)(1 - y)g(0, 0) - x(1 - y)g(1, 0) - (1 - x)yg(0, 1) - xyg(1, 1)$$

agrees with g on $\partial\Omega$.

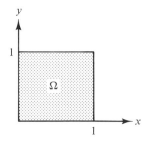

Figure 7.E.1   Unit square.

7.5. Show that if u solves Problem G, and if $u \in H_0^1(\Omega) \cap H^4(\Omega)$, then u solves Problem B.

7.6. Construct a nontrivial function in $H_0^1(\Omega)$ if:

    (a) Ω is the interior of the ellipse $x^2/a^2 + y^2/b^2 = 1$.

    (b) Ω is the interior of the slot shown in Figure 7.E.2.

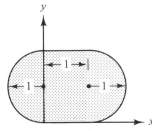

Figure 7.E.2   Slotted region.

7.7. Prove that if U is a finite-dimensional inner product space, U is complete. [*Hint:* Use (6.6.1).]

7.8. Show that if A is the matrix of (7.4.4), then $\mathbf{c}^T A \mathbf{c} > 0$ if $\mathbf{c} \neq \mathbf{0}$.

7.9. Let M be the triangle of Figure 7.6.1 and assume that $v \in C^2(\bar{M})$. Establish (7.6.10) when $m = 1$ if $|\cdot|_{m,M,\infty}$ is defined by (7.6.11).

7.10. If V is a closed subspace of a Hilbert space U, then it is known (Kreyszig [1978]) that every $u \in U$ has a unique representation in the form

$$u = v + w, \tag{1}$$

where $v \in V$ and $(w, z) = 0$ for all $z \in V$. The operator $P: U \to V$, $Pu = v$ is called a *projector*.
(a) Show that P is a bounded, linear operator with $\|P\| = 1$.
(b) Show that P is *idempotent* (i.e., $P^2 = P$).

7.11. Let $\mathbf{z}_j, j = 1, 2, 3$, be three points in R^2 that are not collinear. The *barycentric coordinates* $(\alpha_1, \alpha_2, \alpha_3)$ of a point $\mathbf{z} \in R^2$ are defined by the conditions

$$\mathbf{z} = \alpha_1 \mathbf{z}_1 + \alpha_2 \mathbf{z}_2 + \alpha_3 \mathbf{z}_3,$$
$$1 = \alpha_1 + \alpha_2 + \alpha_3. \tag{2}$$

(a) Show that the barycentric coordinates are uniquely defined for any $\mathbf{z} \in R^2$.
(b) Let Ω denote the interior of the triangle with vertices $\mathbf{z}_j, j = 1, 2, 3$. Show that if $\mathbf{z}$ is any point in $\bar{\Omega}$, then $\alpha_i = A_i/A$, where A is the area of $\bar{\Omega}$ and A_i is the area of the triangular element with vertices $\mathbf{z}, \mathbf{z}_j, j \neq i$.
(c) Conditions (2) define a one-to-one map of the domain

$$K = \{(\alpha_1, \alpha_2, \alpha_3) | 0 \leq \alpha_i \leq 1, i = 1, 2, 3\}$$

onto the triangular element $\bar{\Omega}$ of part (b). What is the map when $\bar{\Omega}$ is the master element $\bar{M}$ of Figure 7.6.1? Use this result and (2) to give another construction of the affine transformation (7.6.1).

7.12. Suppose that $-\infty < x_1 < x_2 < \cdots < x_{N+1} < \infty$ are $N + 1$ points in R and let $\Omega = (x_1, x_{N+1})$, $\Omega_j = (x_j, x_{j+1}), j = 1, \ldots, N$.
(a) Construct an affine transformation of $[0, 1]$ onto $\bar{\Omega}_j$.
(b) If $\bar{E}_i = \bar{\Omega}_{i-1} \cup \bar{\Omega}_i, i = 2, \ldots, N$, use the result of part (a) to construct a basis function $\phi_i: \bar{\Omega} \to R$ such that supp $\phi_i = \bar{E}_i$, $\phi_i \in C^0(\bar{\Omega})$, ϕ_i is a linear function in each $\bar{\Omega}_j$, and $\phi_i(x_j) = \delta_{ij}$. Graph a typical function ψ_i.

7.13. Consider a family of triangulations τ. Denote the maximum and minimum side lengths of a member of τ by h_M and h_m, respectively, and let θ be any vertex angle appearing in this member. Show that if there are constants H and θ_0 such that $h_M/h_m \leq H < \infty$ and $\theta \geq \theta_0 > 0$, then the family is regular.

7.14. Let A and C be real $n \times n$ matrices and assume that A is invertible with $\|A^{-1}\| < \alpha$ for some norm $\|\cdot\|$. Prove that if $\|A - C\| \leq \beta$ and $\alpha\beta < 1$, then C is also invertible and $\|C^{-1}\| \leq \alpha/(1 - \alpha\beta)$. [*Hint:* Show that $\|I - A^{-1}C\| < \alpha\beta$ and apply Theorem 5.5.2 to $A^{-1}C = I - (I - A^{-1}C)$ to deduce the invertibility of C. Then use (5.5.8) to estimate $\|C^{-1}\|$.]

7.15. Figure 7.E.3 shows a part of a triangulation of a region, Ω, on which the following boundary value problem is to be solved:

$$-(u_{xx} + u_{yy}) = 1, \qquad (x, y) \in \Omega,$$

$$u\big|_{\partial\Omega} = 0.$$

Determine the nonzero coefficients of the equation (7.4.3) that corresponds to the origin.

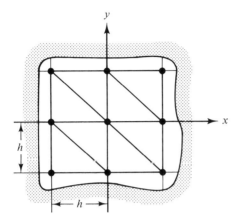

Figure 7.E.3   Portion of a triangulation.

7.16. Consider the isoparametric quadrilateral element shown in Figure 7.E.4.

  (a) Give the explicit form (in terms of x and y) of the basis function corresponding to the node with coordinates $(3, 1)$.

  (b) Find a necessary and sufficient condition on the nodal values of a function v for its interpolant (7.7.3) to be a linear function on the element.

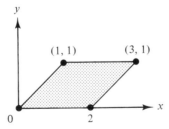

Figure 7.E.4   Isoparametric quadrilateral.

7.17. Consider a family of parallelograms Ξ. Let h_M and h_m denote, respectively, the maximum and minimum side lengths of a member of Ξ, and let θ be any vertex angle appearing in the member. Show that if there are constants H, θ_0, and θ_1 such that $h_M/h_m \leq H < \infty$ and $0 < \theta_0 \leq \theta \leq \theta_1 < \pi$, then (7.7.7) holds.

7.18. Let $u \in C^2[0, 1]$ be the solution of the convection–conduction problem

$$v\,u_x - K u_{xx} = 0, \qquad 0 < x < 1$$

$$u(0) = 0, \qquad u(1) = 1$$

[cf. (1.2.1)]. Further, let U be its piecewise linear finite element approximation in S of the form (1.3.5), where S is defined explicitly in Section 1.3. The function U is determined by (1.3.6). Let $S_0 = \{w \in S: w(0) = w(1) = 0\}$ and define

$$\langle w_1, w_2 \rangle \equiv \int_0^1 [v w_1' w_2 + K w_1' w_2'] \, dx$$

for $w_1, w_2 \in S$.

(1) Prove that $\langle w, w \rangle = K \int_0^1 (w')^2 \, dx$ for all $w \in S_0$.

(2) Prove that $\langle U - u, w \rangle = 0$ for all $w \in S_0$.

(3) Let u_I be the linear interpolant of u as defined in Exercise 1.4. Define $\eta = u - u_I$ and $\phi = u_I - U$. Use (1) and (2) to prove that

$$\left[\int_0^1 (\phi')^2 \, dx \right]^{1/2} \le \frac{|v| + K}{K} \left[\int_0^1 (\eta')^2 \, dx \right]^{1/2}.$$

(4) Hence prove that as $\Delta x \to 0$,

$$\left[\int_0^1 (U(x) - u(x))^2 \, dx \right]^{1/2} = O(\Delta x).$$

[*Hint for* (3): If ε is piecewise continuously differentiable and $\varepsilon(0) = \varepsilon(1) = 0$, then $\int_0^1 [\varepsilon(x)]^2 \, dx \le \int_0^1 [\varepsilon'(x)]^2 \, dx$, which is a special case of the Poincaré inequality.]

Computer Exercises

7.19. Let Ω denote the trapezoid with vertices $(-1, 0)$, $(1, 0)$, $(2, 1)$, and $(-2, 1)$. Verify that the solution of the boundary value problem

$$-(u_{xx} + u_{yy}) = 10y^2 + 8y - 2x^2 - 2, \qquad (x, y) \in \Omega,$$

$$u\Big|_{\partial\Omega} = 0,$$

is

$$u^*(x, y) = (y - y^2)(1 - x^2) + 2y^2 - y^3 - y^4.$$

Use the finite element method to generate numerical solutions of this problem. Make two runs, one with each of the two triangular meshes shown in Figure 7.E.5. The theory implies that if u^h is the finite element solution corresponding to a mesh gauge h, then $\|u^* - u^h\|_0 = O(h^2)$. Do your numerical results support this?

7.20. Consider the electrostatic potential problem given in Example 7.4.1. Solve this problem using four-node isoparametric quadrilaterals. Plot the equipotential lines and compare to Figure 7.4.3.

7.21. As noted in Chapter 2, heat conduction problems may involve a combination of boundary conditions. The variational statement of such problems is given by Theorem 8.2.1. Use this theorem to solve the following axisymmetric heat conduction problem using the finite element method and linear triangles or bilinear quadrilaterals. Find the temperature $u(r, z)$ in the walls of a hollow concrete cylinder of height 2 ft whose inner radius is 0.6 ft and outer radius is 0.9 ft (Figure 7.E.6). Assume that the cylinder contains a fluid at constant temperature 400°F and that the following radiation condition holds at the

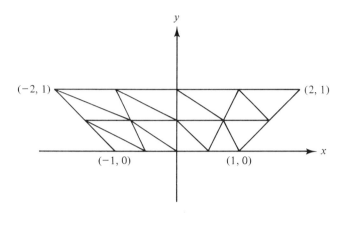

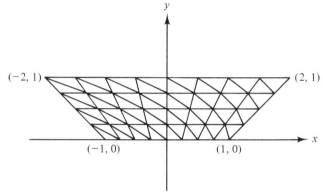

Figure 7.E.5 Trapezoidal region.

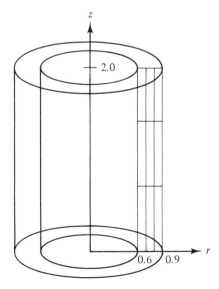

Figure 7.E.6 Hollow concrete cylinder.

outer surface:

$$\frac{\partial u}{\partial r} + 0.7(u - 80) = 0 \text{ at } r = 0.9.$$

Assume further that $\partial u/\partial z = 0$ on the boundaries $z = 0$ and $z = 2$. Verify that your solution is independent of z and compare it to the true solution. (For the true solution, see Exercise 2.3.) Calculate the flux across the outer surface of the cylinder. Compare this finite element calculation with the true value (Carslaw and Jaegar [1959, p. 189])

$$\int_{\substack{\text{outer} \\ \text{surface}}} k \frac{\partial u}{\partial r} \, dA = 642.32 \, k\pi \text{ Btu/hr.}$$

(The thermal conductivity of concrete is $k = 0.79$ Btu/hr-ft-°F.)

7.22. The concrete island drilling system (CIDS) is a platform composed of cellular concrete modules stacked on top of each other, which, in turn, support a barge-mounted drilling rig[5] (see Figure 7.E.7a). The modules can be stacked for siting in water depths of 18 to 55 ft.

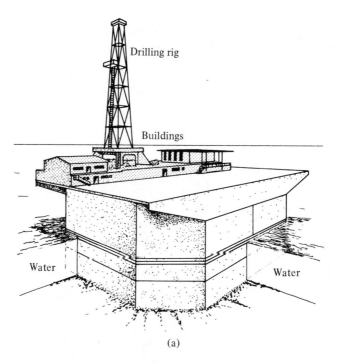

(a)

Figure 7.E.7   (a) Concrete island drilling system; (b) Insulated outer wall of each cell.

---

[5] This problem was suggested by Dr. E. Halteman, Pittsburgh Corning Corp., retired.

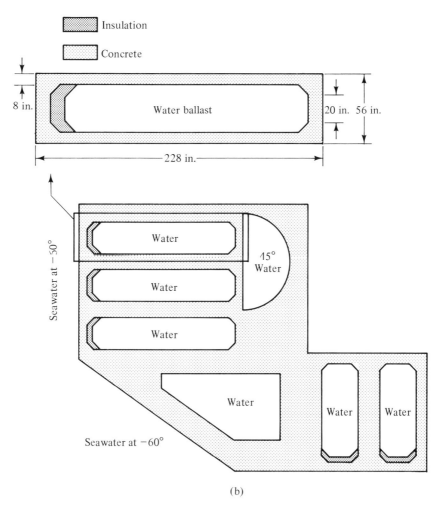

Figure 7.E.7   (Continued)

The concrete honeycomb forms a high-strength, durable structure capable of withstanding cold temperatures and ice loads. The drilling unit is mounted on one of the two deck storage barges and is designed with a 25,000-ft drilling capability. There are quarters for 80 people and 10 months of supplies for long-term operations. The entire system, with drilling rig intact, can be relocated by pumping out the saltwater ballast and towing the CIDS to a new site.

A drilling contractor using a CIDS in the Arctic Ocean is concerned that the water ballast in the outer ring of cells in the barge will freeze and fracture the concrete walls of the honeycomb module. An insulation salesperson suggests insulating the outer walls of each of the cells with roughly 10 in. of insulation, as illustrated in Figure 7.E.7b. The water in the cells that do not border on the perimeter of the barge is kept warm by the drilling activity.

Is the salesperson's suggestion a sound recommendation? Determine the 32°F isotherm in a single cell to justify your answer. You can assume that the heat flow across the walls between cells is zero; that is, these walls are lines of symmetry. Also, compute the integral of the flux (Btu/ft-hr) on each of the four sides of the domain. The sum of these four numbers should be zero. Why? What can you conclude about your discretization?

MATERIAL PROPERTIES

	Thermal conductivity (Btu/ft-hr-°F)	Specific heat (Btu/lbm-°F)	Density (lb/ft³)
Concrete	0.790	0.25	150.0
Water	0.333	1.00	62.4
Insulation	0.028	0.18	8.5

A Short Course in Finite Element Methodology

The finite element method (FEM) is a tool that has been employed for design and analysis purposes in a broad spectrum of engineering and scientific applications. We discuss it in this chapter as a general technique for constructing approximate solutions to boundary value problems. The domain is divided into a finite number of subdomains, called *elements*, and variational formulations are used to construct an approximation to the solution of the boundary value problem. On each element, the finite element approximation is generally a low-degree polynomial.

Piecewise analytic approximation dates back to Archimedes' approach to finding areas of plane figures and volumes of solids. However, the FEM as a method for solving boundary value problems began in the early 1940s with works of Hrennikoff [1941], McHenry [1943], and Courant [1943]. Turner et al. [1956] are generally credited with the first use of "element stiffness matrices" and, as noted in Chapter 7, the term "finite element" was introduced by Clough [1960]. Many engineers and mathematicians have contributed since then to this vast discipline. Texts on various aspects of the FEM abound, a few being those of Becker, Carey, and Oden [1981], Carey and Oden [1984], Davies [1980], Gallagher [1975], Hinton and Owen [1977], and Zienkiewicz [1977].

In earlier chapters we have considered the FEM from the perspective of the mathematician. In this chapter we present a very brief description of the FEM from the perspective of the engineer and/or practitioner. We focus on the linear elasticity problem introduced in Chapter 2.

8.1 SIMPLE SPRING MODEL

To gain some appreciation for finite element methodology as well as the engineering origins of this popular method we consider a simple problem. Recall from basic physics that *Hooke's law* governing the displacement of a linear spring states:

> If a force F is applied to a spring fixed at one end to produce a displacement δ, then there is a linear force–displacement relation:
>
> $$F = k\delta \qquad (k \equiv \text{stiffness of the spring}) \qquad (8.1.1)$$

(see Figure 8.1.1). The *spring constant* or *stiffness k* is dependent on the type of material from which the spring is made. The larger the value of k is, the more force is necessary to effect a given displacement δ.

Now consider a system of springs as indicated in Figure 8.1.2. Each spring is an *element* of the system. Points 1 and 2 have been displaced δ_1 and δ_2 by forces F_1 and F_2, respectively. We refer to these points 1 and 2 as the *nodes* of the element or spring. If the system is in equilibrium,

$$F_1 + F_2 = 0. \qquad (8.1.2)$$

The spring between nodes 1 and 2 acts like the one in Figure 8.1.1, with an overall elongation of $(\delta_2 - \delta_1)$ and a force of F_2; hence

$$F_2 = k(\delta_2 - \delta_1) \qquad (8.1.3)$$

and from (8.1.2)

$$F_1 = -F_2 = k(\delta_1 - \delta_2). \qquad (8.1.4)$$

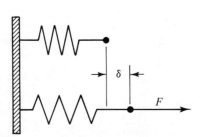

Figure 8.1.1 Single spring.

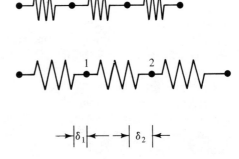

Figure 8.1.2 Spring in a system of springs.

It is convenient to write (8.1.3)–(8.1.4) in matrix form as

$$\mathbf{F}^e = K^e \boldsymbol{\delta}^e \tag{8.1.5}$$

where

$$\mathbf{F}^e = \begin{bmatrix} F_1 \\ F_2 \end{bmatrix}, \quad K^e = \begin{bmatrix} k & -k \\ -k & k \end{bmatrix}, \quad \text{and} \quad \boldsymbol{\delta}^e = \begin{bmatrix} \delta_1 \\ \delta_2 \end{bmatrix}$$

are the *element* (or *spring*) *force vector, stiffness matrix,* and *displacement vector,* respectively. We have one such force–displacement relationship for each spring in the system.

The element force–displacement relations (8.1.5) are now used to analyze general systems of springs in equilibrium. For the two-spring system in Figure 8.1.3, equilibrium implies that

$$F_1 + F_2 + F_3 = 0. \tag{8.1.6}$$

Applying (8.1.4) to spring 1 and (8.1.3) to spring 2, we obtain

$$F_1 = k_1(\delta_1 - \delta_2)$$

and

$$\tag{8.1.7}$$

$$F_3 = k_2(\delta_3 - \delta_2).$$

Equation (8.1.6) then gives

$$F_2 = -k_1\delta_1 + (k_1 + k_2)\delta_2 - k_2\delta_3. \tag{8.1.8}$$

Equations (8.1.7)–(8.1.8) in matrix form are

$$\mathbf{F} = K\boldsymbol{\delta},$$

where

$$\mathbf{F} = \begin{bmatrix} F_1 \\ F_2 \\ F_3 \end{bmatrix}, \quad K = \begin{bmatrix} k_1 & -k_1 & 0 \\ -k_1 & k_1 + k_2 & -k_2 \\ 0 & -k_2 & k_2 \end{bmatrix}, \quad \text{and} \quad \boldsymbol{\delta} = \begin{bmatrix} \delta_1 \\ \delta_2 \\ \delta_3 \end{bmatrix}$$

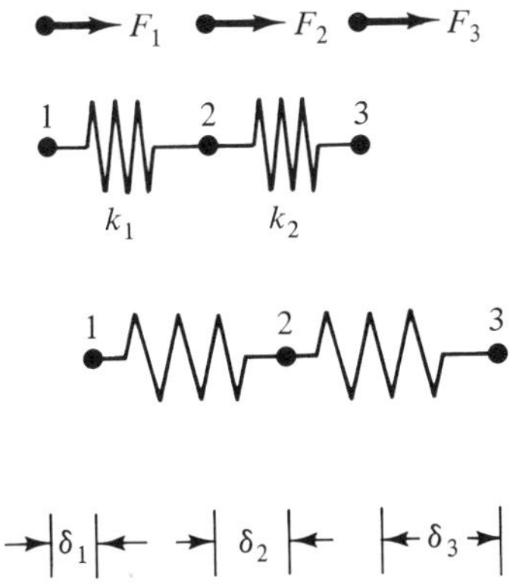

Figure 8.1.3 Two-spring system.

are the *global* (or *overall* or *system*) force vector, stiffness matrix, and displacement vector, respectively.

An important observation is that the global stiffness matrix K is the sum of the element stiffness matrices K^1 and K^2:

$$K = \begin{bmatrix} k_1 & -k_1 & 0 \\ -k_1 & k_1 & 0 \\ 0 & 0 & 0 \end{bmatrix} + \begin{bmatrix} 0 & 0 & 0 \\ 0 & k_2 & -k_2 \\ 0 & -k_2 & k_2 \end{bmatrix}.$$

Furthermore, we note that:

1. K is symmetric, as are K^1 and K^2.
2. $K_{13} = K_{31} = 0$ implies nodes 1 and 3 are not coupled directly. Couplings occur only between nodes in the same element (spring).
3. K is singular, since $K\mathbf{1} = \mathbf{0}$, where the vector $\mathbf{1} = (1, 1, 1)^T$. The vector $\mathbf{1}$ corresponds to the *rigid body motion* of translating the system one unit to the right. If the system is pinned at node 1, then $\delta_1 = 0$, and if $k_1 = k_2 = k$, we have

$$\begin{bmatrix} k & -k & 0 \\ -k & 2k & -k \\ 0 & -k & k \end{bmatrix} \begin{bmatrix} 0 \\ \delta_2 \\ \delta_3 \end{bmatrix} = \begin{bmatrix} F_1 \\ F_2 \\ F_3 \end{bmatrix},$$

which has the solution

$$\delta_2 = \frac{F_2 + F_3}{k}, \qquad \delta_3 = \frac{F_2 + 2F_3}{k},$$

and $F_1 = -k\delta_2$. Hence the singularity can be removed by imposing a constraint that prevents rigid body motions.

This method of analyzing the system of springs has four basic steps:

1. Generate the element stiffness matrices.
2. Assemble the element stiffness matrices into a global system.
3. Impose necessary auxiliary conditions to ensure nonsingularity.
4. Solve the global system.

This is the same basic methodology as that used in implementation of the finite element method to solve general boundary value problems of engineering and science.

8.2 VARIATIONAL FORMULATION

So as to focus our discussion of the FEM and its methodology, we consider the plane elasticity problem derived in Section 2.4. In Chapter 7 we proved that second-order elliptic boundary value problems can be formulated alternatively in terms of variational problems. We now show that the same is true for the plane elasticity problem. For completeness, we restate the differential formulation:[1]

Problem PDE (Plane Elasticity).   *(Cf. Section 2.4.) Let* Ω *be a bounded region in the xy-plane representing a solid of unit thickness whose boundary* $\partial\Omega$ *is piecewise smooth in the sense of Section 6.3. Let u, v* $\in C^2(\bar{\Omega})$. *Find the displacement vector* $\delta = (u, v)$ *satisfying*

$$\begin{cases} \nabla^2 u + \dfrac{1}{1-2v}(u_{xx} + v_{yx}) + \dfrac{X}{G} = 0, \\[2mm] \nabla^2 v + \dfrac{1}{1-2v}(v_{yy} + u_{xy}) + \dfrac{Y}{G} = 0 \end{cases} \tag{8.2.1}$$

for $(x, y) \in \Omega$, *subject to the boundary conditions*

    1. $u(x, y) = b_1(x, y)$ *and* $v(x, y) = b_2(x, y)$ (8.2.2)

for $(x, y) \in \partial\Omega_1$,

    2. $\sigma_x \, dy/ds + \tau_{xy} \, dx/ds = \bar{X}$ *and* $\sigma_y \, dx/ds + \tau_{xy} \, dy/ds = \bar{Y}$ (8.2.3)

for $(x, y) \in \partial\Omega_2$, *where* $\partial\Omega = \partial\Omega_1 \cup \partial\Omega_2$, *and* $(dx/ds, dy/ds)$ *is the tangent vector to* $\partial\Omega$.

Now let us consider another approach to describing the elasticity problem, the *variational* or *energy* formulation.

We make the fundamental assumption that the stress varies *linearly* with strain, or equivalently, that force varies linearly with displacement. For the stress components in Figure 2.4.1, we average σ_x, σ_y, and τ_{xy} on opposite sides of the differential element and associate that value with the centroid. The force $\sigma_x \, dy$ causes a displacement $u_x \, dx$ in the x-direction and does an amount of work

$$\tfrac{1}{2}(\sigma_x \, dy)(u_x \, dx). \tag{8.2.4}$$

The latter quantity is the shaded area in Figure 8.2.1.

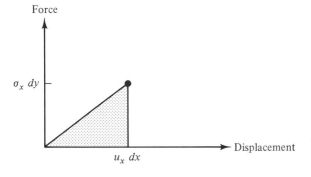

Figure 8.2.1   Force–displacement relationship.

---

[1] We will use the notation of Chapter 6 throughout this chapter.

The force $\tau_{xy}\,dx$ acting on the sides parallel to the x-axis and in the x-direction causes a displacement $u_y\,dy$ and does an amount of work

$$\tfrac{1}{2}(\tau_{xy}\,dx)(u_y\,dy). \tag{8.2.5}$$

In addition to these terms, we interchange the roles of u, v and x, y to find that the total work done by the stress components on the differential element, termed the *strain energy*, is given by

$$\tfrac{1}{2}\big[\sigma_x u_x + \sigma_y v_y + \tau_{xy}(u_y + v_x)\big]\,dx\,dy. \tag{8.2.6}$$

We recognize this as one-half of the inner product of the stress vector $\boldsymbol{\sigma}$ with the strain vector $\boldsymbol{\varepsilon}$, times the area of the element.

Not all of this energy is available, since the boundary and body forces do "negative work." For example, the work done by the body forces X and Y in the x and y directions, respectively, is

$$-(Xu + Yv)\,dx\,dy. \tag{8.2.7}$$

Hence the *potential energy* for the entire body subjected to body forces X, Y in the x, y coordinate directions, respectively, is

$$E(\boldsymbol{\delta}) \equiv \int_{\Omega} (\tfrac{1}{2}\boldsymbol{\sigma}^T\boldsymbol{\varepsilon} - Xu - Yv)\,dx\,dy - \int_{\partial\Omega_2} (\bar{X}u + \bar{Y}v)\,ds, \tag{8.2.8}$$

where $\boldsymbol{\delta} = (u, v)$ and $(\bar{X}, \bar{Y})$ are the (x, y) components of boundary forces specified on $\partial\Omega_2$.

A state of *equilibrium* corresponds to a deformation state $\boldsymbol{\delta} = (u, v)$, which renders the potential energy E a minimum over an appropriate space of admissible states. It is reasonable to assume that u and v are continuous since we do not want the material to rupture or tear under elastic loading. It turns out that we should in fact seek a minimum in a different space of functions which is more appropriate for finite element analyses. If we assume for the time being that $b_1 = b_2 = 0$, an appropriate space is[2]

$$\mathbf{V} \equiv \{\mathbf{w} \mid \mathbf{w} \in V_2(H^1(\Omega)) \text{ and } \mathbf{w} = \mathbf{0} \text{ on } \partial\Omega_1\}.$$

Then we have

Problem VAR.   *Find* $\boldsymbol{\delta}^* = (u^*, v^*) \in \mathbf{V}$ *such that*

$$\min_{\boldsymbol{\delta} \in \mathbf{V}} E(\boldsymbol{\delta}) = E(\boldsymbol{\delta}^*). \tag{8.2.9}$$

Regarding the equivalence of Problems PDE and VAR, we have the following theorem.

---

[2] The linear space $V_k(S)$ is defined to be the space of k-vectors $\mathbf{w} = (w_1, w_2, \ldots, w_k)$, where $w_i \in S$ and S itself is a linear space. This is nothing but the k-fold Cartesian product of S. Furthermore, if $S = H^1(\Omega)$, then by the notation $w_i = 0$ we mean that $\bar{\gamma}w_i = 0$, where $\bar{\gamma}$ is the trace function of Section 6.3.

Theorem 8.2.1.   *If δ^* solves Problem PDE with $b_1 = b_2 = 0$, then it solves Problem VAR. Also, if $u^*, v^* \in C^2(\bar{\Omega})$ and $\delta^* = (u^*, v^*)$ solves Problem VAR, then δ^* also solves Problem PDE with $b_1 = b_2 = 0$.*

This theorem can be proven in a manner similar to that used in Chapter 7 provided that Poincaré's inequality (6.6.2) is replaced by *Korn's inequality* (Korn [1907]); that is, *there is a constant C such that*

$$\|\mathbf{w}\|_1 \leq C(\|\mathbf{w}\|_S^2 + \|\mathbf{w}\|_0^2)^{1/2} \qquad \text{for } \mathbf{w} \in V_2(H^1(\Omega)),$$

where

$$\|\mathbf{w}\|_m \equiv (\|w_1\|_m^2 + \|w_2\|_m^2)^{1/2}, \qquad m = 0, \ 1,$$

and

$$\|\mathbf{w}\|_S \equiv \left[\int_\Omega (\varepsilon_x^2 + \varepsilon_y^2 + \gamma_{xy}^2)\, dx\, dy \right]^{1/2}.$$

This inequality is used to prove that $\|\cdot\|_S$ is equivalent to $\|\cdot\|_1$ over the space $\mathbf{V}$ (see Zeidler [1988]). We now establish this equivalence for a special case. We will need the following identity:

$$\int_\Omega u_x v_y \, dx \, dy = \int_\Omega u_y v_x \, dx \, dy, \tag{8.2.10}$$

which follows from Green's theorem for functions in $C_0^\infty(\Omega)$. The extension to elements $\delta = (u, v) \in V_2(H_0^1(\Omega))$ may be established by a continuity argument since $V_2(C_0^\infty(\Omega))$ is dense in $V_2(H_0^1(\Omega))$.

Lemma 8.2.2.   *The norms $\|\cdot\|_S$ and $\|\cdot\|_1$ are equivalent on $V_2(H_0^1(\Omega))$.*

Proof.   For $\delta = (u, v) \in V_2(H_0^1(\Omega))$ we have from (8.2.10) and the inequality $\pm ab \geq -\frac{1}{2}(a^2 + b^2)$ that

$$\|\delta\|_S^2 = \int_\Omega [\varepsilon_x^2 + \varepsilon_y^2 + \gamma_{xy}^2]\, dx\, dy$$

$$= \int_\Omega [u_x^2 + v_y^2 + (u_y + v_x)^2]\, dx\, dy$$

$$\geq \int_\Omega [\tfrac{1}{2}(u_x^2 + v_y^2) + \tfrac{1}{2}(u_y^2 + v_x^2)]\, dx\, dy = \tfrac{1}{2}|\delta|_1^2,$$

where

$$|\delta|_1 \equiv \int_\Omega (u_x^2 + u_y^2 + v_x^2 + v_y^2)\, dx\, dy.$$

(Note that by adding $\|\delta\|_0^2$ to both sides of this inequality we obtain Korn's inequality for $\delta \in V_2(H_0^1(\Omega))$.) The inequality above and Poincaré's inequality, (6.6.2), imply that there is a constant K_1 such that

$$\|\delta\|_1^2 \leq K_1|\delta|_1^2 \leq 2K_1\|\delta\|_S^2.$$

Also, it is obvious that there exists a constant K_2 such that

$$\|\delta\|_S \leq K_2 \|\delta\|_1,$$

and hence the two norms are equivalent on $V_2(H_0^1(\Omega))$.

Q.E.D.

In a variational formulation such as the one given in Chapter 7, there is an obvious question of how to construct the appropriate functional. Recall that Exercise 7.2 examines the question of constructing the partial differential equation (Euler's equation) that corresponds to a given functional. The following theorem addresses the converse construction. This result is given in the context of abstract operators on Hilbert spaces.

Let H be a real Hilbert space with inner product $(\cdot, \cdot)$ and induced norm $\|\cdot\|$ (see Chapter 6). Let M be a subspace of H and L be a linear operator defined on M. Then the operator $L: M \subset H \to H$ is *self-adjoint* if $(Lu_1, u_2) = (u_1, Lu_2)$ for all u_1, $u_2 \in M$. It is *uniformly positive definite* if there is a positive constant γ such that $(Lu, u) \geq \gamma^2 \|u\|^2$ for all $u \in M$.

Theorem 8.2.3 (Equivalence Theorem).   *Let L be a self-adjoint, uniformly positive definite operator on a dense subspace M of a Hilbert space H, and let $f \in H$ be given. If the equation*

$$Lu = f \tag{8.2.11}$$

has a solution in M, then the functional F defined by

$$F[u] = \tfrac{1}{2}(Lu, u) - (f, u) \tag{8.2.12}$$

assumes its minimum value on M at this solution. Conversely, a function that minimizes $F[u]$ on M satisfies (8.2.11).

Proof. Let u satisfy (8.2.11) and let v be an arbitrary nonzero element of M. Then since L is self-adjoint and positive definite,

$$\begin{aligned}
F[u + v] &= \tfrac{1}{2}(L(u + v), u + v) - (f, u + v) \\
&= \tfrac{1}{2}(Lu, u) - (f, u) + \tfrac{1}{2}(Lu, v) - (f, v) + \tfrac{1}{2}(Lv, v) + \tfrac{1}{2}(Lv, u) \\
&= F[u] + (Lu - f, v) + \tfrac{1}{2}(Lv, v) \\
&= F[u] + \tfrac{1}{2}(Lv, v) > F[u].
\end{aligned}$$

Therefore, F assumes its minimum at u.

Now suppose that u is such that $F[u] \leq F[v]$ for all v in M. Let ε be a positive constant and v belong to M. Then

$$F[u + \varepsilon v] - F[u] \geq 0,$$

which implies by (8.2.12) that

$$\tfrac{1}{2}(L(u + \varepsilon v), u + \varepsilon v) - (f, u + \varepsilon v) - \tfrac{1}{2}(Lu, u) + (f, u) \geq 0,$$

or

$$\tfrac{1}{2}\varepsilon^2(Lv, v) + \varepsilon(Lu - f, v) \geq 0. \tag{8.2.13}$$

Since the left side of (8.2.13) is a quadratic in ε, the inequality can hold only if the coefficient of ε is zero. This in turn implies that $Lu = f$ since v is an arbitrary function in M and M is dense in H.

Q.E.D.

Let us see how this general theory applies to a two-dimensional plane elasticity problem.

We seek $\delta \equiv (u, v)^T$ such that

$$L\delta = \mathbf{f} \quad \text{in } \Omega, \tag{8.2.14}$$

where

$$L\delta \equiv \begin{bmatrix} -G\,\nabla^2 u - \dfrac{G}{1-2v}\,(u_{xx} + v_{xy}) \\[2mm] -G\,\nabla^2 v - \dfrac{G}{1-2v}\,(u_{xy} + v_{yy}) \end{bmatrix} \tag{8.2.15}$$

and

$$\mathbf{f} \equiv \begin{bmatrix} X \\ Y \end{bmatrix}$$

As boundary conditions, suppose that

$$u \equiv v \equiv 0 \quad \text{on the boundary, } \partial\Omega. \tag{8.2.16}$$

Recall that (cf. Section 6.1) $C_0^2(\Omega)$ is the space of functions that vanish near $\partial\Omega$ and have continuous second-order derivatives in Ω. The operator L is defined on the space $M \equiv V_2(C_0^2(\bar{\Omega}))$. It can be shown (Halmos [1951]) that this is a dense subspace of $H \equiv V_2(L_2(\Omega))$, where the inner product on $V_2(L_2(\Omega))$ is

$$(\delta_1, \delta_2) \equiv \int_\Omega \{u_1 u_2 + v_1 v_2\}\, dx\, dy \qquad [\delta_i = (u_i, v_i)],$$

and the corresponding norm is $\|\cdot\|_0$.

Without sacrificing applicability, we assume that $G > 0$ and that $-1 < v < \tfrac{1}{2}$. If $\delta \equiv (u, v)$ is a nonzero element of M, we then have

$$(L\delta, \delta) = \int_\Omega \left\{ \left[-G\,\nabla^2 u - \frac{G}{1-2v}\,(u_{xx} + v_{xy}) \right] u \right.$$

$$\left. + \left[-G\,\nabla^2 v - \frac{G}{1-2v}\,(u_{xy} + v_{yy}) \right] v \right\} dx\, dy$$

$$= \int_\Omega \left[G(u_x^2 + u_y^2 + v_x^2 + v_y^2) + \frac{G}{1-2v}\,(u_x + v_y)^2 \right] dx\, dy.$$

But by Exercise 8.3, there exists a γ^2 such that this last integral is not less than $\gamma^2 \|\delta\|_0^2$, which implies that L is a uniformly positive definite operator on M. It can easily be shown, using integration by parts, that L is also self-adjoint. Theorem 8.2.3 applies, and if a solution to (8.2.14) and (8.2.16) exists in M, then it minimizes over M the functional

$$F[\delta] = \tfrac{1}{2}(L\delta, \delta) - (\mathbf{f}, \delta). \tag{8.2.17}$$

After simplification

$$F[\delta] = \frac{G}{1 - 2v} \int_\Omega \left[(1 - v)u_x^2 + 2vu_xv_y + (1 - v)v_y^2 + \frac{1 - 2v}{2} (u_y + v_x)^2 \right] dx\, dy$$

$$- \int_\Omega (Xu + Yv)\, dx\, dy.$$

One can verify directly that the functional $F[\delta]$ is precisely equal to the *potential energy* $E(\delta)$ given in (8.2.8) with $\bar{X} = \bar{Y} = 0$.

The reader should reflect on the fact that the same plane strain elasticity problem has been cast in a *differential equation formulation* (8.2.14), an *energy formulation* (8.2.9) via physical arguments, and a *variational formulation* (8.2.17) via functional analytic arguments. These are three different *mathematical models* of the same plane strain problem.

The Equivalence Theorem 8.2.3 requires the assumption that the minimizing element u be a member of M. Without this assumption the problem may not have a solution. However, if we enlarge the space M and extend the domain of $F[\delta]$ appropriately, we can sometimes prove that the minimization problem always has a solution. To see how this is done for the two-dimensional plane elasticity problem, we first define a new inner product $[\cdot, \cdot]$ on M. Specifically, we let $[\delta_1, \delta_2] \equiv (L\delta_1, \delta_2)$. Then $\|\delta\|_E \equiv [\delta, \delta]^{1/2}$ is a norm, and direct calculation shows that

$$\|\delta\|_E^2 = \tfrac{1}{2} \int_\Omega \sigma^T \varepsilon \, dx\, dy = \tfrac{1}{2} \int_\Omega \varepsilon^T D\varepsilon \, dx\, dy, \tag{8.2.18}$$

where D is the material stiffness matrix given in (2.4.10). Note that whereas L is defined only on M, we can use (8.2.18) to define $\|\cdot\|_E$ on the larger space $V_2(H_0^1(\Omega))$. (The stress σ and strain ε only involve the first derivatives of the displacements.)

Since D is positive definite, $\|\cdot\|_E$ is equivalent to $\|\cdot\|_S$ on $V_2(H_0^1(\Omega))$, so, by Lemma 8.2.2, it is also equivalent to $\|\cdot\|_1$ on $V_2(H_0^1(\Omega))$. Thus if we take the closure in $V_2(H_0^1(\Omega))$ of M with respect to the norm $\|\cdot\|_E$ (cf. Section 5.1), we obtain a Banach space H_E which we call the *energy space*. (We also call $\|\cdot\|_E$ the *energy norm*, since it is in fact the strain energy.) However, every element in $V_2(H_0^1(\Omega))$ is the limit (with respect to $\|\cdot\|_1$) of a sequence in M (Section 7.3), and since $\|\cdot\|_1$ and $\|\cdot\|_E$ are equivalent, this means that $H_E = V_2(H_0^1(\Omega))$. Moreover, the inner product $[\cdot, \cdot]$ can be extended by continuity from M to H_E. This inner product converts H_E into a Hilbert space having the same topological properties as the Hilbert space $V_2(H_0^1(\Omega))$.

If $\mathbf{f}$ is a fixed element of H, then $(\mathbf{f}, \delta)$ is a bounded linear functional on H_E since by the Cauchy–Schwarz inequality and uniform positive definiteness of L

$$|(\mathbf{f}, \delta)| \leq \|\mathbf{f}\|_0 \|\delta\|_0 \leq \frac{\|\mathbf{f}\|_0}{\gamma} \|\delta\|_E$$

for any $\delta \in H_E$. Thus, by the Riesz Representation Theorem 6.2.1 there is a fixed element $\delta^* \in H_E$ such that $(\mathbf{f}, \delta) = [\delta^*, \delta]$, and we can write

$$F[\delta] = \tfrac{1}{2}[\delta, \delta] - [\delta^*, \delta] \qquad (8.2.19)$$

for $\delta \in H_E$. It is now easy to demonstrate the existence of a minimizing element in H_E.

Theorem 8.2.4.   *The functional $F[\delta]$ defined by (8.2.19) assumes the minimum value $-\tfrac{1}{2}\|\delta^*\|_E^2$ when $\delta = \delta^*$.*

Proof. The result follows immediately from the identity

$$F[\delta] = \tfrac{1}{2}[\delta - \delta^*, \delta - \delta^*] - \tfrac{1}{2}[\delta^*, \delta^*] = \tfrac{1}{2}\|\delta - \delta^*\|_E^2 - \tfrac{1}{2}\|\delta^*\|_E^2.$$

Q.E.D.

If the minimizing element of Theorem 8.2.4 lies in M, then by Theorem 8.2.3 it is also the solution of the differential equation (8.2.14). On the other hand, if $\delta^* \in H_E - M$, then we can regard it as a *generalized solution* of (8.2.14).

8.3 THE FINITE ELEMENT PROCEDURE

In this section we discuss the discretization by the finite element method of the plane strain elasticity boundary value problem formulated in Section 8.2. The true solution to the displacement formulation of linear elasticity given in Section 8.2 is rarely known in closed form. In any numerical discretization we seek an approximate solution by assuming that the displacement can be represented by a finite number of unknowns. In the FEM we idealize the continuum of the structure Ω as a union of *elements* Ω_j (triangles, quadrilaterals, or other simple geometric shapes) which are coupled at a finite number of points known as *nodal points* or *nodes*. Such an idealization is illustrated in Figure 8.3.1. This decomposition is in direct analogy with the spring system in Section 8.1 in which each spring was thought of as an element. Here each element is a triangle, and the nodes are the vertices of the triangles.

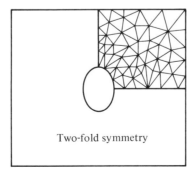

Two-fold symmetry

Figure 8.3.1   Finite element idealization: plate with a hole.

For many structural applications, the governing equilibrium equations are obtained as the Euler equations of an associated functional. We seek the minimizer of a potential energy functional of the form

$$E[\delta] = \tfrac{1}{2} \int_{\Omega} \sigma^T \varepsilon \, dx \, dy - \int_{\Omega} \delta^T \mathbf{p} \, dx \, dy - \int_{\partial\Omega_2} \delta^T \mathbf{q} \, ds, \qquad (8.3.1)$$

where $\sigma =$ stress vector

      $\varepsilon =$ strain vector

      $\delta =$ displacement vector

      $\mathbf{p} =$ vector of body forces per unit volume

      $\mathbf{q} =$ vector of applied boundary forces per unit area.

The linear elastic problem discussed in Section 8.2 is of this generic form, where $\delta = (u, v)^T$.

The finite element method replaces the integrals over Ω in (8.3.1) by a sum of integrals over the elements Ω_j. That is, the potential energy is viewed as a sum of potential energies from the individual component elements. The displacement is assumed to have unknown values only at the nodes, and within element Ω_j it is described in terms of these nodal values δ_j by means of a predetermined interpolation scheme,

$$\delta = N\delta_j. \qquad (8.3.2)$$

For the three-noded triangles considered here, δ_j is 6×1, δ is 2×1, and the 2×6 matrix N contains the appropriate interpolation functions or *shape functions*. We will return to the construction of N for a wide class of elements in the next section. It suffices here to consider the triangular element in Figure 8.3.2, with the associated shape functions, and to note that for this element type

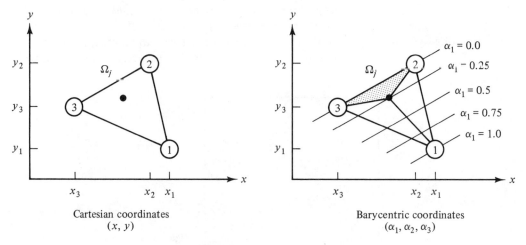

Figure 8.3.2   Constant strain triangle.

$$N = \begin{bmatrix} N_1 & 0 & N_2 & 0 & N_3 & 0 \\ 0 & N_1 & 0 & N_2 & 0 & N_3 \end{bmatrix}$$

Hence $\delta = (u, v)^T$ in (8.3.2) determines u and v as a linear polynomial over Ω_j which depends on the values of u and v, respectively, at the three nodes.

For the triangular element with straight sides the shape functions can be calculated as follows. Let

$$\Delta = \frac{1}{2} \det \begin{bmatrix} 1 & x_1 & y_1 \\ 1 & x_2 & y_2 \\ 1 & x_3 & y_3 \end{bmatrix} = \text{Area } (\Omega_j),$$

$$a_1 = x_2 y_3 - x_3 y_2, \qquad b_1 = y_2 - y_3, \qquad c_1 = x_3 - x_2.$$

Then the shape function for node 1 is

$$N_1 = \frac{a_1 + b_1 x + c_1 y}{2\Delta}$$

The other coefficients and shape functions are obtained by cyclic permutation of subscripts (1, 2, 3). The shape function N_i is the restriction of an associated global basis function of the type discussed in Section 7.6. A convenient coordinate system $(\alpha_1, \alpha_2, \alpha_3)$ for a triangular element is obtained by letting

$$\alpha_i(x, y) = \frac{a_i + b_i x + c_i y}{2\Delta}, \qquad i = 1, 2, 3.$$

This is the so-called *barycentric* (see Exercise 7.11) or *area* coordinate system, and, for example, α_1 is the ratio of the area of the shaded region in Figure 8.3.2 to the area of the triangle Ω_j itself. Also note that $\alpha_i(x_j, y_j) = \delta_{ij}$, the Kronecker delta function. Thus the basis function N_i evaluated at (x, y) is just the ith barycentric coordinate of the point (x, y).

The strains within element Ω_j can be expressed as

$$\varepsilon = B\delta_j, \qquad (8.3.3)$$

where the *strain matrix* B is composed of derivatives of the shape functions. For the two-dimensional linear elastic problem, B is the 3×6 matrix

$$B = \begin{bmatrix} B_1 & B_2 & B_3 \end{bmatrix}$$

with

$$B_i = \begin{bmatrix} \dfrac{\partial N_i}{\partial x} & 0 \\ 0 & \dfrac{\partial N_i}{\partial y} \\ \dfrac{\partial N_i}{\partial y} & \dfrac{\partial N_i}{\partial x} \end{bmatrix}, \qquad 1 \le i \le 3,$$

and $\varepsilon = (\varepsilon_x, \varepsilon_y, \gamma_{xy})^T$.

The element stresses are related to strains, for example by Hooke's law (for plane strain problems)

$$\boldsymbol{\sigma} = D\boldsymbol{\varepsilon}, \tag{8.3.4}$$

where the *elasticity matrix* D is

$$D = \frac{2G}{1 - 2v} \begin{bmatrix} 1 - v & v & 0 \\ v & (1 - v) & 0 \\ 0 & 0 & \dfrac{1 - 2v}{2} \end{bmatrix}$$

Other structural applications can be described with this same formulation and other choices for $\boldsymbol{\varepsilon}$, $\boldsymbol{\sigma}$, and D.

Making the approximations (8.3.2)–(8.3.4) in (8.3.1), we can approximate the potential energy $E[\boldsymbol{\delta}]$ by the sum of energy contributions of the individual elements, that is,

$$E[\boldsymbol{\delta}] \approx E[\mathbf{x}] \equiv \sum_j E_j[\boldsymbol{\delta}_j],$$

where

$$E_j[\boldsymbol{\delta}_j] = \tfrac{1}{2} \int_{\Omega_j} [\boldsymbol{\delta}_j]^T B^T DB[\boldsymbol{\delta}_j] \, dx \, dy$$

$$- \int_{\Omega_j} [\boldsymbol{\delta}_j]^T N^T \mathbf{p} \, dx \, dy - \int_{\partial\Omega_j \cap \partial\Omega_2} [\boldsymbol{\delta}_j]^T N'\mathbf{q} \, ds. \tag{8.3.5}$$

The vector $\mathbf{x}$ is a composite of the element vectors $\boldsymbol{\delta}_j$, and if m is the total number of nodes

$$\mathbf{x} = (u_1, v_1, \ldots, u_m, v_m)^T.$$

The function E of the $2m$ variables x_i will have a minimum value at a point $\mathbf{x}$ only if

$$\frac{\partial E}{\partial x_i} = 0, \qquad 1 \le i \le 2m,$$

which formally produces a system of $2m$ equations, the *global stiffness* system

$$K\mathbf{x} = \mathbf{F}. \tag{8.3.6}$$

As with the spring system in Section 8.1 we derive a relationship between the element displacement $\boldsymbol{\delta}_j$ and element force $\mathbf{F}_j^e$ by considering the element Ω_j in isolation. If the element is in equilibrium, we must have

$$\frac{\partial E_j}{\partial \delta_i} = 0, \qquad 1 \le i \le 3,$$

which yields

$$\int_{\Omega_j} (B^T DB)\boldsymbol{\delta}_j \, dx \, dy = \int_{\Omega_j} N^T \mathbf{p} \, dx \, dy + \int_{\partial\Omega_j \cap \partial\Omega_2} N^T \mathbf{q} \, ds.$$

We rewrite this as the *element stiffness system*

$$K_j^e \boldsymbol{\delta}_j = \mathbf{F}_j^e. \tag{8.3.7}$$

The 6×6 *element stiffness matrix* is

$$K_j^e = \int_{\Omega_j} B^T D B \, dx \, dy$$

and the 6×1 *equivalent nodal force vector* is

$$\mathbf{F}_j^e = \int_{\Omega_j} N^T \mathbf{p} \, dx \, dy + \int_{\partial\Omega_j \cap \partial\Omega_2} N^T \mathbf{q} \, ds,$$

where typically $\mathbf{p}$ and $\mathbf{q}$ are in turn approximated by linear combinations of the shape functions. Note the similarity of the relation (8.3.7) between triangular element displacements and forces, and the relation (8.1.5) between spring displacements and forces.

As in Section 8.1, we assemble the global stiffness matrix K from the element stiffness matrices K_j^e. This assembly process will be covered in more detail later, as will the solution of the global stiffness system. A key feature of the finite element method is this decomposition (both physically and mathematically) of the structure into substructures or elements upon which force–displacement relationships are derived.

8.4 ELEMENT CONSTRUCTION

There are many element types that can be used in two-dimensional analyses. In the preceding section we presented the constant strain triangle. Here we consider a family of quadrilateral elements generated by *transfinite* mappings (Gordon and Hall [1973]).

To conform to curved boundaries, elements with curved edges have been widely used for many years by finite element practitioners. The *transfinite element* is an invertible mapping $\mathbf{T}$ from a square parameter domain $S: [-1, 1] \times [-1, 1]$ onto a closed, bounded, and simply connected region Ω_j in the xy-plane, together with a transfinite or blending-function interpolant of the dependent variable u defined over Ω_j (Figure 8.4.1). The "subparametric," "superparametric," and "isoparametric"

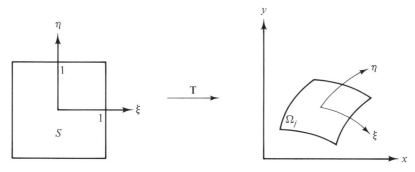

Figure 8.4.1 Domain mapping for transfinite elements.

element types discussed in Zienkiewicz [1977] and Ergatoudis, Irons, and Zienkiewicz [1968] are special cases of transfinite elements.

Let $f(\xi, \eta)$ be a scalar function of two variables $(\xi, \eta) \in S$. Then interpolants to f of the form

$$P_\xi[f](\xi, \eta) = \sum_{i=0}^{m_1} f(\xi_i, \eta)\phi_i(\xi),$$

$$P_\eta[f](\xi, \eta) = \sum_{j=0}^{m_2} f(\xi, \eta_j)\psi_j(\eta), \qquad (8.4.1)$$

where ϕ_i and ψ_j are any functions satisfying

$$\phi_i(\xi_k) = \delta_{ik} \quad \text{and} \quad \psi_j(\eta_k) = \delta_{jk} \qquad \text{(Kronecker deltas)}$$

are *transfinite* interpolants since they agree with or interpolate to f at more than a finite number of points. For example,

$$P_\xi[f](\xi, \eta) = f(\xi, \eta),$$

along the *lines* $\xi = \xi_i$, $0 \le i \le m_1$, and

$$P_\eta[f](\xi, \eta) = f(\xi, \eta),$$

along the *lines* $\eta = \eta_j$, $0 \le j \le m_2$. The functions ϕ_i and ψ_j are called *blending* functions since they blend the curves $\{(\xi_i, \eta, f(\xi_i, \eta)), 0 \le i \le m_1\}$ and $\{(\xi, \eta_j, f(\xi, \eta_j)), 0 \le j \le m_2\}$, respectively, into a surface. We note also that the operators

$$P_\xi: f \to P_\xi[f]$$

and

$$P_\eta: f \to P_\eta[f]$$

are *projectors*, that is, linear transformations such that $P_\xi^2 = P_\xi$ and $P_\eta^2 = P_\eta$ (see Exercise 7.10). These projectors can be combined algebraically to obtain two additional interpolants, the *tensor product interpolant*,

$$P_\xi P_\eta[f](\xi, \eta) = \sum_{i=0}^{m_1} \sum_{j=0}^{m_2} f(\xi_i, \eta_j)\phi_i(\xi)\psi_j(\eta), \qquad (8.4.2)$$

and the *Boolean sum interpolant*,

$$(P_\xi \oplus P_\eta)[f](\xi, \eta) = (P_\xi + P_\eta - P_\xi P_\eta)[f](\xi, \eta). \qquad (8.4.3)$$

The latter is also a transfinite interpolant since

$$(P_\xi \oplus P_\eta)[f](\xi, \eta) = f(\xi, \eta)$$

along the lines $\xi = \xi_i$, $0 \le i \le m_1$, *and* along the lines $\eta = \eta_j$, $0 \le j \le m_2$. The former, the tensor product interpolant, is *not* transfinite since it interpolates to f only at the $m_1 m_2$ points $\{(\xi_i, \eta_j): 0 \le i \le m_1, 0 \le j \le m_2\}$ (see Gordon [1971]).

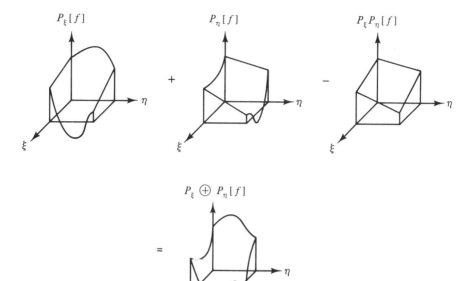

Figure 8.4.2   Boolean sum interpolant.

Figure 8.4.2 illustrates the Boolean sum interpolant, where we have chosen $m_1 = m_2 = 1$ and

$$\phi_0(\xi) = \frac{1 - \xi}{2}, \qquad \psi_0(\eta) = \frac{1 - \eta}{2},$$

$$\phi_1(\xi) = \frac{1 + \xi}{2}, \qquad \psi_1(\eta) = \frac{1 + \eta}{2}. \tag{8.4.4}$$

With these choices for the blending functions, we can construct most of the (serendipity) *isoparametric* elements by the following procedure:

Step 1. Replace the scalar function f in (8.4.3) by the vector-valued vector function

$$\mathbf{F} = \begin{bmatrix} x \\ y \\ u \end{bmatrix},$$

where

$$\begin{bmatrix} x(\xi, \eta) \\ y(\xi, \eta) \end{bmatrix}$$

is to be our mapping from S: $[-1, 1] \times [-1, 1]$ onto Ω^j and u is the dependent variable to be interpolated.

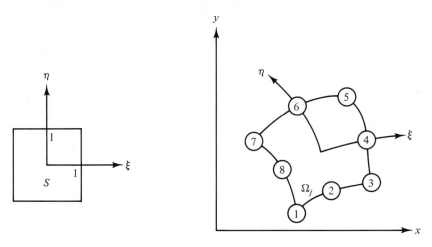

Figure 8.4.3   Eight-node isoparametric element.

Step 2. Choose the images of $\xi = \pm 1$ and $\eta = \pm 1$,

$$\begin{bmatrix} x(\pm 1, \eta) \\ y(\pm 1, \eta) \end{bmatrix} \quad \text{and} \quad \begin{bmatrix} x(\xi, \pm 1) \\ y(\xi, \pm 1) \end{bmatrix}, \quad \text{respectively,}$$

as parametric linear, quadratic, or cubic polynomials which pass through associated nodes on the boundary of Ω_j.

For example, in Figure 8.4.3 the nodes 1, 2, and 3 are connected by the parametric curve

$$\begin{bmatrix} x(\xi, -1) \\ y(\xi, -1) \end{bmatrix} = \frac{\xi(\xi - 1)}{2} \begin{bmatrix} x_1 \\ y_1 \end{bmatrix} + (\xi + 1)(1 - \xi) \begin{bmatrix} x_2 \\ y_2 \end{bmatrix} + \frac{\xi(\xi + 1)}{2} \begin{bmatrix} x_3 \\ y_3 \end{bmatrix}$$

Thus the curve through nodes 1, 2, and 3 is the image of $\eta = -1$, $-1 \leq \xi \leq 1$.

Step 3. The Boolean sum interpolant in (8.4.3) then becomes

$$\begin{aligned}
(P_\xi \oplus P_\eta)[\mathbf{F}](\xi, \eta) &= \frac{1 - \xi}{2} \begin{bmatrix} x(-1, \eta) \\ y(-1, \eta) \\ u(-1, \eta) \end{bmatrix} + \frac{1 + \xi}{2} \begin{bmatrix} x(1, \eta) \\ y(1, \eta) \\ u(1, \eta) \end{bmatrix} \\
&+ \frac{1 - \eta}{2} \begin{bmatrix} x(\xi, -1) \\ y(\xi, -1) \\ u(\xi, -1) \end{bmatrix} + \frac{1 + \eta}{2} \begin{bmatrix} x(\xi, 1) \\ y(\xi, 1) \\ u(\xi, 1) \end{bmatrix} \\
&- \frac{(1 - \eta)(1 - \xi)}{4} \begin{bmatrix} x(-1, -1) \\ y(-1, -1) \\ u(-1, -1) \end{bmatrix} - \frac{(1 - \eta)(1 + \xi)}{4} \begin{bmatrix} x(1, -1) \\ y(1, -1) \\ u(1, -1) \end{bmatrix} \\
&- \frac{(1 + \eta)(1 - \xi)}{4} \begin{bmatrix} x(-1, 1) \\ y(-1, 1) \\ u(-1, 1) \end{bmatrix} - \frac{(1 + \eta)(1 + \xi)}{4} \begin{bmatrix} x(1, 1) \\ y(1, 1) \\ u(1, 1) \end{bmatrix}.
\end{aligned} \quad (8.4.5)$$

Step 4. Expand (8.4.5) and collect terms multiplying the m^e nodal values of **F** to obtain

$$(P_\xi \oplus P_\eta)[\mathbf{F}](\xi, \eta) = \sum_{i=1}^{m^e} N_i(\xi, \eta) \begin{bmatrix} x_i \\ y_i \\ u_i \end{bmatrix}, \qquad (8.4.6)$$

where node P_i has coordinates (x_i, y_i) and $u_i = u(x_i, y_i)$. The functions $N_i(\xi, \eta)$ are *shape functions* for this element type.

The elements generated by the steps above are *isoparametric* since the *same* blending functions are used for the mapping from $S \to \Omega_j$ as are used for the dependent variable u. We could, of course, construct the domain transformation $\mathbf{T}: S \to \Omega_j$ using blending functions of degree d_1 and then use blending functions of degree d_2 to construct the interpolant to $u(\xi, \eta)$. If $d_1 < d_2$, then the resulting element is *subparametric*, and if $d_1 > d_2$, then the resulting element is *superparametric* in the terminology of Zienkiewicz [1977].

For the *bilinearly blended* functions given in (8.4.5) we generate a class of isoparametric elements illustrated in Table 8.4.1. These are so-called *serendipity* elements (Zienkiewicz [1977]).

If we choose $m_1 = m_2 = m > 1$, and choose ϕ_i (*and* ψ_i) as a polynomial of degree m that is 0 at ξ_j for j not equal to i and 1 for j equal to i, where

TABLE 8.4.1   SERENDIPITY ELEMENTS IN THE PLANE

Images of $\xi = \pm 1, \eta = \pm 1$	Nodal numbering	Shape functions
Linear	4 $\cdots$ 3 $\vdots$ $\vdots$ 1 $\cdots$ 2	$N_i = (1 \pm \xi)(1 \pm \eta)/4$
Quadratic	7 $\cdot$ 6 $\cdot$ 5 8 4 1 $\cdot$ 2 $\cdot$ 3	Corners: $\quad N_i = (1 \pm \xi)(1 \pm \eta)(\pm \xi \pm \eta - 1)/4$ Midside: $\quad N_i = (1 \pm \eta)(1 - \xi^2)/2$ $\quad N_i = (1 \pm \xi)(1 - \eta^2)/2$
Cubic	10 $\cdot$ 9 $\cdot$ 8 $\cdot$ 7 11 6 12 5 1 $\cdot$ 2 $\cdot$ 3 $\cdot$ 4	Corners: $\quad N_i = (1 \pm \xi)(1 \pm \eta)(9\xi^2 + 9\eta^2 - 10)/32$ Midside: $\quad N_i = 9(1 \pm \xi)(1 - \eta^2)(1 \pm 3\eta)/32$ $\quad N_i = 9(1 \pm \eta)(1 - \xi^2)(1 \pm 3\xi)/32$

$\xi_i \ (=\eta_i) = (-1 + 2i/m)$ for $0 \le i \le m$, then the tensor product interpolant becomes

$$P_\xi P_\eta[\mathbf{F}] = \sum_{i=0}^{m} \sum_{j=0}^{m} \left(\prod_{\substack{k=0 \\ k \ne i}}^{m} \frac{\xi - \xi_k}{\xi_i - \xi_k} \right) \left(\prod_{\substack{k=0 \\ k \ne j}}^{m} \frac{\eta - \eta_k}{\eta_i - \eta_k} \right) \begin{bmatrix} x(\xi_i, \eta_j) \\ y(\xi_i, \eta_j) \\ u(\xi_i, \eta_j) \end{bmatrix}$$

$$= \sum_{i=0}^{m} \sum_{j=0}^{m} N_i(\xi, \eta) \begin{bmatrix} x(\xi_i, \eta_j) \\ y(\xi_i, \eta_j) \\ u(\xi_i, \eta_j) \end{bmatrix} \tag{8.4.7}$$

Formula (8.4.7) generates another class of standard element types illustrated in Table 8.4.2.

TABLE 8.4.2   FULL TENSOR PRODUCT ELEMENTS

Images of $\xi = \xi_i$ and $\eta = \eta_j$	Nodal numbering	Shape functions
Linear	4 $\cdots$ 3 $\vdots$ $\vdots$ 1 $\cdots$ 2	(8.4.7) with $m = 1$ $\xi_i, \eta_j \in \{-1, 1\}$
Quadratic	7 $\cdot$ 6 $\cdot$ 5 $\cdot$ $\cdot$ $\cdot$ 8 $\cdot$ 9 $\cdot$ 4 $\cdot$ $\cdot$ $\cdot$ 1 $\cdot$ 2 $\cdot$ 3	(8.4.7) with $m = 2$ $\xi_i, \eta_j \in \{-1, 0, 1\}$
Cubic	10 $\cdot$ 9 $\cdot$ 8 $\cdot$ 7 $\cdot$ $\cdot$ $\cdot$ $\cdot$ 11 $\cdot$ 16 $\cdot$ 15 $\cdot$ 6 $\cdot$ $\cdot$ $\cdot$ $\cdot$ 12 $\cdot$ 13 $\cdot$ 14 $\cdot$ 5 $\cdot$ $\cdot$ $\cdot$ $\cdot$ 1 $\cdot$ 2 $\cdot$ 3 $\cdot$ 4	(8.4.7) with $m = 3$ $\xi_i, \eta_j \in \{-1, -\frac{1}{3}, 0, \frac{1}{3}, 1\}$

8.5 CURVED ELEMENTS AND NUMERICAL INTEGRATION

If the element Ω_j has curved edges, we assume, as in the constructions of Section 8.4, that there exists a one-to-one onto mapping $\mathbf{T}$ such that

$$\mathbf{T} \colon [-1, 1] \times [-1, 1] \to \Omega_j.$$

One should be aware that the transfinite mappings used in Section 8.4 are *not* always one-to-one (Exercise 8.6).

The shape functions constructed in Section 8.4 are functions of a local (ξ, η) coordinate system, while the integrals in Section 8.3 are with respect to the (x, y) system. Equations such as (8.4.6) and (8.4.7) provide us with the necessary change of variable formulas. For example, the chain rule of differentiation yields

$$\frac{\partial N_i}{\partial x} = \frac{\partial N_i}{\partial \xi}\frac{\partial \xi}{\partial x} + \frac{\partial N_i}{\partial \eta}\frac{\partial \eta}{\partial x}$$

and

$$\frac{\partial N_i}{\partial y} = \frac{\partial N_i}{\partial \xi}\frac{\partial \xi}{\partial y} + \frac{\partial N_i}{\partial \eta}\frac{\partial \eta}{\partial y},$$

where $\partial \xi/\partial x$, $\partial \xi/\partial y$, $\partial \eta/\partial x$, and $\partial \eta/\partial y$ are obtained from numerically inverting the Jacobian matrix

$$J = \begin{bmatrix} \dfrac{\partial x}{\partial \xi} & \dfrac{\partial x}{\partial \eta} \\ \dfrac{\partial y}{\partial \xi} & \dfrac{\partial y}{\partial \eta} \end{bmatrix}.$$

That is, at an integration point, J is calculated and inverted to determine

$$J^{-1} = \begin{bmatrix} \dfrac{\partial \xi}{\partial x} & \dfrac{\partial \xi}{\partial y} \\ \dfrac{\partial \eta}{\partial x} & \dfrac{\partial \eta}{\partial y} \end{bmatrix}.$$

The stiffness matrix in (8.3.7) can be rewritten in terms of the (ξ, η) system as

$$K_j^e = \int_{\Omega_j} B^T D B \, dx \, dy = \int_{-1}^{1}\int_{-1}^{1} C^T R^T D R C |\det J| \, d\xi \, d\eta, \qquad (8.5.1)$$

where $B = RC$, $C = [C_1 \quad C_2 \quad \cdots \quad C_{m_j}]$, m_j is the number of nodes in element Ω_j,

$$R = \begin{bmatrix} \xi_x & \eta_x & 0 & 0 \\ 0 & 0 & \xi_y & \eta_y \\ \xi_y & \eta_y & \xi_x & \eta_x \end{bmatrix}, \quad \text{and} \quad C_i = \begin{bmatrix} \dfrac{\partial N_i}{\partial \xi} & 0 \\ \dfrac{\partial N_i}{\partial \eta} & 0 \\ 0 & \dfrac{\partial N_i}{\partial \xi} \\ 0 & \dfrac{\partial N_i}{\partial \eta} \end{bmatrix}.$$

As such, the $2m_j \times 2m_j$ stiffness matrix is obtained by numerical integration over the domain $S \equiv [-1, 1] \times [-1, 1]$. Integrals such as those in (8.5.1) are iterated integrals, and hence it is sufficient to consider numerical integration for functions of one variable. For $n = 1, 2, \ldots$ consider the expression

$$I_n(f) \equiv \sum_{i=1}^{n} w_i f(a_i).$$

It is always possible to determine the integration points $\{a_i\}$ and weights $\{w_i\}$ so that

$$I_n(f) = \int_{-1}^{1} f(x)\, dx$$

if f is a polynomial whose degree does not exceed $2n - 1$. (See Exercise 8.7 for the case $n = 2$. In fact, using the theory of orthogonal polynomials, it can be shown (Isaacson and Keller [1966]) that the integration points $\{a_i\}$ are the zeros of the Legendre polynomial of degree n on the interval $[-1, 1]$.) This criterion produces the so-called Gaussian quadrature formulas, the first four of which are defined by the data in Table 8.5.1. When these formulas are used to approximate the integrals in the stiffness matrices, n is typically chosen so that the quadratures are exact if $\Omega_j \equiv S$.

TABLE 8.5.1   GAUSSIAN QUADRATURE FORMULAS

$$\int_{-1}^{1} f(x)\, dx \approx \sum_{i=1}^{n} w_i f(a_i)$$

	a_i	w_i
$n = 1$	0.00000 00000	2.00000 00000
$n = 2$	$\pm$0.57735 02692	1.00000 00000
$n = 3$	$\pm$0.77459 66692	0.55555 55556
	0.00000 00000	0.88888 88889
$n = 4$	$\pm$0.86113 63116	0.34785 48451
	$\pm$0.33998 10436	0.65214 51549

For triangular elements, the integrals involved in calculating stiffness matrices are not iterated integrals with constants as limits of integration. However, formulas have been derived in which no bias is given to any of the barycentric coordinates α_i (see Hammer, Marlowe, and Stroud [1956] and Cowper [1973]). Three such numerical integration formulas are given in Table 8.5.2. They exactly integrate polynomials of degree 1, 2, and 3, respectively.

TABLE 8.5.2 NUMERICAL INTEGRATION ON TRIANGLES

Order	Integration point location	Point	Barycentric coordinates	Weight
Linear		a	1/3, 1/3, 1/3	1
Quadratic		a	1/2, 1/2, 0	1/3
		b	0, 1/2, 1/2	1/3
		c	1/2, 0, 1/2	1/3
Cubic		a	1/3, 1/3, 1/3	$-27/48$
		b	0.6, 0.2, 0.2	25/48
		c	0.2, 0.6, 0.2	25/48
		d	0.2, 0.2, 0.6	25/48

8.6 FRONTAL METHOD

One reason for the rapid growth in the popularity of the FEM was the development of the frontal method, notably by Irons [1970], for the solution of finite element equations. The global system is in essence solved by Gaussian elimination but with two distinctive features:

1. The processes of *assembly* and *elimination* of the global system are intertwined.
2. The ordering of variables is determined by the ordering of elements.

A more straightforward approach would be to generate the entire set of equations making up the global stiffness system, ordering the unknowns so as to minimize bandwidth, and then to apply Gaussian elimination to solve the system (see Section 10.3). But the latter approach turns out to be less efficient, and may in some cases produce a wider bandwidth.

In contrast, the frontal method proceeds by forming, in turn, each element stiffness matrix K_j^e and load vector $\mathbf{F}_j^e$. As they are formed, each is assembled into the global matrix K. But after each element has been processed, a check is made to determine which, if any, rows and columns have been completely assembled.

Column i is said to be complete once all elements containing the node associated with column i have been processed.

Completed columns are eliminated; more elements are processed; more complete columns eliminated; and so on.

The frontal method is very effective when core storage is limited. An array, called the *active matrix*, is set up in core into which the entries of the element stiffness matrices are assembled. At each stage of elimination, the pivot row is written onto peripheral storage such as disks, and its space in the active matrix can then be reused for assembly of more element stiffness matrices. The order in which elements are processed determines the order in which unknowns are encountered and also when a column is complete.

Example 8.6.1

Consider the problem of determining the maximum stress in a square plate $[-6, 6] \times [-6, 6]$ containing a circular cutout (Figure 8.6.1). By symmetry, only half the plate $\Omega = [-6, 6] \times [-6, 0]$ is modeled and eight-node isoparametric elements are used as

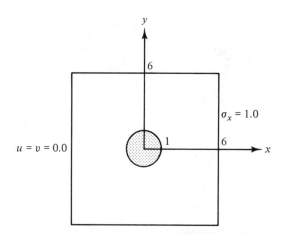

Figure 8.6.1 Plate with a circular hole.

illustrated in Figure 8.6.2. The left boundary is held fixed, the top and bottom are free, and a unit force is applied along the right boundary. The variational formulation is: Find $\delta^* = (u^*, v^*)$ such that

$$F[\delta^*] = \min_{\delta \in S_0} F[\delta],$$

where

$$F[\delta] = \frac{G}{1 - 2v} \int_\Omega \left[(1 - v)u_x^2 + 2vu_x v_y + (1 - v)v_y^2 + \frac{1 - 2v}{2}(u_y + v_x)^2 \right] dx\, dy$$

$$- \int_{y=-6}^{y=0} u(6, y)\, dy,$$

and where $S_0 = \{\delta = (u, v) \mid \delta \in V_2(H^1(\Omega)),$ and $u = v = 0$ along $x = -6\}$. Poisson's ratio is $v = 0.3$ and the shear modulus is $G = 1000$. The maximum stress is known to be 3.0

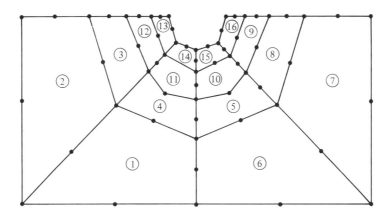

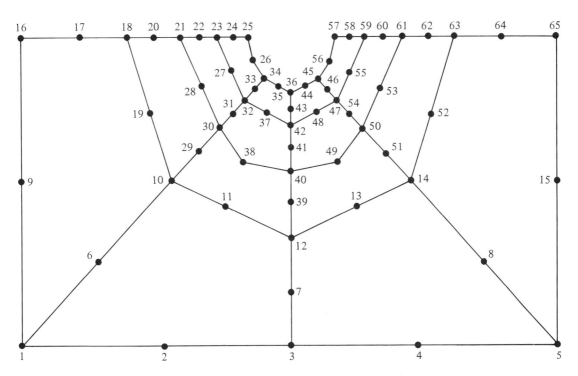

Figure 8.6.2   Finite element idealization of plate with circular cutout.

at $(0, -1)$ and is the maximum value of $\sigma_x(0, y)$, where (see Timoshenko and Goodier [1970, p. 92])

$$\sigma_x(0, y) = \frac{1}{2}\left(2 + \frac{1}{y^2} + \frac{3}{y^4}\right). \tag{8.6.1}$$

The circled numbers in Figure 8.6.2 present an order that allows for the elimination of columns associated with node I after element J has been processed as indicated in Table 8.6.1.

TABLE 8.6.1   FRONTAL ELIMINATION

Element J processed	Nodes I complete columns	Global system size if no variables eliminated	Active matrix size after variables eliminated
1	2	16×16	14×14
2	1, 6, 9	26×26	18×18
3	19	36×36	26×26
4	10, 29, 11	42×42	26×26
5	12, 39, 13	52×52	30×30
6	3, 7, 4	58×58	30×30
7	5, 8, 15	68×68	34×34
8	14, 51, 52	74×74	34×34
9	53	84×84	42×42
10	49, 50, 54	90×90	42×42
11	38, 40, 41	96×96	42×42
12	28, 30, 31	102×102	42×42
13	27	112×112	50×50
14	32, 33, 37	118×118	50×50
15	42, 43, 48	124×124	50×50
16	46, 47, 55	130×130	50×50

Hence, if no elimination were done during assembly of the element stiffness matrices, the global system would be 130×130. In contrast, alternating assembly and elimination produces an active matrix that is no larger than 50×50. The difference would be more dramatic for much finer meshes where the sparsity of the global matrix is much greater.

In Figure 8.6.3 the stress σ_x along the line segment $x = 0$, $-6 \le y \le -1$ calculated by the finite element method is compared to the true solution (8.6.1). The maximum calculated stress is 2.736, and the exact value is 3.0. A refined mesh would give better agreement. Figure 8.6.3 contains a contour plot of the stress σ_x.

In the frontal method, if the stiffness matrix is symmetric, one need only generate and assemble the entries above the diagonal. During the elimination stage of the frontal method, the pivot rows are stored on peripheral storage such as disks for retrieval during the back-substitution phase of Gaussian elimination. For large matrices, this requires one disk write during elimination and one disk read during the back substitution. In contrast, banded algorithms would require many more reads

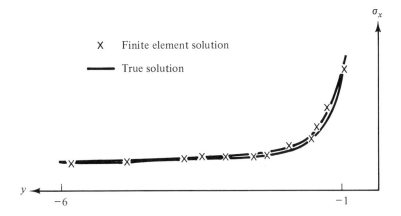

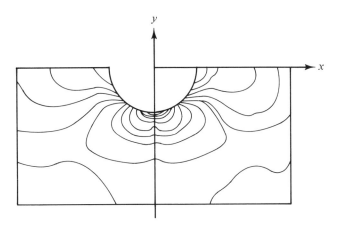

Figure 8.6.3   Stress component σ_x.

and writes to disk during elimination for matrices that were so large as to prohibit the storage of many rows in core. Therein lies one of the big advantages of the frontal method when working on computers with limited core storage.

The frontal method, as illustrated above, is also the basis for a technique called *substructuring*. For example, the union of the 16 elements in Figure 8.6.2 can be viewed as one super element with 130 degrees of freedom and 65 nodes. After elimination of the interior nodes, this substructure or super element has 50 degrees of freedom and 25 nodes, and these are the nodes that are to be shared with other elements in the idealization. Substructuring is a convenient and efficient technique for organizing the assemblage and elimination when an analyst wishes to rerun a problem with only minor changes to the mesh or boundary conditions in a predetermined subregion.

NOTES AND REMARKS

8.1 This development using a system of springs follows Davies [1980]. Similar motivational material for the assembly of elemental *stiffness matrices* has been given in terms of electrical networks (see Zienkiewicz [1977]).

In 1678, Robert Hooke first published his now famous law relating stress and strain as the anagram: CEIIINOSSSTTUV (*UT TENSIO SIC VIS*). This roughly translates into "as the tension goes, thus goes the action." It has been said that this is one of the earliest examples of a scientist *sitting on his data!*

8.2 Theorem 8.2.3 is a very general result concerning operators (not necessarily differential operators) on Hilbert spaces (see Mikhlin [1965]). As proven in Chapter 7, the variational formulation is also equivalent to a weak or Galerkin formulation for many problems. The latter, however, is applicable to a much wider class of boundary value problems than the former. In Chapter 9 we apply Galerkin's method to a parabolic initial–boundary value problem.

8.3 The triangular element in Figure 8.3.2 is called the *constant strain triangle* since the vector ε in (8.3.3) is independent of x and y.

Other structural applications of the finite element method follow the outline given here by changing the definitions of ε, σ, and D. For example, plate bending has the associated vectors and matrix

$$\varepsilon = \begin{bmatrix} -w_{xx} \\ -w_{yy} \\ 2w_{xy} \end{bmatrix}, \qquad \sigma = \begin{bmatrix} M_x \\ M_y \\ M_{xy} \end{bmatrix},$$

and

$$D = \frac{Et^3}{12(1-v^2)} \begin{bmatrix} 1 & v & 0 \\ v & 1 & 0 \\ 0 & 0 & \frac{1-v}{2} \end{bmatrix},$$

where w is the normal deflection of the plate; M_x, M_y, and M_{xy} are bending and twisting moments; E is Young's modulus; t is the thickness of the plate; and v is Poisson's ratio. In this case the integrand of the potential energy involves second-order derivatives, and the shape functions must have continuous gradients between elements. The functional representing potential energy now involves second-ordered derivatives and the solution is sought in subspaces of $H^2(\Omega)$.

For the steady-state heat flow problem (see Section 2.3), the element stiffness system is the same as (8.3.7). If Ω_j has m_j nodes, then

$$K_j^e = \int_{\Omega_j} kB^T B \, dx \, dy$$

and

$$B = \begin{bmatrix} B_1 & B_2 & \cdots & B_{m_j} \end{bmatrix}$$

with

$$B_i = \begin{bmatrix} \dfrac{\partial N_i}{\partial x} \\ \dfrac{\partial N_i}{\partial y} \end{bmatrix}, \qquad 1 \le i \le m_j.$$

Furthermore,

$$\mathbf{F}_j^e = \int_{\Omega_j} N^T f \, dx \, dy$$

with $N^T = [N_1, \ldots, N_{m_j}]$ and

$$\delta_j = [u_1, \ldots, u_{m_j}],$$

where u_i represents the finite element approximation to the temperature at node i of element Ω_j.

For thermal loads the thermal strain vector is

$$\varepsilon^0 = (\alpha T, \alpha T, 0)^T,$$

where α is the *coefficient of thermal expansion* and T is the specified temperature. The associated stresses are

$$\sigma = D(\varepsilon + \varepsilon^0).$$

Equation (8.3.7) then is

$$K_j^e \delta_j = \mathbf{g}_j^e,$$

where

$$\mathbf{g}_j^e = \mathbf{f}_j^e - \int_{\Omega_j} B^T D \varepsilon^0 \, dx \, dy.$$

(see Hinton and Owen [1977] or Zienkiewicz [1977]).

8.4 The method given in Gordon and Hall [1973], and reproduced here, provides an orderly construction of families of *isoparametric elements*. This was not the case when such elements were first introduced in the mid-1960s. The shape functions for such elements were derived by trial and error and often there was an element (no pun intended) of chance as to whether the construction of higher-order elements could be completed. Thus it occurred to Ergatoudis, Irons, and Zienkiewicz [1968] to name the family *serendipity* "after the famous princes of Serendip noted for their chance discoveries (Horace Walpole, 1754)." See Gordon and Hall [1973] or Ciarlet and Raviart [1972] for a general convergence analysis for these element types.

8.5 As noted in the main body of the text, Gaussian quadrature with n sample points integrates exactly polynomials of degree $2n - 1$ or less. Hence *if* Ω_j is a rectangle, and if the degree of N_i is m, then Gaussian quadrature with $n \ge ((m - 1)^2 + 1)/2$ yields "exact" entries for the element stiffness matrix. But *if* Ω_j has curved sides, then in general J^{-1} and hence the integrand in (8.5.1) is a rational function of ξ and η. As such, the entries of K_j^e cannot be integrated exactly by a standard quadrature formula.

8.6 As the elements are processed in the frontal method, a *front* develops in the finite element mesh behind which are elements already processed. Columns associated with nodes that are behind (and not on) the front are complete and hence eliminated. The discovery that such a front develops prompted the name *frontal method*.

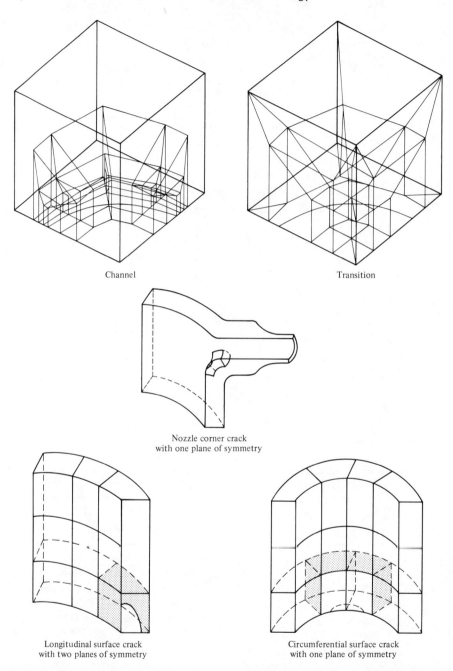

Channel

Transition

Nozzle corner crack
with one plane of symmetry

Longitudinal surface crack
with two planes of symmetry

Circumferential surface crack
with one plane of symmetry

Figure 8.N.1 Macro element.

An example of substructuring is given in Hall, Raymund, and Palusamy [1979]. Reactor components are modeled as a catenation of isoparametric elements so as to isolate a crack region as a macro or super element. Successive computer runs analyzing crack growth involved changes only within this super element and the rest of the reactor component was assembled and internal nodes eliminated once and for all. This macro element was compatible with a 20-node isoparametric element on three faces and thus could easily be configured in a finite element idealization of 20-node elements. It consisted of a channel subregion of 28 elements with variable node density on each edge, surrounded by a transition subregion of 14 elements. Figure 8.N.1 illustrates the undeformed macro element and its placement in a thick-walled structure.

EXERCISES

8.1. Show that the operator $L = -\nabla^2$ is self-adjoint and uniformly positive definite on the space

$$M \equiv \{u \mid u \in C^2(\bar{\Omega}), \quad u(x, y) = 0 \text{ for } (x, y) \in \partial\Omega\}.$$

[It is known that M is dense in $L_2(\Omega)$.]

8.2. Prove that the solution to

$$-\nabla^2 u = f, \qquad (x, y) \in \Omega$$

$$u = 0, \qquad (x, y) \in \partial\Omega$$

also satisfies

$$F[u] = \min_{v \in H_0^1(\Omega)} F[v],$$

where $F[v] \equiv \frac{1}{2} \int_\Omega \{|\nabla v|^2 - 2fv\} \, dx \, dy$. [*Hint:* Use Exercise 8.1 and Theorem 8.2.3.]

8.3. Let the domain Ω be contained in a square K of side length a. Prove that if $u \in C_0^2(\Omega)$ and $u \equiv 0$ on $K - \Omega$, then

$$\|u\|_0^2 \le a^2 \int_\Omega (u_{x_i})^2 \, dx \, dy, \qquad i = 1, 2.$$

8.4. Consider a bar element Ω_j of cross-sectional area A and length L (Figure 8.E.1). Assume that the displacements u_1 and u_2 in the x_1 and x_2 directions, respectively, are approximated by

$$u_1 = \frac{L - x}{L} \delta_1 + \frac{x}{L} \delta_3,$$

$$u_2 = \frac{L - x}{L} \delta_2 + \frac{x}{L} \delta_4, \qquad 0 \le x \le L$$

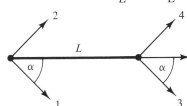

Figure 8.E.1   Bar element.

where the δ_i are components of displacement as indicated. Find the axial strain $\varepsilon_x = du/dx$, where u is the displacement in the x-direction. Assume that the stress $\sigma_x = E\varepsilon_x$ and show that the element stiffness system is

$$K_j^e \delta_j = \mathbf{f}_j^e,$$

where $[\mathbf{f}_j^e]_i$ is the component of the force in the direction corresponding to δ_i and

$$K_j^e = \frac{AE}{L} \begin{bmatrix} \cos^2 \alpha & \sin \alpha \cos \alpha & -\cos^2 \alpha & -\sin \alpha \cos \alpha \\ \sin \alpha \cos \alpha & \sin^2 \alpha & -\sin \alpha \cos \alpha & -\sin^2 \alpha \\ -\cos^2 \alpha & -\sin \alpha \cos \alpha & \cos^2 \alpha & \sin \alpha \cos \alpha \\ -\sin \alpha \cos \alpha & -\sin^2 \alpha & \sin \alpha \cos \alpha & \sin^2 \alpha \end{bmatrix}.$$

8.5. Consider the eight points P_i: (x_i, y_i).

i	x_i	y_i
1	0.0	0.0
2	1.0	1.0
3	2.0	2.0
4	1.0	1.5
5	0.0	1.0
6	−1.0	1.5
7	−2.0	2.0
8	−1.0	1.0

Show that the transfinite mapping associated with the eight-node serendipity element having these nodes is not invertible.

8.6. Prove that the bilinear transfinite map (8.4.5) from $S \to \Omega_j$ is one-to-one and onto if and only if Ω_j is a straight-sided convex quadrilateral.

8.7. Consider the quadrature formula

$$I_2(f) = w_1 f(a_1) + w_2 f(a_2).$$

Show that if $w_1 = w_2 = 1.0$, $a_1 = -\sqrt{3}/3$, and $a_2 = \sqrt{3}/3$, then $I_2(f) = \int_{-1}^{1} f(x)\,dx$ whenever f is a polynomial of degree ≤ 3.

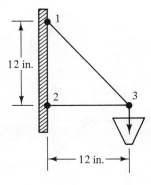

12 in.

12 in.

Figure 8.E.2   Flowerpot hanger of cross section $A = 0.05$ in.

8.8. Suppose that a flowerpot weighing 5 pounds is suspended from a steel hanger ($E = 29 \times 10^6$ psi) as indicated in Figure 8.E.2. Use Exercise 8.4 to determine the forces exerted on the wall at points 1 and 2. What is the deflection at node 3?

Computer Exercises

8.9. Solve the problem in Example 8.6.1 by using linear (constant strain) triangles and taking advantage of the two-fold symmetry. Compare your results to those given in the text for the eight-node element idealization. Refine your mesh in the vicinity of the point $(0, -1)$. Does this improve your approximation to the maximum stress?

8.10. Use the finite element method to solve the following problem (see Figure 8.E.3). Find the temperature T such that

$$\nabla \cdot k \, \nabla T = 0, \qquad \mathbf{x} \in \Omega,$$

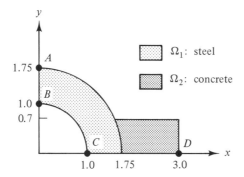

Figure 8.E.3   Problem geometry.

where $k = 30.62$ in Ω_1, $k = 0.79$ in Ω_2,

$$\nabla T \cdot \mathbf{n} = 0 \quad \text{along } \overline{AB} \text{ and } \overline{CD},$$

$$T = 450 \quad \text{along } \overline{BC},$$

and

$$-k \, \nabla T \cdot \mathbf{n} = 0.7(T - 80) \quad \text{along } AD,$$

where $\mathbf{n}$ is the exterior unit normal to $\partial\Omega$. Plot the isotherms.

8.11. In a certain park there is an island in a lake that is accessible only by boat. To enlarge the area available to picnickers, it would be desirable to provide permanent access to the island. One option is to build a pedestrian bridge at the narrowest point between the

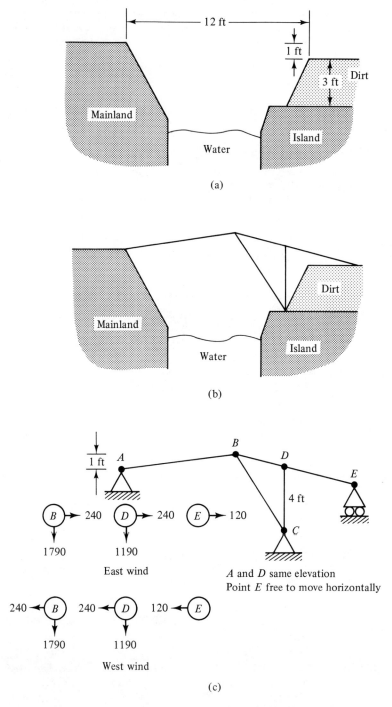

Figure 8.E.4   (a) Island and mainland; (b) Bridge; (c) Truss.

island and the mainland. This site is shown in Figure 8.E.4a, which reveals that the rock required for a solid base for the bridge is at a different elevation on each side of the waterway. To solve this problem, a bridge design is suggested which includes a support on the rockbed on each side of the water and a small extension on the right side to the ground level. The bridge is shown in Figure 8.E.4b. It is to be made of wooden members (Young's modulus: 1.1×10^6 psi) constructed into trusses spaced 4 ft apart (we only consider one of these trusses). Panels 4 ft wide will span the gap between the trusses and will be mounted on the joints of the truss. Specify the size of each member of the trusses.

Loadings on the bridge are due to pedestrians, snow, and wind. The first two are gravity loads and act downward, the last one is a horizontal load and may occur in either direction, east or west. A schematic drawing of the truss is shown in Figure 8.E.4c along with the total loads (in pounds force) at joints B, D, and E. Solve for the stresses on each member for both an east and west wind. Taking the worst case for each member, find the cross-sectional area required for each member, if they are to be made of wood having a strength of 415 psi. (Note that you want the stress in each member to be less than 415 psi.) Assume that members AB, BD, and DE are of one cross-sectional area, that BC is another cross-sectional area, and that DC is a third type. [*Hint:* Use the stiffness matrix in Exercise 8.4 for each member. Guess a cross-sectional area of 1.0 ft^2, solve for the stresses, and then either increase or decrease the area according to how the stresses compare to the strength of the material.]

8.12. A contractor wishes to plant a tree in a planting box that is located close to an underground steamline. She has asked you to advise her on the advantages of lining one side and the bottom of the planting box with an insulation material. She asks you to find the thermal flux across the sides designated AB and BC in Figure 8.E.5a with and without the insulation in place. As additional information, she would like to see a plot of the isotherms in both cases. The physical parameters needed are given in Table 8.E.1.

Assume that the temperature of the steam on the inner surface of the pipe is 400°F, and that the pipe has an inner diameter of 10 in. and an outer diameter of 11.5 in. The insulation around the pipe is 2 in. thick and is assumed to be in place for both calculations. Use a Neumann (symmetry) condition for the soil at a distance far from the pipe and box. The temperature of the air is 90°F and the coefficient of thermal convection into the air is 0.88 Btu/hr-ft^2-°F.

There is a concrete walk over the area which is 4 in. thick; the concrete box is 5 in. thick and 40 in. on a side (outside dimension). The center of the pipe is 36 in. from the outer edge of the side of the box and 36 in. from the surface of the concrete walk. The insulation used as a lining of the one side and bottom of the box is 6 in. thick.

TABLE 8.E.1 MATERIAL PARAMETERS

Material	Density (lbm/ft^3)	Specific heat (Btu/lbm-°F)	Thermal conductivity (Btu/hr-ft-°F)
Steel	489.01	0.11	30.62
Concrete	150.00	0.25	0.79
Insulation	8.5	0.18	0.03
Soil	85.0	0.21	0.90

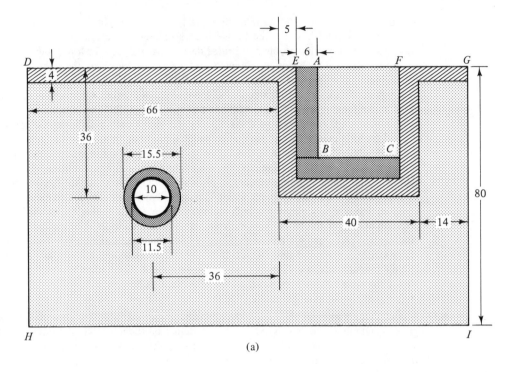

(a)

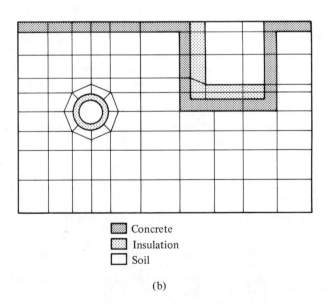

Concrete
Insulation
Soil

(b)

Figure 8.E.5   (a) Planting box geometry; (b) Finite element idealization; (c) Isotherms without insulation; (d) Isotherms with insulation.

Maximum temperature = 400
Minimum temperature = 90.7
Flux = 23.4 Btu/hr

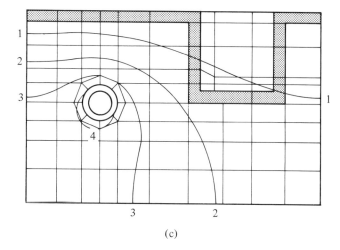

1	110.0
2	129.3
3	148.7
4	168.0

(c)

Maximum temperature = 400
Minimum temperature = 89.9
Flux = 4.7 Btu/hr

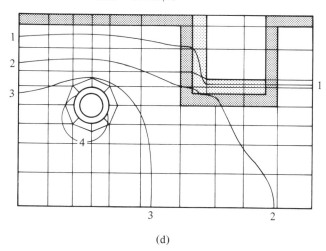

1	109.3
2	128.7
3	148.0
4	167.4

(d)

Figure 8.E.5   (continued)

This is a steady-state heat conduction problem (cf. Chapter 2). The temperature $T(x, y)$ satisfies

$$\mathbf{V} \cdot k\, \mathbf{V}T = 0 \tag{1}$$

in the problem domain Ω, where the conductivity k varies from material to material. The boundary conditions are

$$0.79 \frac{\partial T}{\partial y} = 0.88(T - 90) \quad \text{on } \overline{DE} \text{ and } \overline{FG}$$

$$0.03 \frac{\partial T}{\partial y} = 0.88(T - 90) \quad \text{on } \overline{EA}$$

$$0.90 \frac{\partial T}{\partial y} = 0.88(T - 90) \quad \text{on } \overline{AF}$$

$$T = 400 \quad \text{on the inner surface of the pipe}$$

$$\frac{\partial T}{\partial x} = 0 \quad \text{on } \overline{DH} \text{ and } \overline{GI}$$

$$\frac{\partial T}{\partial y} = 0 \quad \text{on } \overline{HI}.$$

The problem has the following *weak formulation*: Find $T \in H_1(\Omega)$ such that $T = 400$ on the inner surface of the pipe and such that

$$\int_\Omega (k\, \mathbf{V}T \cdot \mathbf{V}v)\, dx\, dy + \int_{\overline{DG}} h(T - 90)v\, dx = 0$$

for all $v \in H_1(\Omega)$ such that $v = 0$ on the inner surface of the pipe. The conductivities k for the various materials are given in Table 8.E.1 and the coefficient of thermal convection h is given as 0.88 Btu/hr-ft^2-$^\circ$F.

This problem was solved using a finite element program and the eight-node isoparametric element. The finite element mesh is illustrated in Figure 8.E.5b and contains 115 elements and 393 nodes. Figure 8.E.5c illustrates the isotherms without the insulation, and Figure 8.E.5d illustrates the isotherms with the insulation in place.

The flux across the segments $\overline{AB}$ and $\overline{BC}$ without the insulation is calculated to be 23.4 Btu/hr, while with the insulation the flux drops to 4.7 Btu/hr. However, the maximum temperature in the planting box only drops from 115°F to 104°F when the insulation is installed.

Use a finite difference or finite element program to reproduce the results given above. Would lining the side $\overline{CF}$ with insulation or increasing the thickness of the insulation around the pipe reduce significantly the temperature and/or flux of heat entering the planting box? What is the time-dependent behavior of the temperature? Why is it impossible for the temperature within the box to fall below 90°F? Make the boundary conditions on the surface time dependent so as to be more realistic.

9

Parabolic Equations: The Finite Element Approach

9.1 SEMIDISCRETE GALERKIN APPROXIMATION

In Chapter 2 we presented the following representative parabolic equation, which describes, for example, the time-dependent flow of heat in an isotropic solid:

$$\rho c u_t - \nabla \cdot k \nabla u = f, \qquad \mathbf{x} \in \Omega, \quad 0 < t \le T < \infty, \tag{9.1.1}$$

where u is the temperature, ρ the density, c the specific heat, k the thermal conductivity, and f a heat source. Here, as in Chapter 2, we assume that Ω is a bounded region (i.e., a connected open set) in R^p (specifically $p = 2$, although most of what follows is true for $p \ge 1$) and that ρ, c, and k are positive functions in Ω that are independent of t.

In addition to (9.1.1), the temperature $u(\mathbf{x}, t)$ is required to satisfy an *initial condition*

$$u(\mathbf{x}, 0) = u_0(\mathbf{x}), \qquad \mathbf{x} \in \Omega, \tag{9.1.2}$$

and *boundary conditions*

$$u(\mathbf{x}, t) = b(\mathbf{x}), \qquad \mathbf{x} \in \partial\Omega_1, \quad 0 < t \le T, \tag{9.1.3}$$

$$-\nabla u \cdot \mathbf{n} = 0, \qquad \mathbf{x} \in \partial\Omega_2, \quad 0 < t \le T, \tag{9.1.4}$$

$$-k \nabla u \cdot \mathbf{n} = h_0(u - u_s), \qquad \mathbf{x} \in \partial\Omega_3, \quad 0 < t \le T, \tag{9.1.5}$$

where the boundary of Ω, $\partial\Omega = \partial\Omega_1 \cup \partial\Omega_2 \cup \partial\Omega_3$, $\mathbf{n}$ is the unit outward normal to $\partial\Omega$, h_0 is the coefficient of heat transfer ($h_0 > 0$), and u_s is the specified temperature of the surrounding medium.

In this chapter we study the finite element solution of such time-dependent parabolic problems. For this purpose, we will freely employ the notation and results of Chapter 6. Henceforth, we also assume that $\partial\Omega$ is piecewise smooth in the sense of Section 6.3.

The initial–boundary value problem (9.1.1)–(9.1.5) is replaced by the following equivalent *Galerkin problem*. Find a function $u(\mathbf{x}, t)$, continuously differentiable with respect to t, such that $u \in S$ and for all $v \in S_0$

$$\int_\Omega \rho c u_t v \, dx + \int_\Omega (k\, \nabla u \cdot \nabla v - fv)\, dx + \int_{\partial\Omega_3} h_0(u - u_s)v \, ds = 0, \qquad (9.1.6)$$

where S is the set[1] of functions

$$S = \{v \mid \text{for each } 0 < t \leq T,\ v(\cdot, t) \text{ and } v_t(\cdot, t) \in H^1(\Omega);\ \text{and } v(\mathbf{x}, t) = b(\mathbf{x}) \text{ on } \partial\Omega_1\}$$

and

$$S_0 = \{v \in H^1(\Omega) \mid v(\mathbf{x}) = 0 \text{ on } \partial\Omega_1\}.$$

The procedure for proving that the solution to the Galerkin problem is also a solution of the initial–boundary value problem (9.1.1)–(9.1.5) is similar to that used in Chapter 7 to prove Theorem 7.1.3. As in Chapter 7, the converse requires a solution to the Galerkin problem to have additional smoothness. For existence and uniqueness results concerning the Galerkin problem, see Browder [1964], Lions [1961], and Ladyzhenskaya [1985].

To simplify the exposition, we assume that $b(\mathbf{x}) \equiv 0$. For each $0 < t \leq T$, we choose a finite-dimensional subspace $S^h \subset S_0$ spanned by $\{\phi_i \colon 1 \leq i \leq N\}$. Here as in Chapter 7, the exponent h is typically a mesh gauge that approaches 0 as $N \to \infty$. Then the *semidiscrete Galerkin approximation* $U(\mathbf{x}, t)$ to $u(\mathbf{x}, t)$ is a one-parameter family of elements in S^h of the form

$$U(\mathbf{x}, t) = \sum_{j=1}^{N} c_j(t)\phi_j(\mathbf{x}), \qquad (9.1.7)$$

where the coefficients $c_j(t)$ are continuously differentiable functions of t on $[0, T]$. These coefficients are determined by the system of equations

$$\int_\Omega \rho c U_t \phi_i \, dx + \int_\Omega (k\, \nabla U \cdot \nabla \phi_i - f\phi_i)\, dx + \int_{\partial\Omega_3} h_0(U - u_s)\phi_i \, ds = 0, \qquad 1 \leq i \leq N.$$

$$(9.1.8)$$

Substituting (9.1.7) into (9.1.8) gives a system of ordinary differential equations:

$$M \frac{d\mathbf{C}}{dt} = -K\mathbf{C} + \mathbf{S}, \qquad (9.1.9)$$

---

[1] The notation $v(\cdot, t) = b$ on $\partial\Omega$ for a function $v \in H^1(\Omega)$ means that $\tilde{\gamma}v = b$, where $\tilde{\gamma}$ is the trace operator of Section 6.3.

where the $N \times N$ *global mass matrix*

$$M \equiv \left[\int_\Omega \rho c \phi_i(\mathbf{x}) \phi_j(\mathbf{x}) \, d\mathbf{x} \right],$$ (9.1.10)

the $N \times N$ *global stiffness matrix*

$$K \equiv \left[\int_\Omega k \, \nabla \phi_j \cdot \nabla \phi_i \, d\mathbf{x} + \int_{\partial\Omega_3} h_0 \phi_j(\mathbf{x}) \phi_i(\mathbf{x}) \, ds \right],$$ (9.1.11)

the $N \times 1$ *source vector*

$$\mathbf{S} \equiv \left[\int_\Omega f(\mathbf{x}) \phi_i(\mathbf{x}) \, d\mathbf{x} + \int_{\partial\Omega_3} h_0 u_s \phi_i(\mathbf{x}) \, ds \right],$$ (9.1.12)

and the $N \times 1$ vector of unknowns

$$\mathbf{C}(t) \equiv [c_i(t)]^T.$$ (9.1.13)

In addition, the initial condition (9.1.2) requires that

$$\mathbf{C}(0) = \mathbf{C}_0 = [c_i^0]^T,$$ (9.1.14)

where

$$U(\mathbf{x}, 0) = \sum_{j=1}^N c_j^0 \phi_j(\mathbf{x}) \approx u_0(\mathbf{x}).$$ (9.1.15)

Usually, $U(\mathbf{x}, 0)$ is an interpolant of $u_0(\mathbf{x})$, or a least squares approximation of $u_0(\mathbf{x})$.

Assuming that the $\{\phi_i\}$ are linearly independent, it can be shown that the matrix M is nonsingular. In fact, if $\mathbf{Z} \in R^N$, $\mathbf{Z} \neq 0$, and $w(\mathbf{x}) = \sum_{i=1}^N z_i \phi_i(\mathbf{x})$, then

$$\mathbf{Z}^T M \mathbf{Z} = \int_\Omega \rho c w^2(\mathbf{x}) \, d\mathbf{x} > 0.$$

Hence M is not only nonsingular, but positive definite. This gives us the next theorem, whose proof is left to the reader.

Theorem 9.1.1.   *For the semidiscrete approximation (9.1.7) to the initial–boundary value problem (9.1.1)–(9.1.5), the coefficient vector (9.1.13) is given by*

$$\mathbf{C}(t) = \exp(-M^{-1}Kt)\,\mathbf{C}_0 + \int_0^t \exp[-M^{-1}K(t-s)]\,M^{-1}\mathbf{S}\,ds.$$ (9.1.16)

Furthermore, if K is nonsingular, then (9.1.16) reduces to

$$\mathbf{C}(t) = \exp(-M^{-1}Kt)(\mathbf{C}_0 - K^{-1}\mathbf{S}) + K^{-1}\mathbf{S}.$$ (9.1.17)

9.2 COMPLETE DISCRETIZATION

In the preceding section, the time-dependent parabolic problem was discretized in space using the Galerkin method. The result was a system of ordinary differential equations (9.1.9) in which time t was still a continuous independent variable. There is an extensive literature concerning the numerical solution of such systems of ODEs and there are standard software packages available for their solution. In this chapter we consider three standard approaches to discretization in time. It follows from (9.1.17) that when K is nonsingular, the solution of the matrix differential equation (9.1.9) subject to (9.1.14) can be discretized in time by using Padé rational approximations of the matrix exponential. Three such approximations are:

1. *Forward approximation:*

$$\exp(-M^{-1}Kt) \approx (I - M^{-1}Kt), \qquad (9.2.1)$$

2. *Backward approximation:*

$$\exp(-M^{-1}Kt) \approx (I + M^{-1}Kt)^{-1}, \qquad (9.2.2)$$

3. *Crank–Nicolson approximation:*

$$\exp(-M^{-1}Kt) \approx \left(I + M^{-1}K\frac{t}{2}\right)^{-1}\left(I - M^{-1}K\frac{t}{2}\right). \qquad (9.2.3)$$

These approximations are accurate only for small t. (Indeed, the last two approximations may not exist unless t is sufficiently small.) However, we can apply them repeatedly using, for example, a uniform partition of $[0, T]$. Thus, let $\Delta t = T/M_0$ where M_0 is some positive integer, and set $t_m \equiv m\,\Delta t$, $m = 0, 1, \ldots, M_0$. Since

$$\exp(-M^{-1}Kt_m) = \exp(-M^{-1}K\,\Delta t)\exp(-M^{-1}K(t_m - \Delta t)),$$

it follows from (9.1.17) that

$$\mathbf{C}(t_m) = \exp(-M^{-1}K\,\Delta t)(\mathbf{C}(t_{m-1}) - K^{-1}\mathbf{S}) + K^{-1}\mathbf{S}. \qquad (9.2.4)$$

Equation (9.2.4) suggests defining $\mathbf{C}^m$, an approximation to $\mathbf{C}(t_m)$, by requiring that

$$\mathbf{C}^m = T(\Delta t)(\mathbf{C}^{m-1} - K^{-1}\mathbf{S}) + K^{-1}\mathbf{S}. \qquad (9.2.5)$$

where $T(\Delta t)$ is an approximation of $\exp(-M^{-1}K\,\Delta t)$. Note that when $T(\Delta t)$ is chosen as

$$T(\Delta t) = I - \Delta t(M + \theta\,\Delta t\,K)^{-1}K, \qquad (9.2.6)$$

we obtain the forward difference, Crank–Nicolson, and backward difference approximations for $\theta = 0, \frac{1}{2}$, and 1, respectively. Formula (9.2.5) is valid only if K^{-1} exists. However, in this case (9.2.5) and (9.2.6) imply that

$$\mathbf{C}^m = T(\Delta t)\mathbf{C}^{m-1} + [I - T(\Delta t)]K^{-1}\mathbf{S}$$
$$= T(\Delta t)\mathbf{C}^{m-1} + \Delta t(M + \theta\,\Delta t\,K)^{-1}\mathbf{S}.$$

Thus, if $T(\Delta t)$ is given by (9.2.6), the approximation

$$\mathbf{C}^m = T(\Delta t)\mathbf{C}^{m-1} + \Delta t(M + \theta\,\Delta t\,K)^{-1}\mathbf{S} \qquad (9.2.7)$$

is equivalent to (9.2.5) for nonsingular K, but it can also be used when K is singular.

Example 9.2.1

Consider the axisymmetric cylindrical steel shell illustrated in Figure 9.2.1. The inner surface is held at a constant temperature of 150°F, and at the outer surface there is a radiative condition of the type (9.1.5) with $u_s = 50$°F. The coefficient of heat transfer on the surface is taken to be 70.40 Btu/hr-ft²-°F. The other properties of steel are given in Table 2.3.1. Initially (at $t = 0$), the cylinder is at a temperature of 50°F, and we seek the temperature response at the midplane $r = 7.5$ due to the sudden change in the inner surface temperature from 50°F to 150°F.

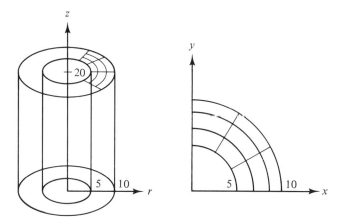

Figure 9.2.1 Cylindrical shell geometry.

Using the fact that the temperature u is independent of z, the parabolic initial–boundary value problem in (x, y) coordinates is[2]
Find $u(x, y, t)$ such that with $r = \sqrt{x^2 + y^2}$ and $\Theta = \sin^{-1}(y/r)$

$$\rho c u_t = \nabla \cdot k \nabla u \quad \text{in } \Omega \equiv \{(x, y) \mid 5 < r < 10\} \qquad (9.2.8)$$

subject to boundary conditions

$$u(x, y, t) = 150 \quad \text{on } \partial\Omega_1 = \{(x, y) \mid r = 5\}, \qquad 0 < t \le 1400, \qquad (9.2.9)$$

$$-k(u_x \cos \Theta + u_y \sin \Theta) = 70.4(u - 50), \quad r = 10, \quad 0 \le \Theta \le \pi/2, \quad 0 < t \le 1400, \quad (9.2.10)$$

$$
\begin{aligned}
u_x(0, y, t) = 0, &\quad 5 \le y \le 10, \quad 0 < t \le 1400, \\
u_y(x, 0, t) = 0, &\quad 5 \le x \le 10, \quad 0 < t \le 1400,
\end{aligned}
\qquad (9.2.11)
$$

and initial condition

$$u(x, y, 0) = 50 \quad \text{in } \Omega. \qquad (9.2.12)$$

The weak formulation is: *Find $u \in S$ such that for all $w \in S_0$,*

$$\int_\Omega \left[\rho c u_t w + k \nabla u \cdot \nabla w \right] dx + \int_0^{\pi/2} 70.4(u - 50) \Big|_{r=10} d\Theta = 0. \qquad (9.2.13)$$

---

[2] In fact, the symmetries of this example imply that the temperature depends only on the radial distance r, so that u satisfies the *one-dimensional* heat equation, $\rho c u_t = (1/r)(kru_r)_r$, subject to the boundary conditions $u(5, t) = 150$, $-ku_r(10, t) = 70.4(u - 50)$.

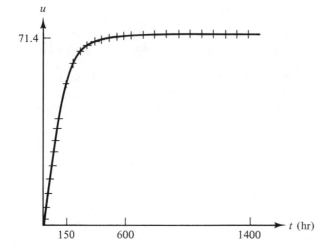

Figure 9.2.2 Temperature response at the midplane of cylinder.

This problem was solved using a Galerkin approximation of the form (9.1.7) on a mesh of nine eight-node isoparametric elements (see Figure 9.2.1). Formula (9.2.7) with $\theta = 1$ was used to advance the solution in time. The results are plotted in Figure 9.2.2.

9.3 CONVERGENCE OF THE SEMIDISCRETE SOLUTION

In this section we establish convergence of the semidiscrete Galerkin approximation $U(\mathbf{x}, t)$ in (9.1.7) to the true solution $u(\mathbf{x}, t)$ for appropriate sequences of finite-dimensional subspaces S^h. To this end, for *fixed t*, let $\tilde{U}(\cdot, t) \in S^h$ be an approximation to $u(\cdot, t)$. For example, if $S^h \subset S_0$ is a space of continuous, piecewise linear functions, then $\tilde{U}(\mathbf{x}, t)$ could be chosen as the piecewise linear interpolant of Theorem 7.6.4. Assume that

$$\tilde{U}(\mathbf{x}, t) \equiv \sum_{j=1}^{N} \tilde{c}_j(t)\phi_j(\mathbf{x}). \tag{9.3.1}$$

Further, assume that the initial condition $u_0(\mathbf{x})$ is such that $\tilde{U}(\mathbf{x}, 0) = U(\mathbf{x}, 0) = u_0(\mathbf{x})$. (This assumption can be relaxed.)

Define, for $1 \leq i \leq N$,

$$k_i(t) \equiv \int_\Omega \rho c \tilde{U}_t \phi_i \, d\mathbf{x} + \int_\Omega (k \, \nabla \tilde{U} \cdot \nabla \phi_i - f\phi_i) \, d\mathbf{x} + \int_{\partial\Omega_3} h_0(\tilde{U} - u_s)\phi_i \, ds. \tag{9.3.2}$$

Let $v = \phi_i$ in (9.1.6). Subtracting (9.1.6) from (9.3.2), we have

$$k_i(t) = \int_\Omega \rho c(\tilde{U} - u)_t \phi_i \, d\mathbf{x} + \int_\Omega k \, \nabla(\tilde{U} - u) \cdot \nabla \phi_i \, d\mathbf{x} + \int_{\partial\Omega_3} h_0(\tilde{U} - u)\phi_i \, ds, \tag{9.3.3}$$

and subtracting (9.1.8) from (9.3.2), we obtain

$$k_i(t) = \int_\Omega \rho c(\tilde{U} - U)_t \phi_i \, d\mathbf{x} + \int_\Omega k \, \nabla(\tilde{U} - U) \cdot \nabla \phi_i \, d\mathbf{x} + \int_{\partial\Omega_3} h_0(\tilde{U} - U)\phi_i \, ds. \tag{9.3.4}$$

Now let $V_1 \equiv \tilde{U} - u$ and $V_2 \equiv \tilde{U} - U = \sum_{i=1}^{N} \varepsilon_i(t)\phi_i(x)$, where $\varepsilon_i = \tilde{c}_i - c_i$. Multiply (9.3.3) and (9.3.4) by $\varepsilon_i(t)$ and sum on i to obtain

$$\sum_{i=1}^{N} \varepsilon_i(t)k_{it}(t) = \int_\Omega \rho c V_{1t}V_2 \, d\mathbf{x} + \int_\Omega k \, \nabla V_1 \cdot \nabla V_2 \, d\mathbf{x} + \int_{\partial\Omega_3} h_0 V_1 V_2 \, ds \quad (9.3.5)$$

and

$$\sum_{i=1}^{N} \varepsilon_i(t)k_{it}(t) = \int_\Omega \rho c V_{2t}V_2 \, d\mathbf{x} + \int_\Omega k \, \nabla V_2 \cdot \nabla V_2 \, d\mathbf{x} + \int_{\partial\Omega_3} h_0 V_2^2 \, ds. \quad (9.3.6)$$

Equating (9.3.5) and (9.3.6), we have

$$\int_\Omega \rho c V_{2t}V_2 \, d\mathbf{x} + \int_\Omega k \, \nabla V_2 \cdot \nabla V_2 \, d\mathbf{x} + \int_{\partial\Omega_3} h_0 V_2^2 \, ds$$

$$= \int_\Omega \rho c V_{1t}V_2 \, d\mathbf{x} + \int_\Omega k \, \nabla V_1 \cdot \nabla V_2 \, d\mathbf{x} + \int_{\partial\Omega_3} h_0 V_1 V_2 \, ds$$

$$\leq \frac{K_1}{2} \|V_{1t}\|_0^2 + \frac{1}{2}\|V_2\|_0^2 + \frac{1}{2}\|k^{1/2}\, \nabla V_1\|_0^2 + \frac{1}{2}\|k^{1/2}\, \nabla V_2\|_0^2$$

$$+ \frac{1}{2}\int_{\partial\Omega_3} (h_0^{1/2} V_1)^2 \, ds + \frac{1}{2}\int_{\partial\Omega_3} (h_0^{1/2} V_2)^2 \, ds, \quad (9.3.7)$$

where $K_1 \equiv \max_\Omega (\rho c)^2$, and we have used the inequality $ab \leq \frac{1}{2}a^2 + \frac{1}{2}b^2$ to obtain the last inequality. Furthermore, using the equalities

$$\int_\Omega V_{2t}V_2 \, d\mathbf{x} = \frac{1}{2}\frac{d}{dt}\int_\Omega V_2^2 \, d\mathbf{x} = \frac{1}{2}\frac{d}{dt}\|V_2\|_0^2,$$

we can rewrite (9.3.7) as

$$\frac{d}{dt}\|V_2\|_0^2 \leq K_2^{-1}\|V_2\|_0^2 + K_1 K_2^{-1}\|V_{1t}\|_0^2 + K_3\|\nabla V_1\|_0^2 + K_4 \int_{\partial\Omega_3} V_1^2 \, ds, \quad (9.3.8)$$

where $K_2 \equiv \min_\Omega (\rho c)$, $K_3 \equiv K_2^{-1} \max_\Omega k$, and $K_4 \equiv K_2^{-1} \max_{\partial\Omega_3} h_0$.

Inequality (9.3.8) can be rearranged as

$$\frac{d}{dt}\|V_2\|_0^2 - K_2^{-1}\|V_2\|_0^2 \leq \xi(t), \quad (9.3.9)$$

where

$$\xi(t) = K_1 K_2^{-1}\|V_{1t}\|_0^2 + K_3\|\nabla V_1\|_0^2 + K_4 \int_{\partial\Omega_3} V_1^2 \, ds.$$

Multiplying (9.3.9) by $e^{-K_2^{-1}t}$, we see that

$$\frac{d}{dt}(e^{-K_2^{-1}t}\|V_2\|_0^2) \leq e^{-K_2^{-1}t}\xi(t).$$

Integrating this inequality from 0 to t, and noting that $V_2|_{t=0} = 0$, we obtain

$$\|V_2\|_0^2 \le \int_0^t e^{K_2^{-1}(t-t')} \xi(t')\,dt'.$$

Therefore,

$$\|\tilde{U} - U\|_0^2 \equiv \|V_2\|_0^2 \le \int_0^t e^{K_2^{-1}(t-t')}\left[K_1 K_2^{-1}\|V_{1t}\|_0^2 + K_3\|\nabla V_1\|_0^2 + K_4\int_{\partial\Omega_3} V_1^2\,ds\right]dt'. \tag{9.3.10}$$

This inequality provides us with the means to prove the following theorem.

Theorem 9.3.1. *Let $u(\mathbf{x}, t)$ be the solution to the parabolic initial–boundary value problem (9.1.1)–(9.1.5) and for each t let $U(\cdot, t)$ be its semidiscrete Galerkin approximation (9.1.7) in S^h. Assume that for each t, $u(\cdot, t)$ and $u_t(\cdot, t)$ belong to $H^{2n}(\Omega)$, and that S^h is a finite-dimensional subspace of S_0 containing an element $\tilde{U}(\cdot, t)$, an interpolant of u of the form (9.3.1), such that*

$$\|u - \tilde{U}\|_m = O(h^{2n-m}), \qquad m = 0, 1,$$

and $\tag{9.3.11}$

$$\int_{\partial\Omega_3} (u - \tilde{U})^2\,ds = O(h^{4n})$$

as the mesh gauge $h \to 0$. Then for $0 \le t \le T$,

$$\|u - U\|_0 \le Kh^{2n-1}, \tag{9.3.12}$$

where K depends on T and u.

Proof. From the triangle inequality,

$$\|u - U\|_0 \le \|u - \tilde{U}\|_0 + \|\tilde{U} - U\|_0.$$

The first term on the right is $O(h^{2n})$, by hypothesis. As for the second, it is bounded by the square root of the right side of (9.3.10). We next note that also by hypothesis,

$$\int_{\partial\Omega_3} V_1^2\,ds = O(h^{4n}) \quad\text{and}\quad \|\nabla V_1\|_0^2 = O(h^{4n-2}).$$

Furthermore,

$$\|V_{1t}\|_0^2 = O(h^{4n}).$$

This last result follows since $\tilde{U}_t$ is an interpolant of u_t and (9.3.11) holds also for $\|u_t - \tilde{U}_t\|_m$. Hence, substituting into (9.3.10), we have that for fixed t,

$$\|\tilde{U} - U\|_0 \equiv \|V_2\|_0 = O(h^{2n-1}).$$

Q.E.D.

As was demonstrated in Chapter 7, the two finite element spaces of *linear isoparametric triangles* and *bilinear isoparametric quadrilaterals* satisfy (9.3.11) for $n = 1$.

9.4 ONE-DIMENSIONAL APPROXIMATION

The convergence results of the preceding section require the construction of a function $\tilde{U}$ that is *close to* u in the sense of (9.3.11). In this section we discuss this construction for the special case when the spatial domain is the finite open interval (a, b). Consider the Galerkin method applied to the simple one-dimensional heat flow problem:

$$u_t = u_{xx}, \qquad a < x < b, \quad 0 < t \leq T, \tag{9.4.1}$$

$$u(a, t) = u(b, t) = 0, \qquad 0 \leq t \leq T, \tag{9.4.2}$$

$$u(x, 0) = u_0(x), \qquad a < x < b. \tag{9.4.3}$$

If $S^h = \text{span}\,(\phi_1, \ldots, \phi_N)$ is a finite-dimensional subspace of $H_0^1((a, b))$ from which we seek an approximation to u, then, as outlined in Section 9.1, the semi-discrete Galerkin approximation

$$U(x, t) = \sum_{i=1}^{N} c_i(t)\phi_i(x) \tag{9.4.4}$$

is determined by a matrix differential equation

$$M\frac{d\mathbf{C}}{dt} = -K\mathbf{C}, \tag{9.4.5}$$

where

$$\mathbf{C} = (c_1, \ldots, c_N)^T, \tag{9.4.6}$$

$$M_{ij} = \int_a^b \phi_i(x)\phi_j(x)\,dx, \qquad 1 \leq i, j \leq N, \tag{9.4.7}$$

and

$$K_{ij} = \int_a^b \phi_i'(x)\phi_j'(x)\,dx, \qquad 1 \leq i, j \leq N. \tag{9.4.8}$$

The rate of convergence of $U(x, t)$ to $u(x, t)$, as the dimension of the subspace S^h increases, is dependent upon the particular sequence of spaces chosen. We now consider a class of piecewise polynomial spaces which have been used extensively to generate semidiscrete Galerkin approximations.

Let the interval $\bar{I} \equiv [a, b]$ be partitioned by

$$\Pi: a = x_0 < x_1 \cdots < x_{m+1} = b,$$

and let

$$h_j \equiv x_j - x_{j-1}, \qquad j = 1, \ldots, m + 1, \qquad h \equiv \max_j h_j.$$

Further, let $P^n(\bar{I}, \Pi)$ be the space of functions that reduce to polynomials of degree $(2n - 1)$ on each interval (x_j, x_{j+1}). The *smooth Hermite space of order* n is, by definition,

$$H^n(\bar{I}, \Pi) \equiv P^n(\bar{I}, \Pi) \cap C^{n-1}(\bar{I}). \tag{9.4.9}$$

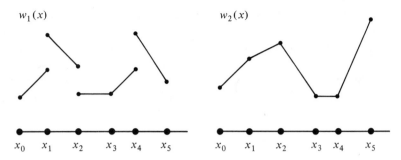

Figure 9.4.1   Piecewise linear polynomials.

Thus $w \in H^n(\overline{I}, \Pi)$ implies that

1. $w(x) = \sum\limits_{i=0}^{2n-1} a_{ij}x^i, \quad x \in (x_j, x_{j+1}), \, 0 \le j \le m,$

2. w and its first $n - 1$ derivatives are continuous on $\overline{I}$.

For example, Figure 9.4.1 shows $w_1(x)$ and $w_2(x)$, both of which are elements of $P^1(\overline{I}, \Pi)$. However, w_2 belongs to $H^1(\overline{I}, \Pi)$ but w_1 does not.

To treat the homogeneous boundary conditions (9.4.2), we define the subspace

$$H_0^n(\overline{I}, \Pi) \equiv \{v \in H^n(\overline{I}, \Pi) \mid v(a) = v(b) = 0\}.$$

Theorem 9.4.1.   *There exists a unique function $\tilde{f} \in H^n(\overline{I}, \Pi)$ satisfying*

$$\tilde{f}^{(k)}(x_j) = f_j^{(k)}, \qquad 0 \le k \le n - 1, \quad 0 \le j \le m + 1$$

where the $f_j^{(k)}$ are given quantities. Hence

$$\dim H^n(\overline{I}, \Pi) = n(m + 2)$$

and

$$\dim H_0^n(\overline{I}, \Pi) = n(m + 2) - 2.$$

For a proof, see Birkhoff, Schultz, and Varga [1968]. The element $\tilde{f}$ is called the *smooth Hermite interpolant* of f if the given set is in fact the values of a function f and its derivatives at the respective points.

For the space $H^1(\overline{I}, \Pi)$, Theorem 9.4.1 implies that choosing the function values at the $m + 2$ mesh points uniquely determines a piecewise linear function that interpolates to those values.

The error in approximating a function f by its smooth Hermite interpolant has been studied, for example, by Birkhoff, Schultz, and Varga [1968] and Swartz and Varga [1972]. These studies utilize Sobolev norms and L_∞ norms. The latter are defined on $C^j(\overline{\Omega})$ as $\|u\|_{j,\infty} \equiv \max\limits_{0 \le |\alpha| \le j} \sup\limits_{\mathbf{x} \in \overline{\Omega}} |D^\alpha u(\mathbf{x})|$ and $\|u\|_\infty \equiv \|u\|_{0,\infty}$.

Theorem 9.4.2.   *If $f \in H^{2n}(I)$ and $\tilde{f} \in H^n(\bar{I}, \Pi)$ is the smooth Hermite interpolant of f, then there is a constant K such that*

$$\|(f - \tilde{f})^{(r)}\|_0 \le K\|f^{(2n)}\|_0 \, h^{2n-r}, \qquad 0 \le r \le n-1. \tag{9.4.10}$$

If $f \in C^{2n}(\bar{I})$, then there are constants M_{nr} such that

$$\|(f - \tilde{f})^{(r)}\|_\infty \le M_{nr}\|f^{(2n)}\|_\infty \, h^{2n-r}, \qquad 0 \le r \le n-1, \tag{9.4.11}$$

where $M_{nr} = 1/[4^{n-r} r!(2n-2r)!]$.

From Theorem 9.4.1 we conclude that there is a unique function ϕ_{jk} such that $\phi_{jk}^{(r)}(x_s) = \delta_{rk}\delta_{js}$ (recall that δ_{rs} is the Kronecker delta function: $\delta_{rs} = 1$, if $r = s$; and $\delta_{rs} = 0$, otherwise), where $0 \le j, s < m+1$, and $0 \le k, r \le n-1$, for each fixed choice of j and k. This in turn gives us the following theorem.

Theorem 9.4.3.   *The vector space $H^n(\bar{I}, \Pi)$ is spanned by*

$$\{\phi_{jk}(x) \,|\, 0 \le j \le m+1, 0 \le k \le n-1\},$$

where $\phi_{jk}(x)$ is the unique element in $H^n(\bar{I}, \Pi)$ characterized by

$$\phi_{jk}^{(r)}(x_s) = \delta_{rk}\delta_{js}.$$

Since these functions are linearly independent they form a basis for $H^n(\bar{I}, \Pi)$. Similarly,

$$\{\phi_{jk}(x) \,|\, 1 \le j \le m, 0 \le k \le n-1\}$$

form a basis for $H_0^n(\bar{I}, \Pi)$.

Basis functions such as those given in Figure 9.4.2 are termed *cardinal* basis functions by some authors and *fundamental* basis functions by others since the coordinates of the smooth Hermite interpolant of f relative to this basis are the Hermite interpolatory data of function values and derivative values at the mesh points. We have, for example,

$$w \in H^1(\bar{I}, \Pi) \quad \text{implies that} \quad w(x) = \sum_{j=0}^{m+1} w(x_j)\phi_{j0}(x)$$

and $\tag{9.4.12}$

$$w \in H^2(\bar{I}, \Pi) \quad \text{implies that} \quad w(x) = \sum_{j=0}^{m+1} \{w(x_j)\phi_{j0}(x) + w'(x_j)\phi_{j1}(x)\}.$$

If it is desirable that the approximation to a function f possess more smoothness than C^{n-1} for $n > 1$, then $\tilde{f}$ can be chosen from the *spline subspace* $S^n(\bar{I}, \Pi)$ of the smooth Hermite space defined by

$$S^n(\bar{I}, \Pi) \equiv H^n(\bar{I}, \Pi) \cap C^{2n-2}(\bar{I}). \tag{9.4.13}$$

$(n = 1)$

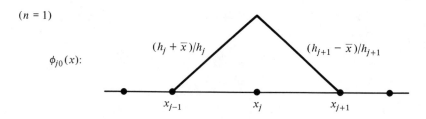

$\phi_{j0}(x)$:

$(h_j + \bar{x})/h_j$ $(h_{j+1} - \bar{x})/h_{j+1}$

x_{j-1} x_j x_{j+1}

$(n = 2)$

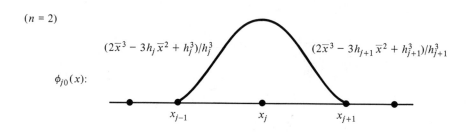

$(2\bar{x}^3 - 3h_j\bar{x}^2 + h_j^3)/h_j^3$ $(2\bar{x}^3 - 3h_{j+1}\bar{x}^2 + h_{j+1}^3)/h_{j+1}^3$

$\phi_{j0}(x)$:

x_{j-1} x_j x_{j+1}

$\phi_{j1}(x)$:

$(\bar{x}^3 - 2h_{j+1}\bar{x}^2 + h_{j+1}\bar{x})/h_{j+1}^2$

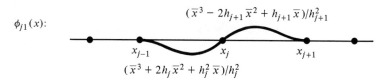

x_{j-1} x_j x_{j+1}

$(\bar{x}^3 + 2h_j\bar{x}^2 + h_j^2\bar{x})/h_j^2$

Figure 9.4.2   Basis functions for $H^1(\bar{I}, \Pi)$ and $H^2(\bar{I}, \Pi)$ where $\bar{x} \equiv x - x_j$.

Thus $w \in S^n(\bar{I}, \Pi)$ implies that

1. $w(x) = \displaystyle\sum_{i=0}^{2n-1} a_i^j x^i, \; x \in (x_j, x_{j+1}), \qquad 0 \le j \le m$

2. w and its first $(2n - 2)$ derivatives are continuous on $\bar{I}$.

As in the case of the Hermite spaces, the boundary conditions (9.4.2) are accommodated by restricting elements of $S^n(\bar{I}, \Pi)$ to the subpace

$$S_0^n(\bar{I}, \Pi) = \{v \in S^n(\bar{I}, \Pi) \mid v(a) = v(b) = 0\}.$$

The following result can be found, for example, in Schoenberg [1946].

Theorem 9.4.4.   *For a given set of values $\{f_i^{(k)}\}$, there exists a unique spline* $\tilde{f} \in S^n(\bar{I}, \Pi)$ *satisfying*

$$\tilde{f}(x_i) = f_i, \qquad 0 \le i \le m + 1,$$

$$\tilde{f}^{(k)}(x_j) = f_j^{(k)}, \qquad j = 0, m + 1, \; 1 \le k \le n - 1.$$

Hence

$$\dim S^n(\bar{I}, \Pi) = m + 2n$$

and

$$\dim S^n_0(\bar{I}, \Pi) = m + 2n - 2.$$

The element $\tilde{f}$ is called the *type 1 spline interpolant* of f if the given set does in fact consist of the values of the function f and its derivatives at the prescribed points. Interpolation in the spline subspace provides approximations with the same order of accuracy as those in the smooth Hermite space, as is seen by the following theorem from Swartz [1968] and Swartz and Varga [1972].

Theorem 9.4.5.   *Let $f \in H^{2n}(I)$ and let $\tilde{f} \in S^n(\bar{I}, \Pi)$ interpolate f in the sense of Theorem 9.4.4, where Π is a uniform partition. Then there exists a constant K such that*

$$\|(f - \tilde{f})^{(r)}\|_0 \le K \|f^{(2n)}\|_0 h^{2n-r}, \qquad 0 \le r \le 2n - 1. \tag{9.4.14}$$

If $f \in C^{2n}(\bar{I})$, then there is a constant K such that

$$\|(f - \tilde{f})^{(r)}\|_\infty \le K \|f^{(2n)}\|_\infty h^{2n-r}, \qquad 0 \le r \le 2n - 1. \tag{9.4.15}$$

Error bounds of the type (9.4.15) that are valid for all types of partitions Π were derived in Hall [1968] for the special case, m = 2, of cubic splines.

There are many bases that one might consider for the space $S^n(\bar{I}, \Pi)$; however, *B-splines* are the most stable from a computational standpoint and also lead to matrices M and K, in Galerkin's method, which have the least number of nonzero elements. The *i*th *B-spline of degree* $2n - 1$ (or *order* $2n$) is defined by

$$B_i(x) = (z_{i+2n} - z_i)[z_i, \ldots, z_{i+2n}](z - x)_+^{2n-1}, \tag{9.4.16}$$

where $\Pi: z_0 < z_1 < \cdots < z_{N+1}$ is a partition of $[a, b]$, $[z_i, \ldots, z_{i+2n}]g(z)$ is the 2*n*th divided difference of g, and the truncated power function

$$x_+ = \begin{cases} 0, & x \le 0, \\ x, & x > 0. \end{cases}$$

We have the following result.

Theorem 9.4.6.   *The ith B-spline satisfies $B_i = 0$ if $x \notin [z_i, z_{i+2n}]$.*

Proof. If $x \notin [z_i, z_{i+2n}]$, then $(z - x)_+^{2n-1}$ is either 0 (if $x \ge z_{i+2n}$), or a polynomial of degree $2n - 1$ (if $x < z_i$). In either case, the 2*n*th divided difference is zero.

Q.E.D.

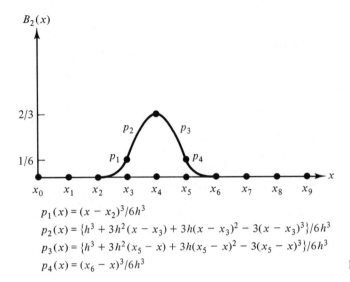

$$p_1(x) = (x - x_2)^3/6h^3$$
$$p_2(x) = \{h^3 + 3h^2(x - x_3) + 3h(x - x_3)^2 - 3(x - x_3)^3\}/6h^3$$
$$p_3(x) = \{h^3 + 3h^2(x_5 - x) + 3h(x_5 - x)^2 - 3(x_5 - x)^3\}/6h^3$$
$$p_4(x) = (x_6 - x)^3/6h^3$$

Figure 9.4.3 *B-spline of degree 3.*

For the case $n = 2$, the cubic polynomials in each of the four subintervals are given in Figure 9.4.3. If we define six mesh points outside the interval $[a, b]$ such that $z_{-3} \le z_{-2} \le z_{-1} \le z_0$ and $z_{m+1} \le z_{m+2} \le z_{m+3} \le z_{m+4}$, then (9.4.16) defines B_i for $-3 \le i \le m$ such that each B_i is nonzero in $[a, b]$. Further, this set of $(m + 4)$ B-splines forms a basis for $S^2(\bar{I}, \Pi)$. In deBoor [1978], identities are given that allow for efficient evaluation of splines expressed in terms of the B-spline basis.

We next give some tables of integrals that are needed to construct the matrices M and K in (9.4.5) for the spaces $H_0^1(\bar{I}, \Pi)$, $H_0^2(\bar{I}, \Pi)$, and $S_0^2(\bar{I}, \Pi)$.

Let $\{\phi_{j0}(x)\}$ be the basis for $H_0^1(\bar{I}, \Pi)$ given in Theorem 9.4.3. Then for the *smooth Hermite space of order* 1:

$$\int_a^b \{\phi_{i0}'(x)\, \phi_{j0}'(x)\}\, dx = \begin{cases} \dfrac{1}{h_{j+1}} + \dfrac{1}{h_j} & i = j, \\[2mm] -\dfrac{1}{h_k}, & |i - j| = 1, \quad k = \max(i, j), \\[2mm] 0, & |i - j| \ge 2, \end{cases}$$

and   (9.4.17)

$$\int_a^b \{\phi_{i0}(x)\, \phi_{j0}(x)\}\, dx = \begin{cases} \dfrac{h_{j+1} + h_j}{3}, & i = j, \\[2mm] \dfrac{h_k}{6}, & |i - j| = 1, \quad k = \max(i, j), \\[2mm] 0, & |i - j| \ge 2. \end{cases}$$

Note that the values of the integrals are independent of the length of interval $[a, b]$.

Let $\{\phi_{j0}(x), \phi_{j1}(x)\}$ be the basis for $H_0^2(\bar{I}, \Pi)$ given in Theorem 9.4.3. Then for the *smooth Hermite space of order* 2:

$$\int_a^b \{\phi_{i0}'(x)\,\phi_{j0}'(x)\}\,dx = \begin{cases} \dfrac{6(1/h_j + 1/h_{j+1})}{5}, & i = j, \\[2mm] -\dfrac{6}{5h_k}, & |i-j| = 1,\ k = \max(i,j), \\[2mm] 0, & |i-j| \geq 2, \end{cases}$$

(9.4.18)

$$\int_a^b \{\phi_{i0}(x)\,\phi_{j0}(x)\}\,dx = \begin{cases} \dfrac{13(h_j + h_{j+1})}{35}, & i = j, \\[2mm] \dfrac{9h_k}{70}, & |i-j| = 1,\ k = \max(i,j), \\[2mm] 0, & |i-j| \geq 2, \end{cases}$$

$$\int_a^b \{\phi_{i1}'(x)\,\phi_{j1}'(x)\}\,dx = \begin{cases} \dfrac{2(h_j + h_{j+1})}{15}, & i = j, \\[2mm] -\dfrac{h_k}{30}, & |i-j| = 1,\ k = \max(i,j), \\[2mm] 0, & |i-k| \geq 2, \end{cases}$$

(9.4.19)

$$\int_a^b \{\phi_{i1}(x)\,\phi_{j1}(x)\}\,dx = \begin{cases} \dfrac{h_j^3 + h_{j+1}^3}{105}, & i = j, \\[2mm] -\dfrac{h_k^3}{140}, & |i-j| = 1,\ k = \max(i,j), \\[2mm] 0, & |i-j| \geq 2, \end{cases}$$

$$\int_a^b \{\phi_{i0}'(x)\,\phi_{j1}'(x)\}\,dx = \begin{cases} 0, & i = j, \\[2mm] \dfrac{1}{10}, & i = j - 1, \\[2mm] -\dfrac{1}{10}, & i = j + 1, \\[2mm] 0, & |i-j| \geq 2, \end{cases}$$

(9.4.20)

and

$$\int_a^b \{\phi_{i0}(x)\,\phi_{j1}(x)\}\,dx = \begin{cases} \dfrac{11(h_{j+1}^2 - h_j^2)}{210}, & i = j, \\[2mm] -\dfrac{13h_{i+1}^2}{420}, & i = j - 1, \\[2mm] \dfrac{13h_i^2}{420}, & i = j + 1, \\[2mm] 0, & |i-j| \geq 2. \end{cases}$$

Let $\{B_i(x)\}_{i=-3}^m$ be the B-spline basis for $S_0^2(\bar{I}, \Pi)$ (uniform mesh). Then for the *cubic spline space* (*uniform mesh*):

$$\int_a^b \{B_i'(x)\, B_j'(x)\}\, dx = \begin{cases} \dfrac{3}{2h}, & i = j, \\[2mm] -\dfrac{9}{32h}, & |i - j| = 1, \\[2mm] -\dfrac{9}{20h}, & |i - j| = 2, \\[2mm] -\dfrac{1}{160h}, & |i - j| = 3, \\[2mm] 0, & |i - j| > 3, \end{cases}$$

and   (9.4.21)

$$\int_a^b \{B_i(x)\, B_j(x)\}\, dx = \begin{cases} \dfrac{151h}{140}, & i = j, \\[2mm] \dfrac{1191h}{2240}, & |i - j| = 1, \\[2mm] \dfrac{3h}{56}, & |i - j| = 2, \\[2mm] \dfrac{h}{2240}, & |i - j| = 3, \\[2mm] 0, & |i - j| > 3. \end{cases}$$

Returning to the Galerkin model (9.4.5), we see that if the mesh Π is uniform and $S^h \equiv H_0^1(\bar{I}, \Pi)$, then the $N \times N$ matrices M and K are

$$M = h \text{ Tridiag } \{\tfrac{1}{6}, \tfrac{2}{3}, \tfrac{1}{6}\}$$

and   (9.4.22)

$$K = \frac{1}{h} \text{ Tridiag } \{-1, 2, -1\},$$

where $h = 1/(N + 1)$. Note that if $Q = \text{Tridiag } \{1, 0, 1\}$, then $K = (2/h)I - (1/h)Q$ and $M = (2h/3)I + (h/6)Q$. Hence $MK = KM$, that is, M and K *commute*, a fact which we utilize later.

If $S^h = H_0^2(\bar{I}, \Pi)$, then for a uniform mesh,

$$M = \text{Block-Tridiag } \left\{ \begin{bmatrix} \dfrac{9h}{70} & \dfrac{13h^2}{420} \\[3mm] -\dfrac{13h^2}{420} & -\dfrac{h^3}{140} \end{bmatrix}, \begin{bmatrix} \dfrac{26h}{35} & 0 \\[3mm] 0 & \dfrac{2h^3}{105} \end{bmatrix}, \begin{bmatrix} \dfrac{9h}{70} & -\dfrac{13h^2}{420} \\[3mm] \dfrac{13h^2}{420} & -\dfrac{h^3}{140} \end{bmatrix} \right\},$$

(9.4.23)

and

$$K = \text{Block-Tridiag} \left\{ \begin{bmatrix} -\dfrac{6}{5h} & \dfrac{1}{10} \\[2mm] -\dfrac{1}{10} & -\dfrac{h}{30} \end{bmatrix}, \begin{bmatrix} \dfrac{12}{5h} & 0 \\[2mm] 0 & \dfrac{4h}{15} \end{bmatrix}, \begin{bmatrix} -\dfrac{6}{5h} & -\dfrac{1}{10} \\[2mm] \dfrac{1}{10} & -\dfrac{h}{30} \end{bmatrix} \right\}.$$

Basis functions can be normalized to guarantee that the entries in (9.4.23) are of the same order of magnitude (see, e.g., Schultz [1973, p. 72]). Also, $MK \neq KM$ by direct calculation.

Finally, if $S^h = S_0^2(\bar{I}, \Pi)$, then

$$M = \frac{h}{2240} \text{ Seven-diag } \{1, 120, 1191, 2416, 1191, 120, 1\}$$

and

$$K = \frac{1}{160h} \text{ Seven-diag } \{-1, -72, -45, 240, -45, -72, -1\}.$$

From Theorems 9.3.1, 9.4.2, and 9.4.5 we deduce the following theorem.

Theorem 9.4.7.   *Let $u(x, t)$ be the solution to the parabolic initial value problem* (9.4.1)–(9.4.3). *Assume that $u(\cdot, t)$ and $u_t(\cdot, t)$ belong to $H^{2n}(I)$, $I = (a, b)$, and that $U(x, t)$ is the semidiscrete Galerkin approximation corresponding to S^h. If $S^h = H_0^n(\bar{I}, \Pi)$ or $S^h = S_0^n(\bar{I}, \Pi)$, then for $0 \leq t \leq T$,*

$$\|u - U\|_0 = O(h^{2n-1}),$$

as $h \to 0$.

For the special choice of $S^h = H_0^1(\bar{I}, \Pi)$ we can establish the L_∞ convergence of the discretization error. We first prove a lemma that gives a bound on the integral of a particular matrix exponential.

Lemma 9.4.8.   *Let $T > 0$ and $0 \leq t \leq T$. Then for all $h > 0$,*

$$\int_0^t \|\exp\left[-M^{-1}K(t - t')\right]\|_\infty \, dt' \leq \frac{\pi^2}{12},$$

where M and K are the tridiagonal matrices of (9.4.22):

$$M = h \text{ Tridiag } \{\tfrac{1}{6}, \tfrac{2}{3}, \tfrac{1}{6}\}$$

$$K = \frac{1}{h} \text{ Tridiag } \{-1, 2, -1\}.$$

Proof. Since M and K are symmetric and commuting matrices, $M^{-1}K$ is also symmetric. Hence there exists an orthogonal matrix P such that

$$P^T(M^{-1}K)P = \text{Diag}\,\{\mu_1, \mu_2, \ldots, \mu_N\} \equiv D.$$

Note that the μ_i are the eigenvalues of $M^{-1}K$. It can be verified that $\mathbf{P}^j$, the jth column of P, is

$$\mathbf{P}^j = \sqrt{\frac{2}{N+1}}\,(\sin\,(j\pi h), \sin\,(2j\pi h), \ldots, \sin\,(Nj\pi h))^T$$

and that

$$\mu_j = \frac{(6/h^2)\sin^2(j\pi h/2)}{1/2 + \cos^2(j\pi h/2)}$$

(see Exercises 9.2 to 9.4). It follows that

$$\mu_j \geq \left(\frac{2}{h}\sin\frac{j\pi h}{2}\right)^2, \qquad 1 \leq j \leq N.$$

Now $x \in (0, \pi/2)$ implies that $(\sin x)/x \geq 2/\pi$, thus

$$\mu_j \geq 4j^2, \qquad 1 \leq j \leq N.$$

The exponential

$$\exp\,(-\tau M^{-1}K) = P\exp\,(-\tau D)P^T,$$

and for $\tau \geq 0$,

$$\left|[\exp\,(-\tau M^{-1}K)]_{ij}\right| = \left|\frac{2}{N+1}\sum_{k=1}^{N}e^{-\tau\mu_k}\sin\frac{ik\pi}{N+1}\sin\frac{jk\pi}{N+1}\right|$$

$$\leq \frac{2}{N+1}\sum_{k=1}^{N}e^{-4\tau k^2}.$$

Thus, since $\sum_{k=1}^{\infty}1/k^2 = \pi^2/6$,

$$\int_0^t \left\|\exp\,[(-(t-t')M^{-1}K]\right\|_\infty\,dt' \leq 2\int_0^t\sum_{k=1}^{N}e^{-4(t-t')k^2}\,dt'$$

$$\leq 2\sum_{k=1}^{N}\frac{1-e^{-4tk^2}}{4k^2} \leq \frac{1}{2}\sum_{k=1}^{N}\frac{1}{k^2} \leq \frac{\pi^2}{12}.$$

$$\text{Q.E.D.}$$

The theorem on L_∞ convergence that we have in mind is the following.

Theorem 9.4.9.   *Let $U(x, t)$ be the semidiscrete Galerkin approximation in $H_0^1(\bar{I}, \Pi)$ for each t, and assume that Π is a uniform mesh. Let $u(x, t)$ be the true solution* *of* (9.4.1)–(9.4.3). *If* $u \in C^3(\bar{I} \times [0, T])$, *then for* $0 < t \le T$,

$$\left\|D^{(r,0)}(U - u)\right\|_\infty \le K(T)h^{2-r}, \tag{9.4.24}$$

$0 \le r \le 2$, *where* $K(T)$ *is a constant independent of* h *and* t.

Proof. Let $\{\phi_{i0}\}$ be the basis for $H^1(\bar{I}, \Pi)$ given in Theorem 9.4.3. (For convenience, we suppress the subscript 0 in the remainder of this proof.) If we multiply (9.4.1) by $\phi_i(x)$, integrate by parts, and subtract from

$$k_i(t) \equiv \int_a^b (D^{(0,1)}\tilde{U})\phi_i \, dx + \int_a^b (D^{(1,0)}\tilde{U})\phi_i' \, dx, \tag{9.4.25}$$

where $\tilde{U} \equiv \sum_{i=1}^N \tilde{c}_i\phi_i$ is the smooth Hermite interpolant in $H_0^1(\bar{I}, \Pi)$ to u, we obtain

$$k_i(t) = \int_a^b [D^{(0,1)}(\tilde{U} - u)]\phi_i \, dx + \int_a^b \lceil D^{(1,0)}(\tilde{U} - u)]\phi_i' \, dx$$

for $1 \le i \le N$. But integration by parts shows that the second integral is zero since $\phi_i'' = 0$ on each subinterval and $(\tilde{U} - u)(a) = (\tilde{U} - u)(b) = 0$.

Hence, by (9.4.11), for $0 < t \le T$,

$$|k_i(t)| \le \int_a^b |D^{(0,1)}(\tilde{U} - u)(\cdot, t)|\phi_i \, dx \le \tfrac{1}{8} \max_{0 \le t \le T} \left\|D^{(2,1)}u(\cdot, t)\right\|_\infty h^3 \equiv K_1(T)h^3,$$

where we have also used the fact that $\int_a^b |\phi_i| \, dx = \int_a^b \phi_i \, dx = h$.

Let $\mathbf{V} = (v_1, v_2, \ldots, v_N)^T$, where $v_i(t) \equiv \tilde{c}_i(t) - c_i(t)$. Then from (9.4.25) and the Galerkin equations

$$\int_a^b (D^{(0,1)}U)\phi_i \, dx + \int_a^b (D^{(1,0)}U)\phi_i' \, dx = 0, \qquad 1 \le i \le N,$$

we have

$$k_i(t) = \int_a^b [D^{(0,1)}(\tilde{U} - U)]\phi_i \, dx + \int_a^b [D^{(1,0)}(\tilde{U} - U)]\phi_i' \, dx.$$

In matrix form this becomes

$$M\frac{d\mathbf{V}}{dt} = -K\mathbf{V} + \mathbf{k}, \tag{9.4.26}$$

where $\mathbf{k} = (k_1, \ldots, k_N)^T$. The $N \times N$ matrices M and K, as given by (9.4.7) and (9.4.8), reduce to the tridiagonal matrices of (9.4.22). We also have

$$\mathbf{V}(0) = \mathbf{0}. \tag{9.4.27}$$

The solution to (9.4.26)–(9.4.27) is

$$\mathbf{V}(t) = \int_0^t \exp\left[-M^{-1}K(t - t')\right]M^{-1}\mathbf{k} \, dt'.$$

But, from Exercise 9.6, $\|M^{-1}\|_\infty \leq 3/h$ and hence

$$\|\mathbf{V}(t)\|_\infty \leq 3K_1(T)h^2 \int_0^t \|\exp[-M^{-1}K(t-t')]\|_\infty \, dt', \qquad 0 \leq t \leq T. \qquad (9.4.28)$$

Next note that for each t,

$$\|D^{(r,0)}(\tilde{U}-U)\|_\infty \leq \|\mathbf{V}(t)\|_\infty \left\| \sum_{i=1}^N |\phi_i^{(r)}| \right\|_\infty.$$

Then, by Theorem 9.4.2 and the triangle inequality,

$$\|D^{(r,0)}(u-U)\|_\infty \leq M_{1r}\|D^{(2,0)}u\|_\infty h^{2-r} + \|\mathbf{V}(t)\|_\infty \left\| \sum_{i=1}^N |\phi_i^{(r)}| \right\|_\infty, \qquad 0 \leq r \leq 2.$$

Now,

$$\left\| \sum_{i=1}^N |\phi_i^{(r)}| \right\|_\infty = \begin{cases} 1 & \text{if } r = 0, \\ \dfrac{2}{h} & \text{if } r = 1, \\ 0 & \text{if } r = 2. \end{cases}$$

Therefore, (9.4.24) follows from (9.4.28) and Lemma 9.4.8.

Q.E.D.

We conclude this section with an example that illustrates the error behavior predicted by the Theorem 9.4.9.

Example 9.4.1

Consider the initial–boundary value problem (9.4.1)–(9.4.3), where

$$u_0(x) = 10 \sin \pi x,$$

and $a = 0$, $b = 1$. The exact solution to this problem is $u(x, t) = 10e^{-\pi^2 t} \sin \pi x$.

We use the space $S^h = H_0^1(\bar{I}, \Pi)$ with a uniform partition for the spatial discretization and formula (9.2.7) with $\theta = \frac{1}{2}$ (Crank–Nicolson) to approximate the solution of (9.4.5). For the mesh spacings considered, the time step is chosen to be small enough ($\Delta t = 10^{-4}$) that we may ignore the effect of the approximate time integration on the discretization error. If U_h is the Galerkin approximation to u from S^h, then from Theorem 9.4.9, we anticipate that

$$\|D^{(r,0)}(U_h - u)\|_\infty \approx K(t)h^{2-r}, \qquad 0 \leq r \leq 2.$$

Hence we define

$$\alpha^{(r)} \equiv \log \frac{\|D^{(r,0)}(U_{h_1} - u)\|_\infty}{\|D^{(r,0)}(U_{h_2} - u)\|_\infty} \Big/ \log \frac{h_1}{h_2} \qquad (9.4.29)$$

for two different values, h_i, of h.

For $t = 0.1$, the data of Table 9.4.1 demonstrate the $O(h^2)$ pointwise convergence of U_h to u as $h \to 0$ as well as the $O(h)$ pointwise convergence of $D^{(1,0)}U_h$ to $D^{(1,0)}u$.

TABLE 9.4.1 ERRORS IN GALERKIN
APPROXIMATION AT $t = 0.1$

h	$\|U_h - u\|_\infty$	$\alpha^{(0)}$	$\|D^{(1,0)}(U_h - u)\|_\infty$	$\alpha^{(1)}$
1/5	1.82×10^{-1}	—	3.58×10^0	—
1/10	4.49×10^{-2}	2.02	1.81×10^0	0.988
1/15	2.02×10^{-2}	1.97	1.21×10^0	0.984
1/20	1.14×10^{-2}	2.01	9.09×10^{-1}	1.000
1/25	7.30×10^{-3}	1.98	7.28×10^{-1}	0.994

9.5 STABILITY

In this section we return to the initial value problem (9.1.9), (9.1.14), under the assumption that the stiffness matrix K is nonsingular. In this case the solution $\mathbf{C}(t)$ is given by (9.1.17), and it is well known (see, e.g., Gantmacher [1959]) that $\mathbf{C}(t)$ is bounded for $t \geq 0$ if Re $\lambda_j < 0$, $1 \leq j \leq N$. Here λ_j denotes the jth eigenvalue of $-M^{-1}K$.

We are interested in the analogous situation for the approximations $\mathbf{C}^m$ given by (9.2.5); that is, we seek conditions such that the vectors $\mathbf{C}^m$, $m = 0, 1, \ldots$, are bounded.

By repeated application of (9.2.5) we see that

$$\mathbf{C}^m = (T(\Delta t))^m (\mathbf{C}^0 - K^{-1}\mathbf{S}) + K^{-1}\mathbf{S}.$$

Therefore, for the $\mathbf{C}^m$ to remain bounded, it is sufficient to have

$$\|T(\Delta t)\| \leq 1 \qquad (9.5.1)$$

for some norm $\|\cdot\|$.

Now suppose that K and M are the tridiagonal matrices of (9.4.22) [i.e., the Galerkin approximation is drawn from $H_0^1(\bar{I}, \Pi)$], and consider the three exponential matrix approximations of Section 9.2 given by (9.2.6) when $\theta = 0, \frac{1}{2}$, and 1. Since M and K are symmetric and commute, the approximate matrix exponential

$$T(\Delta t) = I - \Delta t \, (M + \theta \, \Delta t \, K)^{-1} K$$

is symmetric. Thus if we choose $\|\cdot\|$ to be the Euclidean matrix norm, then (9.5.1) becomes $\rho(T(\Delta t)) \leq 1$, where $\rho(T(\Delta t))$ denotes the spectral radius of $T(\Delta t)$. But this last condition is just the definition of matrix stability given in Section 4.5. Therefore, we can verify (9.5.1) by using Theorem 4.5.1 to determine when $T(\Delta t)$ is stable for $\theta = 0, \frac{1}{2}, 1$. In fact, we know from Section 9.4 that the eigenvalues of $M^{-1}K$ are

$$\mu_j = \frac{(6/h^2) \sin^2 (j\pi h/2)}{\frac{1}{2} + \cos^2 (j\pi h/2)}, \qquad 1 \leq j \leq N.$$

Hence $\mu_j \geq 4$ and it follows from Theorem 4.5.1 that when $\theta = \frac{1}{2}$ or 1, $T(\Delta t)$ is unconditionally stable. If $\theta = 0$, then $T(\Delta t)$ is stable provided that $\Delta t \leq \min_j (2/\mu_j)$. Since $\mu_j \leq 12/h^2$, we see that $T(\Delta t)$ is stable for $\theta = 0$ if $\Delta t \leq h^2/6$.

Note that since $\lambda_j = -\mu_j < 0$ $(1 \leq j \leq N)$, $\mathbf{C}(t)$ is bounded for all $t \geq 0$. We have just proven that the vector approximations $\{\mathbf{C}^m\}_0^\infty$ are also bounded for any $\Delta t \geq 0$ when the Crank–Nicolson $(\theta = \frac{1}{2})$ or backward $(\theta = 1)$ approximations are used, and that they are bounded for $0 \leq \Delta t \leq h^2/6$ when the forward approximation $(\theta = 0)$ is used.

9.6 MULTIDIMENSIONAL HEAT CONDUCTION–CONVECTION

In this section we consider the finite element approximation of the temperature distribution u in a fluid in which there is both conduction and convection of heat. Let $\mathbf{q}$ be a known function of position $\mathbf{x}$ and time t that represents the velocity of the fluid in the domain $\Omega \subset R^p$. The *heat conduction–convection* equation is

$$\rho c u_t - \nabla \cdot k \nabla u + \rho c \mathbf{q} \cdot \nabla u - f = 0, \qquad \mathbf{x} \in \Omega, \qquad (9.6.1)$$

where ρ, c, and k are, respectively, the density, specific heat, and conductivity of the fluid, and f is a source (or sink) of heat (see Section 2.3). In addition, the temperature $u(\mathbf{x}, t)$ is required to satisfy the initial, and boundary, conditions (9.1.2)–(9.1.5).

To illustrate the finite element method, assume that Ω is the interior of a polygon which has been triangulated as in Section 7.6. Further, let S^h be the space of piecewise linear functions on this triangulation defined in that section. Let $S^h = \text{span}(\phi_1, \ldots, \phi_m)$. Then the *semidiscrete Galerkin* approximation

$$U(\mathbf{x}, t) = \sum_{j=1}^m c_j(t)\phi_j(\mathbf{x})$$

satisfies

$$\int_\Omega \rho c U_t \phi_i \, d\mathbf{x} + \int_\Omega \left[k \nabla U \cdot \nabla \phi_i + \rho c (\mathbf{q} \cdot \nabla U)\phi_i - f\phi_i \right] d\mathbf{x}$$

$$+ \int_{\partial\Omega_3} h_0 (U - u_s)\phi_i \, ds = 0, \qquad 1 \leq i \leq N, \qquad (9.6.2)$$

where $S_0^h = \text{span}(\phi_1, \ldots, \phi_N)$ is the space spanned by those basis functions associated with nodes in Ω and nodes on $\partial\Omega_2 \cup \partial\Omega_3$.

Conditions (9.6.2) yield a system of ordinary differential equations of the same generic form as (9.1.9):

$$M \frac{d\mathbf{C}}{dt} = -K\mathbf{C} + \mathbf{S}, \qquad (9.6.3)$$

where M and $\mathbf{S}$ are given in (9.1.10) and (9.1.12), respectively. However, now

$$K = \left[\int_\Omega k \nabla \phi_j \cdot \nabla \phi_i \, d\mathbf{x} + \int_\Omega \rho c (\mathbf{q} \cdot \nabla \phi_j)\phi_i \, d\mathbf{x} + \int_{\partial\Omega_3} h_0 \phi_j(\mathbf{x})\phi_i(\mathbf{x}) \, ds \right]. \qquad (9.6.4)$$

Note that unlike the K defined in (9.1.11) this stiffness matrix is not symmetric, due to the addition of the convective terms.

Convergence of the semidiscrete approximation is established in the following theorem.

Theorem 9.6.1. *Let $u(\mathbf{x}, t)$ be the solution to the heat conduction–convection problem (9.6.1), (9.1.2)–(9.1.5), and let $U(\mathbf{x}, t)$ be its semidiscrete Galerkin approximation corresponding to a finite-dimensional subspace, S^h, of S_0 containing an element $\tilde{U}(\cdot, t)$, an interpolant of u of the form (9.3.1) such that*

$$\|u - \tilde{U}\|_m = O(h^{2n-m}), \qquad m = 0, 1,$$

$$\int_{\partial\Omega_3} (u - \tilde{U})^2 \, ds = O(h^{4n})$$

as the mesh gauge $h \to 0$. Assume that for each fixed t, $u(\cdot, t)$ and $u_t(\cdot, t)$ belong to $H^{2n}(\Omega)$. Then as the mesh gauge $h \to 0$ and for $0 \le t \le T$,

$$\|u - U\|_0 \le K h^{2n-1}, \tag{9.6.5}$$

where K depends on T and u.

Proof. We confine the proof to the case where $b(\mathbf{x})$ in (9.1.3) is identically zero. We proceed as in the proof of Theorem 9.3.1, and present only the necessary changes to that proof. Equation (9.3.2) is replaced by

$$k_i(t) \equiv \int_\Omega \rho c \tilde{U}_t \phi_i \, d\mathbf{x} + \int_\Omega [k \, \nabla\tilde{U} \cdot \nabla\phi_i + \rho c (\mathbf{q} \cdot \nabla\tilde{U})\phi_i - f\phi_i] \, d\mathbf{x}$$

$$+ \int_{\partial\Omega_3} h_0(\tilde{U} - u_s)\phi_i \, ds,$$

and the equality in (9.3.7) is replaced by

$$\int_\Omega \rho c V_{2t} V_2 \, d\mathbf{x} + \int_\Omega k \, \nabla V_2 \cdot \nabla V_2 \, d\mathbf{x} + \int_\Omega \rho c (\mathbf{q} \cdot \nabla V_2) V_2 \, d\mathbf{x} + \int_{\partial\Omega_3} h_0 V_2^2 \, ds$$

$$= \int_\Omega \rho c V_{1t} V_2 \, d\mathbf{x} + \int_\Omega k \, \nabla V_1 \cdot \nabla V_2 \, d\mathbf{x} + \int_\Omega \rho c (\mathbf{q} \cdot \nabla V_1) V_2 \, d\mathbf{x} + \int_{\partial\Omega_3} h_0 V_1 V_2 \, ds. \tag{9.6.6}$$

Similar to the derivation of (9.3.8), we have

$$\frac{d}{dt} \|V_2\|_0^2 + K_2^{-1} \int_\Omega k |\nabla V_2|^2 \, d\mathbf{x} \le \left(K_2^{-1} \|V_2\|_0^2 + K_1 K_2^{-1} \|V_{1t}\|_0^2 \right.$$

$$\left. + K_3 \|\nabla V_1\|_0^2 + K_4 \int_{\partial\Omega_3} V_1^2 \, ds \right) + K_2^{-1} \int_\Omega \rho c \mathbf{q} \cdot (\nabla V_1 - \nabla V_2) V_2 \, d\mathbf{x}. \tag{9.6.7}$$

Note that the second term on the left of the inequality is dropped in the derivation of (9.3.8), but we need it for what follows.

The second integral on the right side of (9.6.7) is bounded as follows:

$$\int_\Omega \rho c \mathbf{q} \cdot (\nabla V_1 - \nabla V_2) V_2 \, d\mathbf{x} \le K_1 \|\mathbf{q}\|_\infty \left[\left(\frac{\varepsilon^2}{2} \int_\Omega |\nabla V_2|^2 \, d\mathbf{x} + \frac{1}{2\varepsilon^2} \|V_2\|_0^2 \right) \right.$$

$$\left. + \left(\frac{1}{2} \int_\Omega |\nabla V_1|^2 \, d\mathbf{x} + \frac{1}{2} \|V_2\|_0^2 \right) \right],$$

where the identity $ab \leq \varepsilon^2 a^2/2 + b^2/(2\varepsilon^2)$ has been used twice, once with a yet-to-be determined ε and the second time with $\varepsilon = 1$. Hence (9.6.7) can be rewritten

$$\frac{d}{dt}\|V_2\|_0^2 + K_2^{-1}\int_\Omega \left(k - K_1\|\mathbf{q}\|_\infty \frac{\varepsilon^2}{2}\right)|\nabla V_2|^2\, d\mathbf{x},$$

$$\leq \left[K_5\|V_2\|_0^2 + K_1 K_2^{-1}\|V_{1t}\|_0^2 + \left(K_3 + \frac{1}{2}\right)\|\nabla V_1\|_0^2 + K_4 \int_{\partial\Omega_3} V_1^2\, ds\right], \qquad (9.6.8)$$

where $K_5 = K_2^{-1}(1 + K_1\|\mathbf{q}\|_\infty[\frac{1}{2} + 1/(2\varepsilon^2)])$. If we choose ε so that the integral on the left-hand side of the inequality is positive, then that integral can be dropped without changing the sense of (9.6.8).

The resulting inequality is analogous to (9.3.8), which held when the convective term was missing (i.e., $\mathbf{q} \equiv \mathbf{0}$). Inequality (9.6.5) then follows from exactly the same argument as in Theorem 9.3.1.

Q.E.D.

If $\Omega \subset R^2$, then S^h can be chosen as the finite element space of linear isoparametric triangles or bilinear isoparametric quadrilaterals studied in Chapter 7, and the conditions of Theorem 9.6.1 are met with $n = 1$.

NOTES AND REMARKS

9.1 The semidiscrete Galerkin approximation is known explicitly in terms of matrix exponentials. However, the dimension of S^h is typically too large to compute these exponentials in closed form. There are two standard approaches to approximating the exponential, the Padé rational approximations (see Varga [1962]) and the Chebyshev rational approximations (see Cody, Meinardus, and Varga [1969]).

9.3 The proof that the semidiscrete Galerkin approximation converges to the true solution was apparently first given in Price and Varga [1970] and generalized in Varga [1971] and Douglas and Dupont [1970].

9.4 Much has been written on the attributes of approximation based on spaces of *piecewise* analytic functions and their inherent advantages over approximation based on analytic functions, such as polynomials or trigonometric functions (see, e.g., Birkhoff and deBoor [1965] and Varga [1971]). The classical example of Runge (see Isaaccson and Keller [1966]) illustrates the catastrophic asymptotic behavior that is possible for the Lagrange interpolation scheme on a uniform grid. If

$$f(x) = \frac{1}{1 + x^2}, \qquad -5 \leq x \leq 5,$$

and Π is a uniform mesh of N points, then analytically it can be shown that there exist points $-5 < \xi < 5$ such that

$$(L_{f,N} - f)(\xi) \to \infty \quad \text{as} \quad N \to \infty,$$

where $L_{f,N}$ is the Lagrange polynomial interpolant to f on Π. Note that $f \in C^\infty[-5, 5]$, yet convergence of $L_{f,N}$ to f is not guaranteed. In contrast, the *piecewise* polynomial interpolants presented in this section converge as $N \to \infty$ under rather mild assumptions on f.

The study of splines was initiated by I. J. Schoenberg [1946] and has since attracted considerable research interest. The term *spline* came from the draftsman's mechanical spline, which is a long thin beam (elastica) woven between weights called *dogs* or *cats*. Mathematically, the segments of the spline are clamped beams, the positions of which are described in terms of cubic polynomials. This, coupled with the continuity of the curvature of the draftsman's spline, gave impetus to the use of the term *spline* for piecewise cubic polynomials of class C^2. The interested reader should consult the books by Schoenberg [1969], deBoor [1978], or Schultz [1973] for additional information.

Approximation theoretic results for higher dimensions can be found, for example, in Birkhoff, Schultz, and Varga [1968], Varga [1971], Ciarlet and Raviart [1972], and Gordon and Hall [1973].

EXERCISES

9.1. Let $f \in C^2(0, 1)$ and let $\tilde{f} \in H^1(\bar{I}, 11)$ be its Hermite interpolant.
   (a) Find linear polynomials $p_1(x)$ and $p_2(x)$ such that $p_1 + p_2 = 1$ and

$$\tilde{f}(x) = p_1(x)f(x_j) + p_2(x)f(x_{j+1})$$

   for $x \in [x_j, x_{j+1}]$.
   (b) Use Taylor's formula to show that

$$\tilde{f}(x) = f(x) - \frac{(x - x_j)(x - x_{j+1})f''(\xi)}{2}$$

   for some $\xi \in (x_j, x_{j+1})$. [*Hint:* Expand $f(x_j)$ and $f(x_{j+1})$ about x.]
   (c) Establish (9.4.10) for the case $n = 1$.

9.2. Let $h = 1/(N + 1)$ for some positive integer N. Verify that the vectors

$$\mathbf{P}^j = \sqrt{\frac{2}{N + 1}} (\sin (j\pi h), \sin (2j\pi h), \ldots, \sin (Nj\pi h))^T, \qquad j = 1, \ldots, N,$$

form an orthonormal set of eigenvectors for the matrix K in (9.4.22) corresponding to the eigenvalues

$$\lambda_j[K] = \frac{4}{h} \sin^2 \frac{j\pi h}{2}.$$

9.3. Verify that the vectors $\{\mathbf{P}^j\}$ of Exercise 9.2 form an orthonormal set of eigenvectors for the matrix M in (9.4.22) corresponding to the eigenvalues

$$\lambda_j[M] = \frac{h}{3}\left(1 + 2\cos^2 \frac{j\pi h}{2}\right).$$

9.4. (a) Show that if the matrices A and B are symmetric and commute, then the eigenvalues of A and B can be ordered so that the eigenvalues of AB are the products of the eigenvalues of A and B. [*Hint:* A necessary and sufficient condition that two symmetric matrices A and B commute is that there exist an orthogonal matrix P such that $P^T A P = \text{Diag}(\lambda_j[A])$ and $P^T B P = \text{Diag}(\lambda_j[B])$. See Wilkinson [1965].]

(b) If M and K are the tridiagonal matrices given by (9.4.22), show that μ_j, the jth eigenvalue of $M^{-1}K$, is

$$\mu_j = \frac{(6/h^2)\sin^2(j\pi h/2)}{\frac{1}{2} + \cos^2(j\pi h/2)}.$$

9.5. If A is an $N \times N$ matrix, prove that

$$\exp\left[-A(t + \Delta t)\right] = \exp\left(-At\right)\exp\left(-A\,\Delta t\right).$$

More generally, prove that

$$\exp(A + B) = \exp(A)\exp(B)$$

for any $N \times N$ matrix B that commutes with A. [*Hint:* The matrix $\exp(A)$ is a polynomial in A of degree at most N^2. Why?]

9.6. Prove that $\|M^{-1}\|_\infty \le 3/h$, where M is given in (9.4.22).

9.7. Let $A = [a_{ij}]$ and $B = [b_{ij}]$ be two $N \times N$ real matrices. Then the *direct* or *Kronecker product* of A and B is defined as the $N^2 \times N^2$ matrix

$$A \otimes B = [a_{ij}B].$$

(a) Show that $(A \otimes B)(C \otimes D) = AC \otimes BD$ and $(A \otimes B)^T = A^T \otimes B^T$.

(b) Show that $(A \otimes B)^{-1} = A^{-1} \otimes B^{-1}$, if the inverses exist.

(c) Show that $\{\lambda_i[A]\lambda_j[B]: 1 \le i, j \le N\}$ is the spectrum of $A \otimes B$, where $\lambda[A]$ and $\lambda_j[B]$ are eigenvalues of A and B, respectively. [*Hint:* Use the Jordan canonical forms and parts (a) and (b).]

9.8. Let $\Omega = (a, b) \times (a, b)$ be a square domain in R^2 and $\Pi \times \Pi$ be a uniform partition of $\bar\Omega$, where $\Pi: a = z_0 < z_1 < \cdots < z_{N+1} = b$ with mesh gauge $h = (b - a)/(N + 1)$. Further, let

$$S^h = H_0^1(\bar I, \Pi) \otimes H_0^1(\bar I, \Pi)$$
$$= \text{span } \{\phi_i(\mathbf{x})\}_{i=1}^{N^2} = \text{span } \{\phi_{j0}(x_1)\phi_{l0}(x_2) \mid 1 \le j, l \le N\}$$

be the so-called tensor product space, where the ϕ_{j0} are given in Theorem 9.4.3. Consider the Galerkin method applied to the two-dimensional problem

$$u_t = \nabla^2 u, \qquad \mathbf{x} \in \Omega, \quad 0 < t \le T,$$

$$u(\mathbf{x}, t) = 0, \qquad \mathbf{x} \in \partial\Omega, \quad 0 \le t \le T,$$

$$u(\mathbf{x}, 0) = u_0(\mathbf{x}), \qquad \mathbf{x} \in \Omega.$$

(a) If $U(\mathbf{x}, t) = \sum_{i=1}^{N^2} c_i(t)\phi_i(\mathbf{x})$ is the semidiscrete Galerkin approximation, where $\mathbf{C}(t) \equiv (c_i(t))$ satisfies

$$\hat M \frac{d\mathbf{C}(t)}{dt} = -\hat K \mathbf{C} + \mathbf{S}, \tag{1}$$

show that by suitably ordering the basis, the matrices $\hat M$ and $\hat K$ can be written as

$$\hat M = M \otimes M \quad \text{and} \quad \hat K = K \otimes M + M \otimes K,$$

where M and K are the $N \times N$ matrices given in (9.4.22).

(b) Show that $\hat M$ and $\hat K$ are symmetric commuting matrices.

(c) Show that the eigenvalues of K and M can be ordered so that the eigenvalues of $\hat{K}$ are

$$\lambda_{ij}[\hat{K}] = \lambda_i[K]\lambda_j[M] + \lambda_i[M]\lambda_j[K],$$

where $\lambda_k[A]$ denotes the kth eigenvalue of A. [*Hint:* See Exercise 9.4.]
(d) Use Exercises 9.2 to 9.4 and part (c) to prove that the forward difference scheme applied to (1) is stable if

$$\Delta t \leq \frac{h^2}{12}.$$

Computer Exercises

9.9. Use the finite element method to compute the temperature response at the midplane of a cylindrical shell, $r_i \leq r \leq r_e$, with external surface temperature at $r = r_e$ maintained at $u = 150°F$ after a sudden change in internal surface temperature $r = r_i$ from $150°F$ when $t = 0$ to $400°F$ when $t > 0$. Assume that the diffusivity is 1.0. Try different ratios of $R = r_i/r_e$ and compare to the graph in Figure 9.E.1 which can be found, for example, in

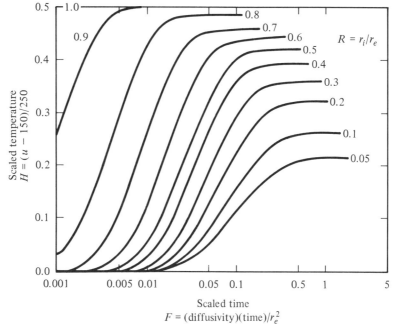

Figure 9.E.1 Temperature response.

Schneider [1963]. Note that because of problem symmetries, this problem can be modeled using (x, y, z, t), (r, z, t), or (x, y, t) coordinates. [As noted in Section 9.2, the temperature in this problem is in fact the solution of a one-dimensional heat equation in (r, t).]

9.10. Solve the problem in Example 9.2.1 on a sequence of mesh refinements. Estimate the rate of convergence of your sequence of finite elemenp approximations.

10

Elliptic Equations: The Finite Difference ───── Approach ─────

A treatment of elliptic boundary value problems by the finite element method has been presented in Chapter 7. In this chapter we analyze an alternative approach that employs finite difference methods. Although such methods do not possess the inherent flexibility of finite element methods, they are simpler to formulate and have the additional advantage that *pointwise* error estimates emerge quite naturally from the analysis. The reader should compare this situation with that of Chapter 7, wherein the error was measured in terms of the *integral* norms on $L_2(\Omega)$ and $H^1(\Omega)$.

10.1 FINITE DIFFERENCE METHODS FOR ELLIPTIC EQUATIONS

We consider the second-order partial differential equation,

$$Lu = f, \tag{10.1.1}$$

where

$$Lu \equiv -\left(\frac{\partial}{\partial x}, \frac{\partial}{\partial y}\right)\begin{bmatrix} a_{11} & a_{12} \\ a_{21} & a_{22} \end{bmatrix}\begin{bmatrix} \dfrac{\partial u}{\partial x} \\ \dfrac{\partial u}{\partial y} \end{bmatrix} + cu. \tag{10.1.2}$$

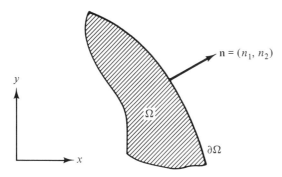

Figure 10.1.1 Unit exterior normal vector.

This equation is to hold on a bounded region[1] Ω, whose boundary $\partial\Omega$ is piecewise smooth in the sense of Section 6.3. We assume in (10.1.1) and (10.1.2) that on $\bar{\Omega} \equiv \Omega \cup \partial\Omega$, the functions[2] c, $f \in C(\bar{\Omega})$, $a_{ij} \in C^1(\bar{\Omega})$, and $c(x, y) \geq 0$. Furthermore, we suppose that for each $(x_1, x_2) \in \Omega$ and for any real numbers t_1, t_2, there exists a positive constant μ such that

$$\sum_{i,j=1}^{2} a_{ij}(x_1, x_2)t_i t_j \geq \mu \sum_{i=1}^{2} t_i^2. \tag{10.1.3}$$

This is the condition that L is *uniformly elliptic* in Ω.

Throughout this chapter we identify $x_1 \equiv x$ and $x_2 \equiv y$ so that (10.1.2) may also be written as

$$Lu = -\sum_{i=1}^{2} \frac{\partial}{\partial x_i} \left(\sum_{j=1}^{2} a_{ij} \frac{\partial u}{\partial x_j} \right) + cu. \tag{10.1.4}$$

Another commonly used notation is

$$Lu = -\nabla \cdot A \,\nabla u + cu.$$

We partition $\partial\Omega$ as $\partial\Omega = \partial\Omega_1 \cup \partial\Omega_2 \cup \partial\Omega_3$ and distinguish three types of *boundary conditions*:

1. *Dirichlet (or first) boundary condition*:

$$u(P) = g_1(P) \quad \text{for} \quad P \in \partial\Omega_1. \tag{10.1.5}$$

2. *Neumann (or second) boundary condition*:

$$\sum_{i,j=1}^{2} a_{ij} \frac{\partial u}{\partial x_j} (P) \, n_i = g_2(P) \quad \text{for} \quad P \in \partial\Omega_2, \tag{10.1.6}$$

where $\mathbf{n} \equiv (n_1, n_2)$ is the unit exterior (outward) normal vector to $\partial\Omega_2$ (Figure 10.1.1).

---

[1] As in previous chapters, we use the term *region* to denote a connected, open set.

[2] $C^m(\Omega)$ denotes the set of functions that are m-times continuously differentiable on Ω, and $C^m(\bar{\Omega})$ denotes the set of restrictions to $\bar{\Omega}$ of functions in $C^m(R^2)$ (see Section 6.1).

3. *Mixed (or third) boundary condition*:

$$\sum_{i,j=1}^{2} \left[a_{ij} \frac{\partial u}{\partial x_j} (P) \, n_i \right] + \sigma \, u(P) = g_3(P) \quad \text{for} \quad P \in \partial\Omega_3. \tag{10.1.7}$$

In (10.1.5)–(10.1.7), σ and the g_i are presumed to be given functions.

In Section 2.3 a steady-state heat flow problem was presented that corresponds to $a_{11} = a_{22} = k$ (where k is the conductivity) and $a_{12} = a_{21} = c = 0$. In this case (10.1.6) reduces to a specified flux condition,

$$k \, \nabla u \cdot \mathbf{n} = g_2,$$

and the third boundary condition reduces to a radiative boundary condition,

$$k \, \nabla u \cdot \mathbf{n} + \sigma \, u = g_3,$$

where, in the notation of Section 2.3, $\sigma = h$ and $g_3 = h u_s$.

To develop a discretization of (10.1.1) in which the derivatives are approximated by difference quotients, we assume that the problem domain Ω is the interior of a polygon which has been partitioned into *rectangular* and *triangular cells* by a mesh or grid Π_Ω. This is a *rectangular* network of lines that are parallel to the coordinate axes and intersect the boundary of Ω only at points where they themselves intersect (cf. Figure 10.1.2).

We can regard Ω as being embedded in a rectangle $\bar{\Omega}^*$ in such a way that the lines of Π_Ω,

$$\{x = x_i\}_{i=0}^{M_1} \cup \{y = y_j\}_{j=0}^{M_2} \tag{10.1.8}$$

partition $\bar{\Omega}^*$ as well as Ω. This permits an easy reference frame for the mesh which partitions the nonrectangular region Ω. The points of intersection of the members of Π_Ω are called *mesh (or grid) points*, and the *mesh gauge h* is defined as the maximum

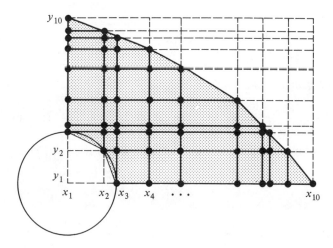

Figure 10.1.2 Partitioned domain imbedded in rectangle $\bar{\Omega}^*$.

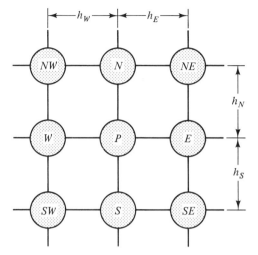

Figure 10.1.3 Compass frame of reference for a mesh point.

of the set $\{|x_i - x_{i-1}|, |y_j - y_{j-1}|\}$. The mesh points which belong respectively to Ω and $\partial\Omega$ form two sets denoted by Ω_h and $\partial\Omega_h$. Also, $\bar{\Omega}_h \equiv \Omega_h \cup \partial\Omega_h$.

Our problem is to construct a *mesh* (or *grid*) *function* $U: \bar{\Omega}_h \rightarrow R$ such that U is a "good" approximation to u on $\bar{\Omega}_h$. This mesh function is determined by solving a system of *finite difference equations*. These equations are obtained from (10.1.1) by approximating the differential equation at each point by an algebraic equation in which the derivatives have been replaced by appropriate difference approximations.

Obviously, the boundary conditions are going to affect the equations that are associated with boundary points. We defer consideration of this issue for the present, and first discuss the mechanics of approximating the derivatives. We adopt the standard compass designations of neighbors and denote a typical mesh point with coordinates (x, y) by P and its neighbors by compass abbreviations (cf. Figure 10.1.3). The following theorem presents the desired approximations to the derivatives in (10.1.2) as well as an asymptotic $(h \rightarrow 0)$ behavior of the associated truncation error. The proof, which is omitted, is an extended exercise in the use of Taylor's theorem and may be found in Forsythe and Wasow [1960].

Theorem 10.1.1.   *Suppose that $u \in C^4(\bar{\Omega})$ and $P \in \Omega$. Then as $h \rightarrow 0$,*

$$u_x(P) = \frac{h_W}{h_E(h_E + h_W)} u(E) + \frac{(h_E - h_W)}{h_E h_W} u(P) - \frac{h_E}{h_W(h_E + h_W)} u(W) + O(h^2), \quad (10.1.9)$$

$$u_y(P) = \frac{h_S}{h_N(h_N + h_S)} u(N) + \frac{(h_N - h_S)}{h_N h_S} u(P) - \frac{h_N}{h_S(h_N + h_S)} u(S) + O(h^2), \quad (10.1.10)$$

$$u_{xx}(P) = \frac{2}{h_E(h_E + h_W)} u(E) - \frac{2}{h_W h_E} u(P) + \frac{2}{h_W(h_W + h_E)} u(W) + O((h_W - h_E) + h^2),$$

$$(10.1.11)$$

$$u_{yy}(P) = \frac{2}{h_N(h_N + h_S)} u(N) - \frac{2}{h_S h_N} u(P) + \frac{2}{h_S(h_S + h_N)} u(S) + O((h_S - h_N) + h^2),$$

(10.1.12)

$$u_{xy}(P) = -\frac{h_E}{h_W(h_E + h_W)} \left[-\frac{h_N}{h_S(h_N + h_S)} u(SW) + \frac{(h_N - h_S)}{h_N h_S} u(W) \right.$$
$$\left. + \frac{h_S}{h_N(h_S + h_N)} u(NW) \right] + \frac{(h_E - h_W)}{h_E h_W} \left[-\frac{h_N}{h_S(h_N + h_S)} u(S) + \frac{(h_N - h_S)}{h_N h_S} u(P) \right.$$
$$\left. + \frac{h_S}{h_N(h_S + h_N)} u(N) \right] + \frac{h_W}{h_E(h_E + h_W)} \left[-\frac{h_N}{h_S(h_N + h_S)} u(SE) + \frac{(h_N - h_S)}{h_N h_S} u(E) \right.$$
$$\left. + \frac{h_S}{h_N(h_S + h_N)} u(NE) \right] + O((h_E - h_W) + (h_N - h_S) + h^2).$$

(10.1.13)

Now let $M(\Omega_h)$ and $M(\bar{\Omega}_h)$ denote the sets of grid functions whose domains are, respectively, Ω_h and $\bar{\Omega}_h$. When the order terms in Theorem 10.1.1 are ignored, the right-hand sides of (10.1.9)–(10.1.13) define[3] *finite difference operators* $u_X, u_Y, \ldots, u_{XY}$ from $M(\bar{\Omega}_h)$ to $M(\Omega_h)$. These correspond to the partial derivatives $u_x, u_y, \ldots, u_{xy}$. With these definitions, we define the *finite difference operator* $L_h: M(\bar{\Omega}_h) \to M(\Omega_h)$ by the condition that for $P \in \Omega_h$,

$$(L_h U)P \equiv -[a_{11} U_{XX} + (a_{12} + a_{21}) U_{XY} + a_{22} U_{YY} + (a_{11}^{(1,0)} + a_{21}^{(0,1)}) U_X$$
$$+ (a_{22}^{(0,1)} + a_{12}^{(1,0)}) U_Y] + cU, \qquad (10.1.14)$$

where $a_{ij}^{(p,q)} = \partial^{p+q} a_{ij} / \partial x^p \partial y^q$, and the right-hand side is evaluated at P. We note that (10.1.14) may also be written in the form

$$(L_h U)P = \sum_Q A(P, Q) U(Q), \qquad (10.1.15)$$

where the only possible nonzero *couplings* $A(P, Q)$ are given by the formulas

$$A(P, P) = a_{11} \frac{2}{h_W h_E} - (a_{12} + a_{21}) \frac{(h_E - h_W)(h_N - h_S)}{h_N h_S h_E h_W} + a_{22} \frac{2}{h_N h_S} + c$$
$$- (a_{11}^{(1,0)} + a_{21}^{(0,1)}) \frac{h_E - h_W}{h_E h_W} - (a_{22}^{(0,1)} + a_{12}^{(1,0)}) \frac{h_N - h_S}{h_N h_S},$$

$$A(P, E) = -a_{11} \frac{2}{h_E(h_E + h_W)} - (a_{12} + a_{21}) \frac{h_W(h_N - h_S)}{h_N h_S h_E(h_E + h_W)}$$
$$- (a_{11}^{(1,0)} + a_{21}^{(0,1)}) \frac{h_W}{h_E(h_E + h_W)},$$

---

[3] If f is any function defined on Ω (or $\partial \Omega$), then its restriction to Ω_h (or $\partial \Omega_h$) is a grid function which we also denote by f.

$$A(P, W) = -a_{11} \frac{2}{h_W(h_W + h_E)} + (a_{12} + a_{21}) \frac{h_E(h_N - h_S)}{h_N h_S h_W(h_E + h_W)}$$

$$+ (a_{11}^{(1,0)} + a_{21}^{(0,1)}) \frac{h_E}{h_W(h_E + h_W)},$$

$$A(P, N) = -(a_{12} + a_{21}) \frac{h_S(h_E - h_W)}{h_E h_W h_N(h_N + h_S)} - a_{22} \frac{2}{h_N(h_N + h_S)}$$

$$- (a_{22}^{(0,1)} + a_{12}^{(1,0)}) \frac{h_S}{h_N(h_N + h_S)},$$

$$A(P, S) = (a_{12} + a_{21}) \frac{h_N(h_E - h_W)}{h_E h_W h_S(h_N + h_S)} - a_{22} \frac{2}{h_S(h_N + h_S)}$$

$$+ (a_{22}^{(0,1)} + a_{12}^{(1,0)}) \frac{h_N}{h_S(h_N + h_S)},$$

$$A(P, NW) = (a_{12} + a_{21}) \frac{h_E h_S}{h_W h_N(h_N + h_S)(h_E + h_W)},$$

$$A(P, SW) = -(a_{12} + a_{21}) \frac{h_E h_N}{h_W h_S(h_N + h_S)(h_E + h_W)},$$

$$A(P, NE) = -(a_{12} + a_{21}) \frac{h_W h_S}{h_E h_N(h_N + h_S)(h_E + h_W)},$$

$$A(P, SE) = (a_{12} + a_{21}) \frac{h_W h_N}{h_E h_S(h_N + h_S)(h_E + h_W)}.$$

In these formulas, the coefficient functions a_{ij} as well as their derivatives are evaluated at the point P. For a *uniform* mesh, these couplings reduce to

$$A(P, P) = \frac{2}{h^2}(a_{11} + a_{22}) + c,$$

$$A(P, E) = \frac{1}{h^2}\left[-a_{11} - \frac{h}{2}(a_{11}^{(1,0)} + a_{21}^{(0,1)})\right],$$

$$A(P, W) = \frac{1}{h^2}\left[-a_{11} + \frac{h}{2}(a_{11}^{(1,0)} + a_{21}^{(0,1)})\right],$$

$$A(P, N) = \frac{1}{h^2}\left[-a_{22} - \frac{h}{2}(a_{22}^{(0,1)} + a_{12}^{(1,0)})\right],$$

$$A(P, S) = \frac{1}{h^2}\left[-a_{22} + \frac{h}{2}(a_{22}^{(0,1)} + a_{12}^{(1,0)})\right],$$

$$A(P, NW) = A(P, SE) = -A(P, NE) = -A(P, SW) = \frac{1}{4h^2}(a_{12} + a_{21}).$$

The derivatives $a_{11}^{(1,0)}$, $a_{21}^{(0,1)}$, $a_{12}^{(1,0)}$, and $a_{22}^{(0,1)}$ can also be *approximated* using the appropriate formulas from Theorem 10.1.1, thus yielding couplings which depend only on functional values $a_{ij}(P)$ and $c(P)$.

10.2 BOUNDARY CONDITIONS

The *finite difference equation*

$$(L_h U)P = f(P), \qquad P \in \Omega_h, \tag{10.2.1}$$

is equivalent to a (rectangular) linear system of equations which may be written in matrix form as

$$\tilde{A}\tilde{\mathbf{U}} = \mathbf{K}. \tag{10.2.2}$$

The equation associated with the mesh point P "approximates" the partial differential equation (10.1.1) at the point P. Dirichlet boundary conditions are easily accommodated. For example, if $P \in \partial\Omega_h \cap \partial\Omega_1$, and (10.1.5) holds, we simply set

$$U(P) = g_1(P). \tag{10.2.3}$$

Obviously (10.2.3) can be used to eliminate the unknowns in (10.2.2) that correspond to mesh points on $\partial\Omega_1$.

We next make a few remarks about the treatment of boundary conditions involving the normal derivatives which occur in (10.1.6)–(10.1.7) when $a_{ij} = k\delta_{ij}$ ($\delta_{ij} =$ Kronecker delta). We delineate two cases and in each case assume that a normal direction is well defined at the mesh point $P \in \partial\bar{\Omega}_h$.

Case 1. If the normal direction is a coordinate direction, we may incorporate the boundary condition

$$\frac{\partial u}{\partial \mathbf{n}}(P) \equiv \nabla u \cdot \mathbf{n} = g_2(P) \quad \text{for} \quad P \in \partial\Omega_2 \tag{10.2.4}$$

into the finite difference model in the following two ways:

I At each point $P \in \partial\Omega_h \cap \partial\Omega_2$, a new difference equation is constructed for that point (see Figure 10.2.1). For each such point we approximate (10.2.4) by a one-sided difference approximation, yielding the equation

$$U(P) - U(W) = h_W\, g_2(P).$$

We now have as many equations as unknowns.

II. Auxiliary points are added to the mesh $\bar{\Omega}_h$ (as illustrated in Figure 10.2.2) so that a *centered difference approximation* can be used to approximate $\partial u/\partial \mathbf{n}$. For example,

$$U_x(P) = \frac{h_W}{h_E(h_E + h_W)} U(E) + \frac{h_E - h_W}{h_E h_W} U(P) - \frac{h_E}{h_W(h_E + h_W)} U(W).$$

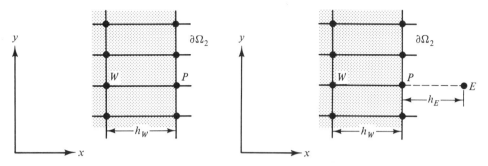

Figure 10.2.1 Normal derivative:
one-sided difference approximation.

Figure 10.2.2 Normal derivative:
centered difference approximation.

In this case, a difference equation of the form (10.2.1) holds at each mesh point of $\bar{\Omega}_h$, including boundary points such as P in Figure 10.2.2. Associated with the auxiliary mesh points such as E in Figure 10.2.2 are equations of the form

$$\frac{h_W}{h_E(h_E + h_W)} U(E) + \frac{h_E - h_W}{h_E h_W} U(P) - \frac{h_E}{h_W(h_E + h_W)} U(W) = g_2(P),$$

which incorporates the boundary condition. Again we have the same number of equations as unknowns.

Case 2. If the normal direction is *not* a coordinate direction, we may proceed as follows. A perpendicular to $\partial\Omega_2$ is constructed at P and extended to the point of intersection, P', of an interior grid line of $\bar{\Omega}_h$ (see Figure 10.2.3). Then the Neumann condition (10.2.4) is approximated at $P \in \partial\Omega_h \cap \partial\Omega_2$ by

$$\frac{\partial u}{\partial \mathbf{n}}(P) \approx \frac{\cos\alpha}{h_W}\left[U(P) - U(P')\right] = g_2(P),$$

where $U(P') = (1/h_S)[(h_S - h_W \tan\alpha)U(W) + (h_W \tan\alpha)U(SW)]$. The finite difference model contains an equation of the type (10.2.1) for each point $P \in \Omega_h$, while at each

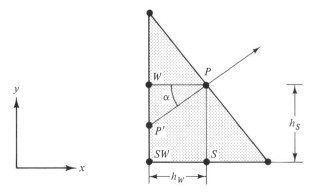

Figure 10.2.3 Normal derivative:
oblique boundary.

boundary point such as P in Figure 10.2.3 an equation of the form

$$[\cos \alpha] U(P) - \left(\cos \alpha - \frac{h_W}{h_S} \sin \alpha \right) U(W) - \left(\frac{h_W}{h_S} \sin \alpha \right) U(SW) = h_W g_2(P)$$

(10.2.5)

holds.

In all the cases above we have constructed finite difference models which consist of a system of (say) M linear equations in M unknowns. We shall see later that finite difference models based on variational formulations handle normal derivative boundary conditions with considerably less effort. For ease of exposition, in the following discussion, we assume $\partial \Omega_1 = \partial \Omega$. This boundary value problem is called the *Dirichlet problem*.

The $M \times M$ system of linear equations that results from (10.2.2) after (10.2.3) has been used to eliminate the boundary unknowns may be written as

$$A\mathbf{U} = \mathbf{K}.$$

(10.2.6)

If $\bar{\Omega}$ is the rectangle of Figure 10.2.4, and the unknowns are given the "lexicographical" ordering shown in this figure, then $M = m_1 m_2$ and the coefficient matrix A may be

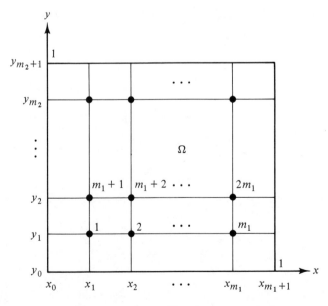

$$\bar{\Omega} = [0, 1] \times [0, 1], \bar{\Omega}_h = \{P_{ij} = (x_i, y_j)\}$$

Figure 10.2.4   Rectangular domain $\bar{\Omega}$.

partitioned as a *block-tridiagonal* matrix,

$$
A = \begin{bmatrix}
A_{11} & A_{12} & & & & \\
A_{21} & A_{22} & A_{23} & & & \\
& \cdot & \cdot & \cdot & & \\
& & \cdot & \cdot & \cdot & \\
& & & \cdot & \cdot & \\
& & & & A_{m_2,m_2-1} & A_{m_2,m_2}
\end{bmatrix},
\tag{10.2.7}
$$

where each nonzero block is itself an $m_1 \times m_1$ tridiagonal matrix. In fact, with this partitioning we have

$$
\mathbf{U} = (\mathbf{U}_1, \mathbf{U}_2, \ldots, \mathbf{U}_{m_2})^T,
$$

where

$$
\mathbf{U}_j = (U_{1j}, U_{2j}, \ldots, U_{m_1,j})^T
$$

and

$$
U_{ij} = U(P_{ij}), \qquad P_{ij} = (x_i, y_j).
$$

Furthermore, if we denote the element in row i and column k of matrix A_{pq} by $[A_{pq}]_{ik}$, and let

$$
J = \{(i, k) \mid i = 1, \ldots, m_1; \; k = i - 1, i, i + 1; \; k \neq 0, m_1 + 1\},
$$

then for $j = 1, \ldots, m_2$,

$$
[A_{jj}]_{ik} = \begin{cases} A(P_{ij}, P_{kj}), & (i, k) \in J \\ 0, & \text{otherwise} \end{cases}
$$

$$
[A_{j,j+1}]_{ik} = \begin{cases} A(P_{ij}, P_{k,j+1}), & (i, k) \in J \\ 0 & \text{otherwise} \end{cases}
$$

$$
[A_{j,j-1}]_{ik} = \begin{cases} A(P_{ij}, P_{k,j-1}), & (i, k) \in J \\ 0 & \text{otherwise}. \end{cases}
$$

The source term $\mathbf{K}$ in (10.2.6) is given by

$$
\mathbf{K} = (\mathbf{K}_1, \mathbf{K}_2, \ldots, \mathbf{K}_{m_2})^T,
$$

where for $2 \leq j \leq m_2 - 1$,

$$
[\mathbf{K}_j]_i = \begin{cases} f_{1j} - \sum_{k=j-1}^{j+1} A(P_{1j}, P_{0k})U_{0k}, & i = 1 \\ f_{ij}, & 2 \leq i \leq m_1 - 1 \\ f_{m_1,j} - \sum_{k=j-1}^{j+1} A(P_{m_1,j}, P_{m_1+1,k})U_{m_1+1,k}, & i = m_1, \end{cases}
$$

while

$$
[\mathbf{K}_1]_i = \begin{cases}
f_{11} - \displaystyle\sum_{k=0}^{2} A(P_{11}, P_{0k})U_{0k} - \sum_{k=1}^{2} A(P_{11}, P_{k0})U_{k0}, & i = 1 \\[4mm]
f_{i1} - \displaystyle\sum_{k=0}^{2} A(P_{11}, P_{k0})U_{k0}, & 2 \le i \le m_1 - 1 \\[4mm]
f_{m_1,1} - \displaystyle\sum_{k=0}^{2} A(P_{m_1,1}, P_{m_1+1,k})U_{m_1+1,k} \\[4mm]
\qquad\qquad - \displaystyle\sum_{k=m_1-1}^{m_1} A(P_{m_1,1}, P_{k0})U_{k0}, & i = m_1
\end{cases}
$$

and $\mathbf{K}_{m_2}$ is defined analogously.

Note that if $a_{12} = a_{21} = 0$, the off-diagonal blocks in (10.2.7) reduce to diagonal matrices. Moreover, when the mesh gauge h is sufficiently small, it can be shown that A is nonsingular, and consequently system (10.2.6) has a unique solution[4]. We return to this question of invertibility in Section 10.4.

We remark that the symmetry of the matrix $[a_{ij}]$ in (10.1.2) does not guarantee the symmetry of A. However, if we use the following difference operators:

$$
(a_{11}U_x)_x \equiv \frac{2[h_E a_{11}(W/2) - (h_E - h_W)a_{11}(P)]}{h_W^2(h_E + h_W)}\, U(W)
$$

$$
+ \frac{2[-h_W^3 a_{11}(E/2) + (h_E^2 - h_W^2)(h_E - h_W)a_{11}(P) - h_E^3 a_{11}(W/2)]}{h_E^2 h_W^2 (h_E + h_W)}\, U(P)
$$

$$
+ \frac{2[h_W a_{11}(E/2) + (h_E - h_W)a_{11}(P)]}{h_E^2(h_E + h_W)}\, U(E), \tag{10.2.8}
$$

$$
(a_{22}U_y)_y \equiv \frac{2[h_N a_{22}(S/2) - (h_N - h_S)a_{11}(P)]}{h_S^2(h_S + h_N)}\, U(S)
$$

$$
+ \frac{2[-h_S^3 a_{11}(N/2) + (h_N^2 - h_S^2)(h_N - h_S)a_{11}(P) - h_N^3 a_{11}(S/2)]}{h_N^2 h_S^2 (h_N + h_S)}\, U(P)
$$

$$
+ \frac{2[h_S a_{11}(N/2) + (h_N - h_S)a_{11}(P)]}{h_N^2(h_N + h_S)}\, U(N), \tag{10.2.9}
$$

where $a_{11}(E/2) = a_{11}(x + h_E/2, y)$, and so on, then for a *uniform* mesh these reduce to

$$
(a_{11}U_x)_x = \frac{1}{h^2}\left[a_{11}\left(\frac{W}{2}\right)U(W) - \left(a_{11}\left(\frac{W}{2}\right) + a_{11}\left(\frac{E}{2}\right)\right)U(P) + a_{11}\left(\frac{E}{2}\right)U(E) \right]
$$

---

[4] When $a_{12} = a_{21} = 0$ and h is sufficiently small, A becomes a so-called *irreducibly diagonally dominant* matrix (Varga [1962]). It is well known that such matrices are invertible.

and

$$(a_{22}U_Y)_Y = \frac{1}{h^2}\left[a_{22}\left(\frac{S}{2}\right)U(S) - \left(a_{22}\left(\frac{S}{2}\right) + a_{22}\left(\frac{N}{2}\right)\right)U(P) + a_{22}\left(\frac{N}{2}\right)U(N)\right].$$

Thus the associated coefficient matrix is symmetric [i.e., $A(P, Q) = A(Q, P)$]. Moreover, it is not difficult to see that for smooth functions these last operators approximate the corresponding partial derivatives with an error that is $O(h^2)$.

10.3 A BRIEF SURVEY OF SOLUTION METHODS FOR LINEAR EQUATION SYSTEMS

In this book we have, for the most part, avoided the description of solution methods for the systems of equations that arise from the discretization of partial differential equations. However, equation systems generated by discretizations of elliptic boundary value problems, such as those presented in this chapter (and Chapter 7), have received so much attention in the numerical analysis literature that some discussion of their solution is in order.

Broadly speaking, solution methods for such systems may be classified as either *direct* (in which a solution that is exact except for roundoff errors is produced in a predictable number of operations) or *iterative* (in which recursive approximations of the exact solution are produced and the number of operations depends on a preselected convergence criterion). There are also methods that are more properly regarded as *hybrid*, since they incorporate significant aspects of both direct and iterative methods.

Most direct methods utilize some form of the classical Gaussian elimination procedure. The more sophisticated algorithms exploit the *sparse* and/or *banded* structure[5] of the coefficient matrix. With a proper ordering of the equations and unknowns, many discrete elliptic systems possess sparse, banded coefficient matrices. There are a number of high-level software packages for the direct solution of linear (general, as well as the more specially structured) systems. We mention, in particular, the modules of the LINPACK software system (Dongarra et al. [1979]) and those contained in the commercially available IMSL (IMSL [1980]) and NAG (NAG [1980]) software libraries. A substantial collection of routines for sparse matrix calculations is also available from IMSL as the *Yale Sparse Matrix Package*. For a survey of sparse matrix calculations, see Reid [1977, 1987].

Certain important special cases of the elliptic equation (10.1.1) admit natural discretizations that may be solved by a class of techniques known as *fast direct*

---

[5] A matrix is sparse if only a relatively small number of its elements is nonzero. It is banded if all of its nonzero elements are confined to its main diagonal and a relatively small number of contiguous super and subdiagonals.

methods. For example, if Ω is a rectangular region and the Poisson equation,

$$u_{xx} + u_{yy} = f(x, y),$$

is subject to the Dirichlet condition $u|_{\partial\Omega} = 0$, then the system (10.2.6) obtained from applying the difference operators U_{XX} and U_{YY} on a uniform mesh can be solved by either the *fast Fourier transform* or *cyclic reduction methods* (Door [1970]). The first of these methods employs discrete Fourier transforms to invert system (10.2.6). The transforms themselves are evaluated by some version of the fast Fourier transform algorithm of Cooley and Tukey [1965]. If the problem is solved on, say, an n by n grid, the number of unknowns is n^2 and the fast Fourier method obtains this solution in $O(n^2 \log_2 n)$ operations. This should be compared with the $O(n^4)$ operations that would be required by a Gaussian elimination method that exploited the banded nature of the matrix and the $O(n^6)$ operations that a "naive" elimination method would use.

In the cyclic reduction method (Buzbee, Golub, and Nielson [1970]), half of the unknowns are eliminated by an algebraic manipulation that leaves the resulting system with the same structure as the original. Thus repeated applications of the process reduce the system to a simple tridiagonal one. The tridiagonal system may be efficiently solved by a direct factorization technique, and the previously eliminated unknowns recovered by back solving additional tridiagonal systems. Again, the number of operations for an n by n grid is $O(n^2 \log_2 n)$. A variant of this method is the *Fourier analysis and cyclic reduction* (FACR) method (Hockney [1965], Swarztrauber [1977], Temperton [1980]), which interweaves the features of the cyclic reduction and fast Fourier methods. A careful application of FACR can improve the solution time over either the fast Fourier or cyclic reduction methods by about a factor of 4 (Press et al. [1986]).

Another class of "fast" methods first converts the discrete boundary value problem into an initial value problem, and then obtains the solution of the latter by a *marching* procedure (see Bank and Rose [1977] and Bank [1977, 1978] for descriptions of these methods).

Each of the foregoing fast methods is formally restricted to problems that are amenable to solution by separation of variables on rectangular domains. However, it may be possible to remove these restrictions at the expense of an increase in computing costs. For instance, nonseparable problems may be treated iteratively as a sequence of separable problems (Gunn [1965], Concus and Golub [1973]). Furthermore, in the case of the Helmholtz equation,

$$u_{xx} + u_{yy} + cu = f,$$

one may remove the dependence on rectangular domains by the *capacitance matrix* method (Proskurowski [1979], O'Leary and Widlund [1979]).

Iterative methods offer an alternative to direct solution techniques. General surveys of these methods may be found, for example, in Kincaid and Young [1979] or Hageman and Young [1981]. These references contain discussions of the classical *Jacobi, Gauss–Seidel,* and *successive overrelaxation* (SOR) schemes. The books by

Varga [1971] and Young [1971] lay the theoretical foundations of these and other iterative methods.

The advantage of iterative methods is that for large sparse systems of the type typically encountered in the solution of elliptic equations, the storage requirements and number of operations per iteration are usually quite modest. This is because the implementation of these methods normally requires only the computation of matrix–vector products involving parts of the coefficient matrix. Thus, only the nonzero entries of this matrix need to be stored. Moreover, unlike direct methods, the iterative process itself produces no "fill-in" (i.e., it creates no new nonzero entries).

The disadvantage of iterative methods is that one is unable to make an a priori determination of the minimum number of iterations required to achieve a specified accuracy in the solution. Therefore, the precise number of operations that a given method will need for convergence is not known in advance. On the other hand, there is a well-developed theory for the estimation of asymptotic (as the number of iterations approaches ∞) convergence rates, and in many instances this permits valuable comparisons of different methods. For example, for our model Poisson problem, this theory shows that the number of iterations required by the Jacobi method to reduce the error by a factor of 10^{-p} is about $\frac{1}{2}pn^2$. If the Gauss–Seidel method is used, this number is reduced by a factor of 2. But if an optimal implementation of the SOR scheme is employed, the number drops to $\frac{1}{3}pn$. Obviously, for large n the choice of the iterative methods makes a tremendous difference in the amount of computational work involved!

Various *acceleration* procedures have been developed to increase the convergence rates of basic schemes such as the Jacobi and SOR methods. In this connection, the *Chebyshev semi-iterative* and *conjugate gradient* acceleration methods are widely used. See Hageman and Young [1981] for descriptions of these. It has also been found that the use of a *preconditioning* matrix, which transforms the coefficient matrix into one having a high convergence rate with respect to a given acceleration procedure, can greatly improve the performance of such a procedure (Meijerink and van der Vorst [1977], Evans [1983], Axelsson, Brinkkemper, and Il'in [1984]). The iterative methods discussed above are part of the ITPACK software package (Kincaid et al. [1981]) and are available from IMSL, Inc.

Multigrid methods stand out as an especially impressive class of hybrid schemes for the solution of linear systems arising from discretizations of elliptic partial differential equations. In these methods, a basic iterative technique such as the Jacobi scheme is first applied to eliminate the high-frequency Fourier modes of the error. This is called the *smoothing* part of the algorithm. Next, a computable measure of the smoothed error, called the "defect," is restricted to a "coarse" subgrid of the original (fine) grid. (The coarse grid is typically obtained by doubling the original mesh spacing.) Using the coarse grid defect, equations for the coarse grid error are developed. Frequently, these equations are of the same generic form as the original difference equations. At this point, the coarse grid error can be determined by one of the methods discussed above and the fine grid error recovered by interpolation—or, what is immensely more significant, the whole smoothing-restriction process can be applied to the newly obtained *coarse grid error*. In this way, an algorithm is obtained on a nested sequence of grids of exponentially decreasing size. When the coarsest grid has been reached, and the error there is determined, the computations proceed back to the original grid by a series of interpolations. Since the restriction and interpolation operations that are used to perform the grid transfers reintroduce errors, the overall algorithm is iterative in nature. However, the convergence rates of these methods are very large (and usually independent of the size of the grid). Indeed, when properly implemented, multigrid methods can produce operation counts as low as $O(n^2)$ on an n by n grid.

The multigrid literature is vast and appears to be growing exponentially. From this plethora, we mention the article by Brandt [1977], the collections by Hackbusch and Trottenberg [1982] and McCormick [1987], and the monograph by Hackbusch [1985].

We conclude this brief survey by calling to the reader's attention the ELLPACK software system for solving elliptic boundary value problems (Rice and Boisvert [1985]). ELLPACK includes a high-level problem statement language as well as an extensive (and extensible) library of problem-solving modules. Using a Fortran-like language, and the variety of finite difference formulas and linear equation solvers included in the module library, the user can generate a grid, discretize the differential equation, and solve the resulting linear equation system without ever leaving the ELLPACK framework.

10.4 MAXIMUM PRINCIPLES

Maximum principles provide an effective way to study the convergence of approximations of the type encountered in Section 10.1. Consequently, in this section we develop maximum principles for both differential and difference operators. We begin with a consideration of the differential operator,

$$Lu = -\nabla \cdot A \, \nabla u + cu, \tag{10.4.1}$$

where $A = [a_{ij}]$, and ∇ is the gradient $(\partial/\partial x, \partial/\partial y)$. Concerning the functions a_{ij} and c, we make the same assumptions as in Section 10.1. We also assume that L is uniformly elliptic. Then we have the following lemma.

Lemma 10.4.1.   *Let* $v \in C(\bar{\Omega}) \cap C^2(\Omega)$. *If* $\max_{\bar{\Omega}} v > 0$, *and if this maximum is assumed at a point in* Ω, *then* $Lv \geq 0$ *at that point.*

Proof. By the well-known necessary conditions for a maximum, we have $v_x = v_y = 0$, $v_{xx} \leq 0$, $v_{yy} \leq 0$, and $v_{xy}^2 \leq v_{xx} v_{yy}$. (Here, and in the rest of the proof, all expressions are evaluated at a point in Ω where the maximum occurs.) Thus

$$Lv = -[a_{11}v_{xx} + (a_{12} + a_{21})v_{xy} + a_{22}v_{yy}] + cv.$$

If $v_{xx} = v_{yy} = 0$, then also $v_{xy} = 0$, and $Lv = cv \geq 0$. Otherwise, we may assume without loss of generality that $v_{xx} < 0$. Since L is uniformly elliptic, we have $a_{22} \geq 0$. Hence

$$Lv = \frac{a_{11}v_{xx}^2 + (a_{12} + a_{21})v_{xx}v_{xy} + a_{22}v_{xx}v_{yy}}{-v_{xx}} + cv$$

$$\geq \frac{a_{11}v_{xx}^2 + (a_{12} + a_{21})v_{xx}v_{xy} + a_{22}v_{xy}^2}{-v_{xx}} + cv \geq 0,$$

where the last inequality follows again from the uniform ellipticity of L.

Q.E.D.

Lemma 10.4.1 leads directly to a maximum principle.

Theorem 10.4.2.   *Let $u \in C(\bar{\Omega}) \cap C^2(\Omega)$. If u satisfies the conditions*

$$Lu \leq 0 \quad \text{on } \Omega,$$

$$u\big|_{\partial\Omega} \leq 0,$$

then $\max_{\bar{\Omega}} u \leq 0$.

Proof. Let $v = u + \varepsilon e^{\alpha x}$, where ε and α are parameters. Then

$$Lv = Lu - \varepsilon[a_{11}\alpha^2 + (a_{11}^{(0,1)} + a_{21}^{(0,1)})\alpha - c]e^{\alpha x}.$$

Since $a_{11} \geq \mu$, where μ is the positive constant of (10.1.3), we can choose $\alpha > 0$ such that for any $\varepsilon > 0$, we have $Lv < 0$ on Ω. It follows from the contrapositive form of Lemma 10.4.1 that for such v at least one of the following conditions holds: (a) $\max_{\bar{\Omega}} v \leq 0$, or (b) $\max_{\bar{\Omega}} v = \max_{\partial\Omega} v$. In case (a),

$$\max_{\bar{\Omega}} u \leq \max_{\bar{\Omega}} v \leq 0,$$

and the theorem is proven. In case (b),

$$\max_{\bar{\Omega}} u \leq \max_{\partial\Omega} v \leq \max_{\partial\Omega} u + \varepsilon \max_{\partial\Omega} e^{\alpha x} \leq \varepsilon \max_{\partial\Omega} e^{\alpha x},$$

and the result again follows by letting $\varepsilon \to 0$.

Q.E.D.

With a maximum principle such as the one we have just established, it is possible to give a priori estimates of the size of a solution of the Dirichlet boundary value problem: Find $u \in C(\bar{\Omega}) \cap C^2(\Omega)$ such that

$$Lu = f \quad \text{on } \Omega,$$

$$u\big|_{\partial\Omega} = g, \tag{10.4.2}$$

where $f \in C(\bar{\Omega})$ and $g \in C(\partial\Omega)$. For this purpose, we introduce the notion of a *comparison function* for solutions of (10.4.2). This is a function $\phi \in C(\bar{\Omega}) \cap C^2(\Omega)$ that satisfies the conditions

$$L\phi \geq \sup_{\Omega} |f| \quad \text{on } \Omega,$$

$$\phi\Big|_{\partial\Omega} \geq \sup_{\partial\Omega} |g|.$$

Then we can prove the following theorem.

Theorem 10.4.3. *Let u solve the boundary value problem* (10.4.2) *and let* ϕ *be a comparison function for solutions of* (10.4.2). *Then* $|u| \leq \phi$ *at all points of* $\bar{\Omega}$.

Proof. At each point of Ω we have

$$L(\pm u) = \pm Lu = \pm f \leq \sup_{\Omega} |f| \leq L\phi.$$

Thus $L(\pm u - \phi) \leq 0$ on Ω. Also, at any point of $\partial\Omega$,

$$\pm u \leq |g| \leq \sup_{\partial\Omega} |g| \leq \phi.$$

Therefore, $\pm u - \phi \leq 0$ on $\partial\Omega$. Applying Theorem 10.4.2 to the function $\pm u - \phi$, we conclude that $\pm u \leq \phi$ on $\bar{\Omega}$.

$$\text{Q.E.D.}$$

It is now a simple matter to show that problem (10.4.2) has at most one solution in $C(\bar{\Omega}) \cap C^2(\Omega)$. For if u and v are two such solutions, then $w = u - v$ solves (10.4.2) with $f = 0$, $g = 0$. Thus $\phi \equiv 0$ is a comparison function for w, and so, according to Theorem 10.4.3, $w \equiv 0$ on $\bar{\Omega}$.

We turn now to a somewhat parallel development for the finite difference operator L_h defined by (10.1.15) under the assumption that L_h is of *nonnegative type*. By this we mean that for all $P \in \Omega_h$ the couplings $A(P, Q)$ in (10.1.15) satisfy the conditions

1. $A(P, P) > 0$, $A(P, Q) \leq 0$, $P \neq Q$,

2. $A(P, P) \geq - \sum_{Q \neq P} A(P, Q)$.

The analogue of Theorem 10.4.2 is the following.

Theorem 10.4.4. *Let* L_h *be of nonnegative type. If* $U \in M(\bar{\Omega}_h)$ *satisfies the conditions*

$$L_h U \leq 0 \quad \text{on } \Omega_h,$$

$$U\Big|_{\partial\Omega_h} \leq 0,$$

then $\max_{\bar{\Omega}_h} U \leq 0$.

Proof. Suppose that $\max_{\bar{\Omega}_h} U = U(P)$ for some $P \in \Omega_h$. If $R \neq P$ is any point such that $A(P, R) \neq 0$, we assert that $U(P) = U(R)$. This follows since otherwise

$(L_h U)P \leq 0$, $U(Q) \leq U(P)$, $Q \neq P$, and $U(R) < U(P)$ combine to imply that

$$U(P) \leq \sum_{Q \neq P} \frac{-A(P, Q)}{A(P, P)} U(Q) < \left[\sum_{Q \neq P} \frac{-A(P, Q)}{A(P, P)} \right] U(P) \leq U(P),$$

which is a contradiction. However, the point P is connected to a point $R \in \partial\Omega_h$ by a finite sequence of points $P = P_0, P_1, \ldots, P_n = R$ such that $A(P_i, P_{i+1}) \neq 0, i = 0, \ldots, n - 1$. It follows by repeated application of the above argument that $U(P) = U(R) \leq 0$.

Q.E.D.

Consider the discrete boundary value problem: Find $U \in M(\bar{\Omega}_h)$ such that

$$L_h U = f \quad \text{on } \Omega_h,$$

$$U\Big|_{\partial\Omega_h} = g, \tag{10.4.3}$$

where f and g are as in (10.4.2). To estimate the size of U, we introduce a comparison function for solutions of (10.4.3). The grid function $\Phi \in M(\bar{\Omega}_h)$ is a comparison function for solutions of (10.4.3) if it satisfies the conditions

$$L_h \Phi \geq \max_{\Omega_h} |f| \quad \text{on } \Omega_h,$$

$$\Phi\Big|_{\partial\Omega_h} \geq \max_{\partial\Omega_h} |g|.$$

Here is the analogue of Theorem 10.4.3.

Theorem 10.4.5.   *Let U solve the discrete boundary value problem* (10.4.3) *where L_h is of nonnegative type, and let Φ be a comparison function for solutions of* (10.4.3). *Then $|U| \leq |\Phi|$ at all points of $\bar{\Omega}_h$.*

The proof is left as Exercise 10.6.

It is a corollary of Theorem 10.4.5 that the linear system represented by (10.4.3) has a unique solution when L_h is of nonnegative type.

Corollary 10.4.6.   *If L_h is of nonnegative type, then* (10.4.3) *possesses a unique solution.*

Proof. Suppose that $f = 0$, $g = 0$. Then $\Phi \equiv 0$ is a comparison function for solutions of (10.4.3), and Theorem 10.4.5 implies that the only solution of (10.4.3) in this case is $U \equiv 0$. Thus the alternative principle[6] for finite-dimensional linear systems yields the desired conclusion.

Q.E.D

---

[6] In the case of (10.4.3), this states that either the homogeneous system (which occurs when $f = 0$, $g = 0$) has a nontrivial solution or the inhomogeneous system has a unique solution.

10.5 *CONVERGENCE OF THE FINITE DIFFERENCE SOLUTION*

In this section we develop an estimate of the size of the *discretization error,*

$$E: \bar{\Omega}_h \to R, \quad E(P) \equiv u(P) - U(P),$$

where u and U are solutions of (10.4.2) and (10.4.3), respectively. If we introduce the *local truncation error,*

$$\tau: \Omega_h \to R, \quad \tau(P) \equiv (L_h u - Lu)P,$$

we see that on Ω_h,

$$L_h E = L_h u - L_h U = L_h u - f = L_h u - Lu = \tau.$$

Also, $E|_{\partial \Omega_h} = 0$. Thus E is a solution of the problem: Find $V \in M(\bar{\Omega}_h)$ such that

$$L_h V = \tau \quad \text{on } \Omega_h$$

$$V\Big|_{\partial \Omega_h} = 0. \tag{10.5.1}$$

We wish to apply Theorem 10.4.5 to problem (10.5.1). This requires that L_h be of nonnegative type and that a comparison function exist for the solution of (10.5.1). These requirements can be met if, for example, the matrix $A = [a_{ij}]$ appearing in (10.4.1) is a constant, diagonal matrix. Under this simple condition, we can produce an explicit comparison function for the solution of (10.5.1). We assume, without loss of generality, that Ω is contained in the strip $\{(x, y) | -\infty < a < x < b < \infty\}$.

Lemma 10.5.1.   *If $A = [a_{ij}]$ is a diagonal matrix of constants, then the finite difference operator L_h given by (10.1.15) is of nonnegative type. Furthermore, $\Phi \in M(\bar{\Omega}_h)$,*

$$\Phi(P) \equiv \frac{1}{2\mu}(r^2 - x^2) \max_{\Omega_h} |\tau|, \quad [P = (x, y)],$$

where $r = \max(|a|, |b|)$ and μ is the positive constant of (10.1.3), is a comparison function for the solution of (10.5.1).

The proof amounts to a verification of the stated conclusions and is left as Exercise 10.9.

If we combine the results of Theorem 10.4.5 and Lemma 10.5.1, we obtain an estimate of $|E|$ on $\bar{\Omega}_h$.

Corollary 10.5.2.   *Let the hypotheses of Lemma 10.5.1 hold. Then*

$$|E(P)| \le \frac{r^2}{2\mu} \max_{\Omega_h} |\tau|, \quad P \in \bar{\Omega}_h.$$

In view of Corollary 10.5.2, convergence of the finite difference solution U to the solution u of the Dirichlet problem (10.4.2) may be established by simply estimating the order of τ. Different results can be obtained by varying the assumed smoothness of u. The proof of the following convergence theorem employs the order estimates of Theorem 10.1.1 and is left to the reader.

Theorem 10.5.3.   *Let $A = [a_{ij}]$ be a diagonal matrix of constants, let $u \in C^4(\bar{\Omega})$ be the solution of the Dirichlet problem (10.4.2), and let U satisfy (10.4.3). Then*

$$\max_{\bar{\Omega}_h} |u - U| = O(h^{\alpha}),$$

where $\alpha = 2$ if the mesh spacings are uniform and $\alpha = 1$ otherwise.

We conclude this section with an example that illustrates the preceding analysis.

Example 10.5.1

Let $\bar{\Omega} \equiv [0, 1] \times [0, 1]$ and consider the partial differential equation,

$$-v_{xx} - v_{yy} + (x^2 + y^2)v = 40(2 - x - y + 4xy)e^{xy}, \qquad (x, y) \in \Omega,$$

subject to the boundary condition $v|_{\partial\Omega} = g$, where g is chosen as the restriction to $\partial\Omega$ of

$$u(x, y) = \{10 - 20[(x - \tfrac{1}{2})^2 + (y - \tfrac{1}{2})^2]\}e^{xy}.$$

One verifies that $u(x, y)$ is also the solution of this boundary value problem. Let U_h denote the solution of the finite difference equations (10.4.3) when the mesh has uniform spacing h. Table 10.5.1 presents $U_h(P)$ at 16 points $P = (x, y)$ for $h = 0.2, 0.1,$ and 0.05.

TABLE 10.5.1   FINITE DIFFERENCE SOLUTION[a]

	$x = 0.2$	$x = 0.4$	$x = 0.6$	$x = 0.8$
$y = 0.2$	6.6520	8.6491	8.9979	7.4912
	6.6588	8.6618	9.0142	7.5054
	6.6606	8.6651	9.0185	7.5092
	6.6612	8.6663	9.0200	7.5105
$y = 0.4$	8.6491	11.2346	12.1645	10.9828
	8.6618	11.2575	12.1936	11.0081
	8.6651	11.2636	12.2014	11.0148
	8.6663	11.2657	12.2040	11.0170
$y = 0.6$	8.9979	12.1645	13.7093	12.8830
	9.0142	12.1936	13.7466	12.9166
	9.0185	12.2014	13.7566	12.9255
	9.0200	12.2040	13.7600	12.9286
$y = 0.8$	7.4912	10.9828	12.8830	12.0930
	7.5054	11.0081	12.9166	12.1255
	7.5092	11.0148	12.9255	12.1344
	7.5105	11.0170	12.9286	12.1375

[a] The first value in each group is for $h = 0.2$, the second is for $h = 0.1$, the third is for $h = 0.05$, and the fourth is the true value.

If we assume that the discretization error is of the form $(u - U_h)(P) = Mh^\alpha$, then for a mesh of gauge $(h/2)$, we have $(u - U_{h/2})(P) = M(h/2)^\alpha$, from which we deduce that

$$\alpha = \log \frac{(u - U_h)(P)}{(u - U_{h/2})(P)}\bigg/ \log 2.$$

Applying this, for example, to the point $P = (0.6, 0.6)$ in Table 10.5.1 when $h = 0.1$, we find that

$$\alpha = \log \frac{0.0134}{0.0034}\bigg/ \log 2 = 1.98,$$

which is consistent with the asymptotic result of Theorem 10.5.3.

10.6 THE LAPLACE OPERATOR

Perhaps the most widely studied elliptic operator is the *Laplace operator*, ∇^2, defined in two dimensions by $\nabla^2 u \equiv u_{xx} + u_{yy}$. The notation $\Delta \equiv \nabla^2$ is also in common use. In Figure 10.6.1 we give three stencils for the Laplace operator for uniform spacings h. The first, a *five-point* formula, $\Delta_h u$, follows from the approximations in Section 10.1; the second, $\Delta_h^{\times} u$, is obtained by rotating the coordinate system 45 degrees; the last is the so-called *nine-point* formula, $\Delta_h^9 u$. Note that

$$\Delta_h^9 u = \tfrac{2}{3}\Delta_h u + \tfrac{1}{3}\Delta_h^{\times} u,$$

and by Taylor series developments similar to those used to prove Theorem 10.1.1 we can prove the following theorem.

Theorem 10.6.1.   *Let $u \in C^4(\Omega)$. Then as $h \to 0$,*

$$(\Delta_h u - \Delta u)(P) = \frac{h^2}{12}\left[u^{(4,0)}(\xi, y_p) + u^{(0,4)}(x_p, \eta)\right] = O(h^2),$$

where ξ lies on the line segment connecting mesh points E and W and η is on the segment connecting mesh points N and S. Similarly,

$$(\Delta_h^{\times} u - \Delta u)(P) = \frac{h^2}{12}\left[u^{(4,0)}(Q_1) + u^{(2,2)}(Q_2) + u^{(0,4)}(Q_3)\right] = O(h^2),$$

where the points Q_i belong to the square determined by P and its immediate neighbors. Finally, for $u \in C^8(\Omega)$,

$$(\Delta_h^9 u - \Delta u)(P) = (1/2)h^2\Delta^2 u(P) + \frac{2}{6!}h^4\left[\Delta^3 u(P) + 2(\Delta u)^{(2,2)}(P)\right] + O(h^6) \quad as\ h \to 0.$$

If u is *harmonic* (i.e., $\nabla^2 u = 0$), then the nine-point formula Δ_h^9 is *sixth* order; otherwise, all three stencils in Figure 10.6.1 are asymptotically equivalent.

$\Delta_h u$:

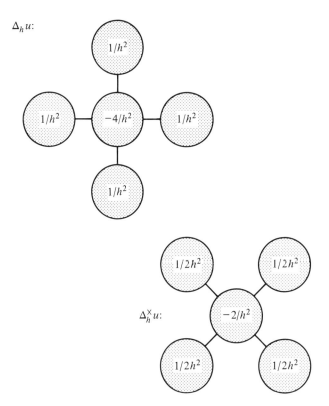

$\Delta_h^{\times} u$:

$\Delta_h^9 u$:

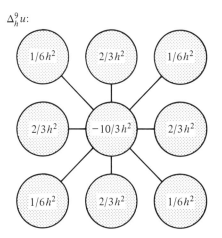

Figure 10.6.1   Three finite difference stencils for $\nabla^2 u$ on a uniform mesh.

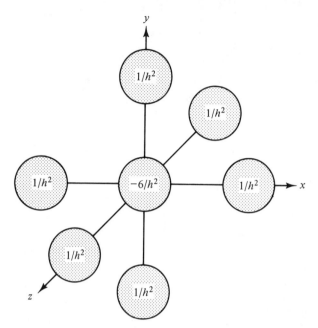

Figure 10.6.2 Finite difference stencil for $u_{xx} + u_{yy} + u_{zz}$.

The Laplace operator ∇^2 in three dimensions is defined by $\nabla^2 u = u_{xx} + u_{yy} + u_{zz}$ for a Cartesian coordinate system. The analogous stencil for $\Delta_h u$ is given in Figure 10.6.2.

10.7 FINITE DIFFERENCE EQUATIONS FROM THE VARIATIONAL FORMULATION

In this section the variational formulation of elliptic boundary value problems is used to generate finite difference equations. The mesh lines of Π_Ω partition Ω into a union of rectangles and triangles, and it facilitates the discussion if an *auxiliary* or *dual* system Π'_Ω of horizontal and vertical mesh lines is constructed in such a way that the lines of Π'_Ω fall halfway between the lines of Π_Ω (cf. Figure 10.7.1). A subregion, R, bounded by mesh lines of Π'_Ω, Π_Ω, and possibly $\partial\Omega$ is called a *cell*. Each cell is either a rectangle or a triangle and contains exactly one mesh point.

For the second-order elliptic problem with Dirichlet boundary conditions (10.1.5), the variational formulation asks for the minimization over

$$S = \{w \in H^1(\Omega) \mid w(P) = g_1(P), \ P \in \partial\Omega_1\}$$

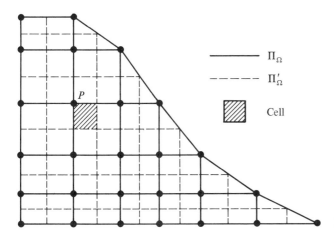

$$
\begin{array}{ll}
\rule{2.5em}{0.4pt} & \Pi_\Omega \\
\text{-----} & \Pi'_\Omega \\
\text{▨} & \text{Cell}
\end{array}
$$

Figure 10.7.1   Finite difference mesh.

of the functional

$$
I[w] = \frac{1}{2} \sum_R \int_R \left(\sum_{i,j=1}^{2} a_{ij} \frac{\partial w}{\partial x_i} \frac{\partial w}{\partial x_j} + cw^2 - 2fw \right) dx\, dy, \qquad (10.7.1)
$$

where the sum is over all cells R determined by Π'_Ω, Π_Ω, and $\partial\Omega$ (see Section 7.2). Thus we seek $u \in S$ such that

$$
\min_{w \in S} I[w] = I[u].
$$

Let u and its derivatives be approximated by constants over each cell; for example, in the shaded cell of Figure 10.7.1,

$$
u \approx U(P), \qquad u_x \approx \frac{U(E) - U(P)}{h_E}, \qquad u_y \approx \frac{U(S) - U(P)}{h_S},
$$

and so on. Systematic substitution of such approximations into $I[u]$ gives rise to a function J whose arguments are the grid function values $\{U(P) \mid P \in \bar{\Omega}_k\}$. The variational problem is then replaced by the finite dimensional minimization problem: Find $U^* \in M(\bar{\Omega}_h)$ such that

$$
J(U^*) = \min_{S_h} J(U), \qquad (10.7.2)
$$

where

$$
S_h = \{U \in M(\bar{\Omega}_h) \mid U(P) = g_1(P),\ P \in \partial\Omega_h \cap \partial\Omega_1\}.
$$

Since this is a conventional minimization problem for a function of several variables, a minimum can only be attained at a point where the gradient of J is zero.

Hence (10.7.2) leads to the system of equations

$$\frac{\partial J}{\partial U(P)} = 0, \qquad P \in \bar{\Omega}_h - \partial\Omega_1. \tag{10.7.3}$$

Formally, this is the finite difference system generated by the variational formulation of the boundary value problem.

The condition (10.7.3) is equivalently written as

$$(L_h U)P \equiv \sum_Q A(P, Q)U(Q) = S(P), \qquad P \in \bar{\Omega}_h - \partial\Omega_1,$$

where the only possible nonzero couplings are

$$A(P, P) = [a_{11}(P) + a_{11}(W)] \frac{h_S + h_N}{4h_W} + [a_{11}(P) + a_{11}(E)] \frac{h_S + h_N}{4h_E}$$

$$+ [a_{22}(P) + a_{22}(S)] \frac{h_E + h_W}{4h_S} + [a_{22}(P) + a_{22}(N)] \frac{h_E + h_W}{4h_N} + c(P) \frac{(h_E + h_W)(h_S + h_N)}{4},$$

$$A(P, E) = -[a_{11}(P) + a_{11}(E)] \frac{h_S + h_N}{4h_E},$$

$$A(P, W) = -[a_{11}(P) + a_{11}(W)] \frac{h_S + h_N}{4h_W},$$

$$A(P, N) = -[a_{22}(P) + a_{22}(N)] \frac{h_E + h_W}{4h_N},$$

$$A(P, S) = -[a_{22}(P) + a_{22}(S)] \frac{h_E + h_W}{4h_S},$$

$$A(P, SW) = -\frac{1}{4}[a_{12}(W) + a_{12}(S)],$$

$$A(P, NE) = -\frac{1}{4}[a_{12}(N) + a_{12}(E)],$$

$$A(P, SE) = \frac{1}{4}[a_{12}(E) + a_{12}(S)],$$

$$A(P, NW) = \frac{1}{4}[a_{12}(W) + a_{12}(N)],$$

and

$$S(P) = f(P) \frac{(h_S + h_N)(h_E + h_W)}{4}.$$

The couplings above were obtained by approximating each function u, a_{kj}, c, and f in a cell of Π'_Ω by its value at the mesh point of Π_Ω which determines the cell.

For example, if R is the shaded cell in Figure 10.7.1,

$$\int_R a_{11}(x, y)\, dx\, dy \approx a_{11}(P)\, \frac{h_E h_S}{4}.$$

Other quadratures could just as easily have been used.

We conclude this section with an example involving more complicated boundary conditions. This is the steady-state heat flow problem (7.2.3). Assume that $\Omega = \bigcup_i \Omega_i$, where the conductivity $k \equiv k_i$ in Ω_i. The *differential equation formulation* is: Find a function u such that

$$-\nabla \cdot k \, \nabla u = f \quad \text{in } \Omega,$$

and

$$u = g \quad \text{on } \partial\Omega_1,$$

$$-\nabla u \cdot \mathbf{n} = 0 \quad \text{on } \partial\Omega_2,$$

$$-k \, \nabla u \cdot \mathbf{n} = h_0(u - u_s) \quad \text{on } \partial\Omega_3.$$

The more general boundary conditions require a functional that is different from (10.7.1) in the variational formulation of this problem. This functional is given in Section 7.2 and leads to the following problem: Find a function u such that

$$\min_{w \in S} I[w] = I[u],$$

where $S = \{w \in H^1(\Omega) \mid w(P) = g(P), P \in \partial\Omega_1\}$ and

$$I[w] = \tfrac{1}{2} \sum_i \int_{\Omega_i} \left[k_i(w_x^2 + w_y^2) - 2fw \right] dx\, dy + \int_{\partial\Omega_3} \left(\tfrac{1}{2} h_0 w^2 - h_0 u_s w \right) ds. \qquad (10.7.4)$$

If R is an auxiliary cell of Π'_Ω, we make the following approximations in $I[u]$:

$$\int_R u_x^2 \, dx\, dy \approx \frac{1}{h_E^2} \int_R \left[U(E) - U(P) \right]^2 dx\, dy,$$

$$\int_R u_y^2 \, dx\, dy \approx \frac{1}{h_S^2} \int_R \left[U(S) - U(P) \right]^2 dx\, dy,$$

$$\int_{\partial\Omega_3 \cap \partial R} \left(\tfrac{1}{2} h_0 u^2 - h_0 u_s u \right) ds \approx \int_{\partial\Omega_3 \cap \partial R} \left\{ \tfrac{1}{2} h_0(P)[U(P)]^2 - h_0(P) u_s(P) U(P) \right\} ds.$$

The result is then

$$J(U) = \frac{1}{2} \left(\sum_R \int_R \left[k_R \left\{ \left[\frac{U(E) - U(P)}{h_E} \right]^2 + \left[\frac{U(S) - U(P)}{h_S} \right]^2 \right\} - 2f(P)U(P) \right] dx\, dy \right)$$

$$+ \sum_R \int_{\partial\Omega_3 \cap \partial R} \left\{ \tfrac{1}{2} h_0(P)[U(P)]^2 - h_0(P) u_s(P) U(P) \right\} ds,$$

where $k \equiv k_R$ in the cell R, and the sum is over all possible cells. For the point P designated in Figure 10.7.1 we finally obtain the difference equation

$$0 = \frac{\partial J}{\partial U(P)} = \left[\frac{k(NE)h_N + k(SE)h_S}{2h_E} + \frac{k(NW)h_N + k(SW)h_S}{2h_W} + \frac{k(NW)h_W + k(NE)h_E}{2h_N} \right.$$

$$\left. + \frac{k(SW)h_W + k(SE)h_E}{2h_S} \right] U(P) - \frac{k(SE)h_S + k(NE)h_N}{2h_E} U(E)$$

$$- \frac{k(SE)h_E + k(SW)h_W}{2h_S} U(S) - \frac{k(NE)h_E + k(NW)h_W}{2h_N} U(N)$$

$$- \frac{k(NW)h_N + k(SW)h_S}{2h_W} U(W) - \tfrac{1}{4} f(P)[h_E h_N + h_E h_S + h_W h_N + h_S h_W],$$

where $k(NE)$ is the value for k in the four cells bounded by the mesh points P, N, NE, E, and so on.

Note that the resulting system of equations is symmetric and that the diagonal term dominates, in absolute value, the sum of the absolute values of the off-diagonal terms. As in the case of (10.2.6), it can be shown that this system has a unique solution. Note also that the boundary integral will affect only the diagonal term, and then, only for cells that contain the mesh point P and are coincident with $\partial\Omega_3$. If P is such a point, then in fact P is a boundary mesh point, and

$$\frac{\partial}{\partial U(P)} \int_{\partial R} \{\tfrac{1}{2} h_0(P)[U(P)]^2 - h_0(P)u_s(P)U(P)\} \, ds = [h_0(P)U(P) - h_0(P)u_s(P)]L,$$

where L is the length of the side of the cell containing P that is coincident with $\partial\Omega_3$. The incorporation of such boundary conditions into the finite difference equations is quite easy compared to the earlier approach associated with the finite difference equations derived from the differential equation formulation.

NOTES AND REMARKS

10.1 We have used Theorem 10.1.1, which is based on Taylor's formula, to generate a difference operator on rectangular grids. It is also possible to use Taylor's formula and the method of undetermined coefficients to derive a finite difference operator $L_h U$ that is a formal approximation of Lu on an irregularly spaced set of points. If a point at which the approximation is to be made is, for example, the origin, and the "neighbors" entering into the approximation have coordinates, say, $(h\xi_i, h\eta_i)$, then the error made in replacing L by L_h is usually $O(h)$ (see Forsythe and Wasow [1960] for details). Unfortunately, in this general case, the resulting difference operator may not be of nonnegative type in the sense of Section 10.3 (Motzkin and Wasow [1953]).

10.2 Although we have assumed that the boundary of Ω is a polygon, it is not difficult to devise interpolation schemes to accommodate Dirichlet conditions on boundaries having more general shapes. In fact, similar statements can be made concerning the Neumann and mixed boundary conditions. For specific interpolation formulas, the reader is referred to texts such as Forsythe and Wasow [1960], Smith [1978], or Vemuri and Karplus [1981].

10.4 The maximum principles that we have presented represent only a small part of a more general theory. An extensive treatment of maximum principles for differential equations may be found in Protter and Weinberger [1984]. The discrete case is considered by Ciarlet [1970] and Brandt [1973], while a discussion of both cases is contained in Garabedian [1986].

10.5 The method that we have used to establish the discretization error estimates given by Theorem 10.5.3 stems from a paper by Gerschgorin [1930]. While it provides information on the order of magnitude of the error as a function of the mesh gauge, it cannot be used to obtain *computable* bounds on the error unless corresponding bounds on the derivatives of u, the unknown solution of the boundary value problem, are available. Moreover, the method applies only to problems whose data are sufficiently smooth to guarantee the boundedness of the derivatives of u that enter into the proof arguments. In contrast to this, there is another approach to the convergence problem that does not assume the existence of u. Indeed, this existence is deduced from the convergence of the finite difference solution itself. Such proofs are much more intricate, and in some respects less useful to the numerical analyst since they usually give no appraisal of the order of the discretization error. The paper by Courant, Friedrichs, and Lewy [1928] is a paradigm of this approach (see also Ladyzhenskaya [1985] and Garabedian [1986]).

The presence of the mixed derivative u_{xy} in (10.1.1) complicates the convergence analysis since the natural discretization of this term as given by Theorem 10.1.1 does not lead (even for constant coefficients and uniform mesh spacings) to a finite difference operator of nonnegative type. In some instances, this difficulty can be circumvented by first transforming the problem into one in which this term is absent (Exercises 10.2 to 10.4). Another approach is to utilize nonstandard discretizations of the u_{xy} term that lead to difference operators of nonnegative type. This has been done by Bramble and Hubbard [1963] (see also Stepleman [1971]).

10.6 Various finite difference formulas for square nets are contained in Bickley [1948] and Collatz [1960]. High-order discretizations of the Laplace operator have been given by Lynch and Rice [1978] and Boisvert [1981].

10.7 Other presentations of the use of a variational principle to derive finite difference equations are contained in Forsythe and Wasow [1960] and Vemuri and Karplus [1981].

EXERCISES

10.1. Consider the change of variables

$$T: \begin{cases} x = \left(r + \dfrac{1}{2}\right) \cos \dfrac{\theta\pi}{2} \\ y = \left(r + \dfrac{1}{2}\right) \sin \dfrac{\theta\pi}{2} \end{cases}$$

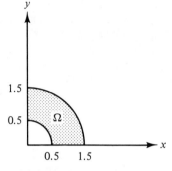

Figure 10.E.1   Quarter annulus Ω.

$0 \le r \le 1, 0 \le \theta \le 1$. Verify that T maps the unit square one-to-one, onto the quarter annulus illustrated in Figure 10.E.1. Graph several coordinate lines of the (r, θ) system. Prove that Laplace's equation $u_{xx} + u_{yy} = 0$ defined on Ω is transformed via T into

$$u_{rr} + \frac{1}{r + \frac{1}{2}} u_r + \frac{4}{\pi^2 (r + \frac{1}{2})^2} u_{\theta\theta} = 0, \qquad 0 \le r, \theta \le 1.$$

Verify that this can also be written as

$$\frac{\partial}{\partial r} \left[\frac{\pi}{2} \left(r + \frac{1}{2} \right) u_r \right] + \frac{\partial}{\partial \theta} \left[\frac{2}{\pi} \left(r + \frac{1}{2} \right)^{-1} u_\theta \right] = 0.$$

10.2. Consider the partial diffferential equation

$$\left[\frac{\partial}{\partial x}, \frac{\partial}{\partial y} \right] \begin{bmatrix} x + y^2 & \frac{1}{2}(1 - 2x)^{1/2} \\ \frac{1}{2}(1 - 2x)^{1/2} & y^2 \end{bmatrix} \begin{bmatrix} \dfrac{\partial u}{\partial x} \\ \dfrac{\partial u}{\partial y} \end{bmatrix} = 0, \qquad 0 \le x, \; y \le \tfrac{1}{2}. \qquad (1)$$

Verify that the change of variables

$$\begin{cases} s = y + \frac{1}{3}(1 - 2x)^{3/2} \\ t = y - (1 - 2x)^{1/2} \end{cases}$$

transforms (1) into a partial differential equation having no term involving u_{st}.

10.3. Consider the elliptic partial differential equation

$$Lu = a_{11} \frac{\partial^2 u}{\partial x^2} + 2a_{12} \frac{\partial^2 u}{\partial x \, \partial y} + a_{22} \frac{\partial^2 u}{\partial y^2} = 0,$$

where the a_{ij} are constants and $a_{ii} > 0$. Let

$$s = \frac{a_{11} x - a_{12} y}{(a_{11} a_{22} - a_{12}^2)^{1/2}},$$

$$t = y,$$

and establish that

$$Lu = \frac{\partial^2 u}{\partial s^2} + \frac{\partial^2 u}{\partial t^2} = 0.$$

10.4. Consider the partial differential equation

$$Lu = a(x, y)u_{xx} + b(x, y)u_{xy} + c(x, y)u_{yy} + d(x, y)u_x + e(x, y)u_y + f(x, y)u = 0,$$

and assume that L is elliptic in the sense of Section 2.1. Let $s = s(x, y)$, $t = t(x, y)$ define a change of coordinates, where s is any function such that $2as_x + bs_y \neq 0$. Show that if $t = $ constant on solutions of

$$\frac{dy}{dx} = \frac{b\,\partial s/\partial x + 2c\,\partial s/\partial y}{2a\,\partial s/\partial x + b\,\partial s/\partial y},$$

then in the (s, t) coordinate system, L is an elliptic operator that is devoid of the mixed derivative term u_{st}.

10.5. If u satisfies

$$-\nabla^2 u + D(x, y)u_x + E(x, y)u_y = F(x, y) \quad \text{in } \Omega,$$

where $F < 0$, prove that

$$\max_{\bar{\Omega}} u = \max_{\partial\Omega} u.$$

10.6. Prove Theorem 10.4.5.

10.7. Define Lu by (10.4.1) and assume that L is uniformly elliptic and that $c \geq 0$. Show that if $u \in C(\bar{\Omega}) \cap C^2(\Omega)$ satisfies $Lu = 0$ on Ω, then $\max_{\bar{\Omega}} |u| = \max_{\partial\Omega} |u|$.

10.8. Define $L_h U$ by (10.1.15) and assume the L_h is of nonnegative type. Show that if $U \in M(\bar{\Omega}_h)$ satisfies $L_h U = 0$ on Ω_h, then $\max_{\bar{\Omega}_h} |U| = \max_{\partial\Omega_h} |U|$.

10.9. Prove Lemma 10.5.1.

10.10. Let $u \in C^4(\bar{\Omega})$ satisfy

$$-[a(x, y)u_{xx} + b(x, y)u_{yy}] = f \quad \text{on } \Omega,$$

$$u\big|_{\partial\Omega} = g,$$

where a, b, $f \in C(\bar{\Omega})$, $g \in C(\partial\Omega)$, and a, $b \geq \mu > 0$ for some constant μ. Define $L_h U: M(\bar{\Omega}_h) \to M(\Omega_h)$,

$$L_h U(P) = a(P)U_{XX}(P) + b(P)U_{YY}(P), \quad P \in \Omega_h,$$

where U_{XX} and U_{YY} are the finite difference operators obtained from Theorem 10.1.1 with uniform spacing h.

(a) Show that L_h is of positive type.

(b) Find a comparison function for solutions of the problem

$$L_h U = f \quad \text{on } \Omega_h,$$

$$U\big|_{\partial\Omega_h} = g. \tag{2}$$

(c) Prove that if U solves (2), then $\max_{\bar{\Omega}_h} |u - U| = O(h^2)$. What happens to this result if u is only a member of $C^3(\bar{\Omega})$; if u is only a member of $C^2(\bar{\Omega})$?

Computer Exercises

10.11. For Example 10.5.1, compute the maximum mesh point error $E(h)$ for the three meshes given, where

$$E(h) \equiv \max |U_h - u|,$$

and the maximum is over the 16 points of Table 10.5.1. Plot $E(h)$ as a function of h.

10.12. Consider the solution to Example 10.5.1 as given by Table 10.5.1. Sketch a contour plot of the approximate solution.

10.13. Use the finite difference method to solve the boundary value problem

$$-\nabla^2 u = (x - 2)^2 + e^{xy} \quad \text{in } \Omega \equiv (0, 1) \times (0, 1),$$

where the Dirichlet boundary conditions are chosen so that the true solution is

$$u(x, y) = (x - 2)^2 + e^{xy}.$$

Using a sequence of uniform meshes with $h = \frac{1}{4}, \frac{1}{8}, \frac{1}{16}, \ldots$, compare the approximate and true solutions at the mesh points, and assess the asymptotic convergence rate.

10.14. Solve Exercise 7.21 using the finite difference method presented in Section 10.1.

11

Case Studies

In this chapter we present five case studies of real-world applications that involve the numerical solution of partial differential equations. These examples were chosen, first, to illustrate the practicality of numerical methods of the type discussed in the previous chapters, and second, to provide a basis for student projects that involve supplemental reading and significant computation. Each case study includes a description of the problem, details on the finite difference or finite element approximation, sample computer simulations, and suggestions for further investigations.

11.1 FUEL ROD QUENCHING

Fuel rod quenching is one of the events of a postulated *loss-of-coolant accident* (LOCA) in boiling-water or pressurized-water nuclear reactors. The coolant loss results in a degradation of heat transfer at the rod surfaces and a subsequent temperature excursion in the rods. In such an emergency, the rods are quenched either by a top spraying or bottom flooding of coolant. Thus the physical process to be analyzed is the rewetting of a hot vertical surface by a falling or rising layer of liquid. An important analysis goal is the prediction of the time required to bring the rod temperature down to a normal operating level. The problem of rewetting a surface

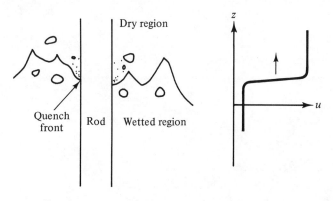

Figure 11.1.1   Quench front and thermal wave.

also occurs in industrial processes such as the metallurgical quenching of hot solids and the filling of containers with a cryogenic liquid.

The mathematical formulation of the rod quenching problem involves the equation of heat conduction (Section 2.3) and certain boundary conditions, including one that induces a traveling thermal wave. The location of this wave marks the front of the rewetting agent (Figure 11.1.1). In this section we consider a model based on an infinitely long, homogeneous, axisymmetric fuel rod. Thus, in terms of cylindrical coordinates (r, z), the problem domain is the strip shown in Figure 11.1.2. The rod temperature $u(r, z, t)$ is the solution of the nonlinear initial–boundary value problem:

$$\rho c u_t = \frac{1}{r}(kru_r)_r + (ku_z)_z + Q, \qquad 0 < r < r_w, \quad -\infty < z < \infty, \quad t > 0, \qquad (11.1.1)$$

$$u(r, -\infty, t) = u_s, \qquad u(r, \infty, t) = u_w, \qquad 0 < r < r_w, \quad t \ge 0, \qquad (11.1.2)$$

$$u_r(0, z, t) = 0, \qquad -\infty < z < \infty, \quad t > 0, \qquad (11.1.3)$$

$$-ku_r(r_w, z, t) = \begin{cases} g_{nb}(z, t, u,) & \text{if } u \le u^*, \\ g_{fb}(z, t, u) & \text{if } u > u^*, \end{cases} \qquad -\infty < z < \infty, \quad t > 0, \qquad (11.1.4)$$

$$u(r, z, 0) = u^0(r, z), \qquad 0 < r < r_w, \quad -\infty < z < \infty. \qquad (11.1.5)$$

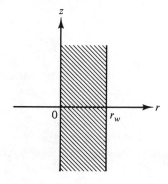

Figure 11.1.2   Problem domain.

The data appearing in (11.1.1)–(11.1.5) are the density $\rho(r, z, t, u)$; the specific heat $c(r, z, t, u)$; the thermal conductivity $k(r, z, t, u)$; the external heat source $Q(r, z, t)$; the saturation and wall temperatures u_s, u_w; the nucleate boiling and film boiling heat transfer functions at the wall $g_{nb}(z, t, u)$, $g_{fb}(z, t, u)$; the wetting temperature u^*; and the initial condition $u^0(r, z)$.

Typically, $0 \approx g_{fb} \ll g_{nb}$, and it is this property of (11.1.4) that generates the thermal wave. Other mathematical models of this problem have been considered by various authors (see, e.g., Duffey and Porthouse [1973] or Thompson [1974]).

A conventional numerical approach to (11.1.1)–(11.1.5) is fraught with difficulties. This is due primarily to the presence of the traveling thermal wave, which manifests itself as a steep axial gradient in u that moves along the rod. Consequently, an extremely fine mesh in the z-direction is needed to preserve the accuracy of the numerical solution.

The *isotherm-migration method* (Dix and Cizek [1971], Durack and Wendroff [1977], Gurcak, Porsching, and Spencer [1980]) circumvents this difficulty by interchanging the roles of u and z. Thus, instead of $u = u(r, z, t)$, we write $z = z(r, u, t)$. Of course, for this inversion to be meaningful, u must be a strictly monotone (say, increasing) function of z for each r and t. Assuming that this is the case, we can then transform (11.1.1) to obtain an equation for the new dependent variable z.

The isotherm migration method is particularly well suited to the calculation of steeply traveling wavefronts. This is because the steep moving front in the (r, z) system (Figure 11.1.3a) becomes a translating flat in the (r, u) system (Figure 11.1.3b). Correspondingly, the large number of mesh lines required to resolve the front in the (r, z) system reduces to a moderate number in the (r, u) system.

The fundamental identity defining the inversion of u and z in the isotherm migration method is $z \equiv z(r, u(r, z, t), t)$. By differentiating this expression, we may

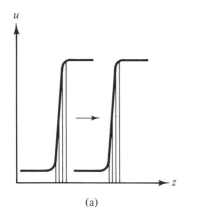
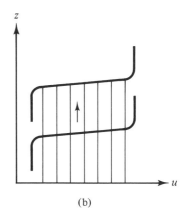

Figure 11.1.3   Moving wavefront and mesh lines.

deduce the following relationships:

$$\frac{1}{r} u_{rr} = \frac{1}{z_u} \left[\left(\frac{z_r^2}{z_u} \right)_u - \frac{1}{r} (rz_r)_r \right],$$

$$u_{zz} = \frac{1}{z_u} \left(\frac{1}{z_u} \right)_u.$$

It then follows that (11.1.1) transforms into

$$\rho c z_t + \left[\frac{k(z_r^2 + 1)}{z_u} \right]_u - \frac{1}{r} (rkz_r)_r + Qz_u = -k_z, \qquad 0 < r < r_w, \quad u_s < u < u_w, \quad t > 0.$$

$$(11.1.6)$$

If the temperature $u(r, z, t)$ is a smooth function of z, then (11.1.2) implies that

$$z_u(r, u_s, t) = z_u(r, u_w, t) = \infty, \qquad 0 < r < r_w, \quad t > 0. \tag{11.1.7}$$

Moreover, the initial condition (11.1.5) becomes

$$z(r, u, 0) = z^0(r, u) \qquad 0 < r < r_w, \quad u_s < u < u_w, \tag{11.1.8}$$

where $z^0(r, \cdot)$ is the function inverse to $u^0(r, \cdot)$.

Regarding the transformed boundary conditions, we have from (11.1.3) and (11.1.4) that

$$z_r(0, u, t) = 0, \qquad u_s < u < u_w, \quad t > 0, \tag{11.1.9}$$

and

$$\left. \frac{kz_r}{z_u} \right|_{(r_w, u, t)} = \begin{cases} g_{nb}(z, t, u) & \text{if } u_s < u \le u^* \\ g_{fb}(z, t, u) & \text{if } u^* < u < u_w, \end{cases} \quad t > 0. \tag{11.1.10}$$

The motion of the isotherms is governed by the system (11.1.6)–(11.1.10).

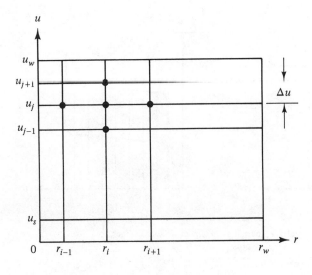

Figure 11.1.4 Finite difference mesh.

We now proceed to the difference equations. As shown in Figure 11.1.4, we overlay the region $0 < r < r_w$, $u_s < u < u_w$ with a rectangular mesh of lines:

$$\{r = r_i, i = 1, \ldots, I, r_i < r_{i+1}\}, \qquad \{u = u_j, j = 1, \ldots, J, u_j = u_s + j \, \Delta u\},$$

where for simplicity we have chosen a uniform temperature increment[1] $\Delta u \equiv (u_w - u_s)/(J + 1)$. We denote $z(r_i, u_j, t_{n+1})$ by $z_{i,j}^{n+1}$, where $t_{n+1} = t_n + \Delta t$, Δt being the (non-uniform) time step. Furthermore, $k(r_i, z_{i,j}^n, t_n, u_j) = k_{i,j}^n$, and so on. At mesh points (i.e., the intersections of the previously defined mesh lines), we replace (11.1.6) by an appropriate difference equation. Consider first the term $(d/z_u)_u$, where $d \equiv k(z_r^2 + 1)$. If subscript $j \pm \frac{1}{2}$ denotes evaluation at $u_j \pm \Delta u/2$, then by Taylor's theorem, at any time in the interval $[t_n, t_{n+1}]$,

$$\left(\frac{d}{z_u}\right)_u\bigg|_{i,j} = \frac{(d/z_u)_{i,j+1/2} - (d/z_u)_{i,j-1/2}}{\Delta u} + O(\Delta u)^2$$

$$= \frac{d_{i,j+1/2}}{(z_{i,j+1} - z_{i,j})/\Delta u} - \frac{d_{i,j-1/2}}{(z_{i,j} - z_{i,j-1})/\Delta u} \Big/ \Delta u + O(\Delta u)$$

$$= \frac{d_{i,j+1/2}(z_{i,j} - z_{i,j-1}) + d_{i,j-1/2}(z_{i,j} - z_{i,j+1})}{(z_{i,j+1} - z_{i,j})(z_{i,j} - z_{i,j-1})} + O(\Delta u)$$

$$= \frac{d_{i,j+1/2}^n(z_{i,j}^{n+1} - z_{i,j-1}^{n+1}) + d_{i,j-1/2}^n(z_{i,j}^{n+1} - z_{i,j+1}^{n+1})}{(z_{i,j+1}^n - z_{i,j}^n)(z_{i,j}^n - z_{i,j-1}^n)} + O(\Delta u + \Delta t).$$

From this it follows quite naturally that

$$\left(\frac{d}{z_u}\right)_u\bigg|_{i,j} \approx \frac{D_{i,j+1/2}^n(Z_{i,j}^{n+1} - Z_{i,j-1}^{n+1}) + D_{i,j-1/2}^n(Z_{i,j}^{n+1} - Z_{i,j+1}^{n+1})}{(Z_{i,j+1}^n - Z_{i,j}^n)(Z_{i,j}^n - Z_{i,j-1}^n)}, \qquad (11.1.11)$$

where $Z_{i,j}^n$ is the finite difference approximation of $z_{i,j}^n$,

$$D_{i,j+1/2}^n \equiv K_{i,j+1/2}^n \left\{ \left[\frac{Z_{i+1,j}^n - Z_{i-1,j}^n + Z_{i+1,j+1}^n - Z_{i-1,j+1}^n}{2(r_{i+1} - r_{i-1})} \right]^2 + 1 \right\},$$

and

$$K_{i,j+1/2}^n \equiv k\left(r_i, \frac{Z_{i,j+1}^n + Z_{i,j}^n}{2}, t_n, \frac{u_j + u_{j+1}}{2}\right).$$

A similar, but less involved, line of reasoning leads to

$$-\frac{1}{r}(rkz_r)_r\bigg|_{i,j} \approx \frac{(r_i + r_{i+1})K_{i+1/2,j}^n \dfrac{Z_{i,j}^{n+1} - Z_{i+1,j}^{n+1}}{r_{i+1} - r_i} + (r_{i-1} + r_i)K_{i-1/2,j}^n \dfrac{Z_{i,j}^{n+1} - Z_{i-1,j}^{n+1}}{r_i - r_{i-1}}}{r_i(r_{i+1} - r_{i-1})},$$

$$(11.1.12)$$

where $K_{i+1/2,j}^n$ is an approximation of $k_{i+1/2,j}^n$.

---

[1] The generalization to nonuniform temperature increments is not difficult.

The remaining approximations in (11.1.6) are simply

$$(\rho c z_t)_{i,j} \approx (RC)_{i,j}^n \frac{Z_{i,j}^{n+1} - Z_{i,j}^n}{\Delta t} \tag{11.1.13}$$

and

$$(Q z_u)_{i,j} \approx Q_{i,j}^n \frac{Z_{i,j}^{n+1} - Z_{i,j-1}^{n+1}}{\Delta u} \qquad (Q_{i,j}^n \geq 0), \tag{11.1.14}$$

RC denoting the analogue of K for the product ρc.

If we make the indicated approximations, the difference equation resulting from (11.1.6) may be written

$$A_{i,j}^n Z_{i,j}^{n+1} - A_{i,j-1}^n Z_{i,j-1}^{n+1} - A_{i,j+1}^n Z_{i,j+1}^{n+1} - A_{i-1,j}^n Z_{i-1,j}^{n+1} - A_{i+1,j}^n Z_{i+1,j}^{n+1} = b_{i,j}^n, \tag{11.1.15}$$

where $A_{i,j}^n$, $A_{i\pm1,j}^n$, $A_{i,j\pm1}^n$, and $b_{i,j}^n$ are readily constructed from (11.1.11)–(11.1.14). Assuming the strict monotonicity of $Z_{i,j}^n$ as a function of j, we see that these coefficients satisfy the inequalities $A_{i\pm1,j}^n \geq 0$, $A_{i,j\pm1}^n \geq 0$, and

$$A_{i,j}^n \geq A_{i,j+1}^n + A_{i,j-1}^n + A_{i+1,j}^n + A_{i-1,j}^n.$$

Such conditions define an "equation of nonnegative type" in the sense of Section 10.4, and as shown in Section 4.4, yield an unconditionally stable numerical method for the *linear* heat conduction equation.[2] It is known that in the presence of steep temperature gradients, the "explicit" version of these equations, which is obtained by replacing superscript $n+1$ by n in all difference approximations except (11.1.13), leads to an unstable method unless the time step is severely restricted. (See Section 4.3 for a discussion of this phenomenon.)

Equation (11.1.15) applies for $1 < j < J$ and $r_1 < r_i < r_w$. The remaining cases require either a modification of terms in (11.1.15) or a new difference equation. For example, if $j = J$ and $r_1 < r_i < r_w$, we incorporate the effect of the boundary condition (11.1.7) as follows. With $d = k(z_r^2 + 1)$ as before, we have

$$\left(\frac{d}{z_u} \right)_u \Big|_{i,J} = \frac{(d/z_u)_{i,w} - (d/z_u)_{i,J-1/2}}{3\Delta u/2} + O(\Delta u)$$

$$= -\frac{2}{3} \frac{d_{i,J-1/2}}{z_{i,J} - z_{i,J-1}} + O(\Delta u) = \frac{2}{3} \frac{d_{i,J-1/2}^n}{z_{i,J-1}^{n+1} - z_{i,J}^{n+1}} + O(\Delta u + \Delta t)$$

$$= \frac{2}{3} d_{i,J-1/2}^n \left[\frac{2}{z_{i,J-1}^n - z_{i,J}^n} + \frac{z_{i,J}^{n+1} - z_{i,J-1}^{n+1}}{(z_{i,J-1}^n - z_{i,J}^n)^2} \right] + O(\Delta u + \Delta t),$$

Therefore, in (11.1.6) we replace the term $(d/z_u)_u$ by the expression

$$\frac{2}{3} D_{i,3/2}^n \left[\frac{2}{Z_{i,2}^n - Z_{i,1}^n} + \frac{Z_{i,1}^{n+1} - Z_{i,2}^{n+1}}{(Z_{i,2}^n - Z_{i,1}^n)^2} \right].$$

---

[2] Of course, the present problem is nonlinear, but it is not unreasonable to expect that the behavior of the difference equations will be similar to those of the linear case.

where $D_{i,J-1/2}^n$ is defined as in (11.1.11). In the same way, the analogous replacement for $j = 1, r_1 < r_i < r_w$, is

$$\frac{2}{3} D_{i,3/2}^n \left[\frac{2}{Z_{i,2}^n - Z_{i,1}^n} + \frac{Z_{i,1}^{n+1} - Z_{i,2}^{n+1}}{(Z_{i,2}^n - Z_{i,1}^n)^2} \right].$$

Note that in both of these cases the result is again a linear equation of nonnegative type having the form (11.1.15).

To close the set of implicit difference equations, it remains to consider the lines $r = 0$, and $r = r_w$. On $r = 0$, we approximate condition (11.1.9) by

$$Z_{0,j}^{n+1} - Z_{1,j}^{n+1} = 0, \qquad j = 1, \ldots, J,$$

while on $r = r_w$, we apply an upwind difference method (cf. Section 3.4) to (11.1.10) to obtain

$$K_{w,j}^n \frac{Z_{w,j}^{n+1} - Z_{w-1,j}^{n+1}}{r_w - r_{w-1}} = \frac{\Phi_{w,j}^n}{\Delta u} \left[\frac{Z_{w,j}^{n+1} - Z_{w,j-1}^{n+1}}{Z_{w,j+1}^{n+1} - Z_{w,j}^{n+1}} \right], \qquad j = 2, \ldots, J-1, \qquad (11.1.16)$$

where

$$\Phi_{w,j}^n = \begin{cases} (g_{nb})_{w,j}^n & \text{if } u_s < u_j \le u^*, \\ (g_{fb})_{w,j}^n & \text{if } u^* < u_j < u_w, \end{cases}$$

and the upper or lower line of the bracketed term is to be used as $\Phi_{w,j}^n$ is either negative or nonnegative. In (11.1.16) we have introduced w as an index for mesh points on r_w. For $j = 1, J$ in (11.1.16) we difference away from the corresponding boundary indices $j = 0, J + 1$.

The linear system defined by the aggregate of these difference equations has a structure which is identical to that resulting from the usual "five-point" discretization of Laplace's equation (Section 10.6). Thus, as noted in Section 10.3, there are many efficient algorithms available for its solution.

To illllustrate the performance of the isotherm migration difference method, we consider a rod for which $r_w = 0.0175833$ ft, $\rho c = 48$ Btu/ft^3-$^\circ$F, and $k = 0.003333$ Btu/sec-ft-$^\circ$F. The boundary condition at the wall is of the form

$$-ku_r = \begin{cases} 2.64(u - 200) & \text{if } u < 420, \\ 0 & \text{if } u \ge 420. \end{cases}$$

Also, $Q = 0$, $u_s = 200^\circ$F, and $u_w = 1300^\circ$F. We discretize the (r, u) problem domain by using 10 radial and 17 (nonuniform) temperature mesh lines. Specifically, we have[3]

$$10^2 r_i = (0, 1.52875, 0.382175), 1.55683, 1.62333, 1.69083, 1.75733, 1.75833 \text{ ft}$$

and

$$u_j = 205, 210, 225, 250, (300, 1200, 100), 1250, 1275, 1295^\circ\text{F}.$$

---

[3] The notation $x = (a, b, c)$ means step x from a to b in increments of c.

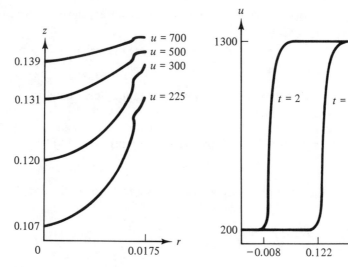

Figure 11.1.5 Isotherms at 25 sec.   **Figure 11.1.6** Development of thermal wave.

For the initial isotherms, we set $z^0(r_i, u_j) = \phi_j$, $i = 1, \ldots, 10$, where

$$10^3\phi_j = -6.0, -4.0, -3.0, -2.0, -1.0, -0.50, 0.50, 1.0, 2.5, 4.0, 5.5, 7.0,$$
$$11.0, 15.0, 20.0, 25.0, 51.0 \text{ ft.}$$

This problem was solved using a composite fuel rod model (Gurcak, Porsching, and Spencer [1980]) which allows for the presence of a gap in the rod's materials. This introduces an additional boundary condition but does not affect the basic difference equations described above. Output from that solution forms the basis of Figure 11.1.5, which shows selected isotherms at 25 sec. The jump in isotherm position at $r \approx 0.015$ ft is due to the gap. Figure 11.1.6 shows the thermal wave at the rod's surface at 2 and 25 sec. The wave speed is about 0.0057 ft/sec.

SUGGESTIONS FOR FURTHER INVESTIGATIONS

1. Solve the sample problem by the isotherm migration difference method, and by comparing this solution to the one given, assess the effect of the gap on the isotherm and thermal wave positions.

2. If the explicit version of the difference equations is used, a common necessary condition for stable calculations is

$$\Delta t < \frac{z_u^2 \rho c}{2k} (\Delta u)^2.$$

TABLE 11.1.1   POSITION OF THERMAL WAVE AT 25 SEC

$u(°F)$	z (ft)
205	0.12247
210	0.12668
225	0.13201
250	0.13534
300	0.13805
400	0.14017
500	0.14091
600	0.14197
700	0.14344
800	0.14538
900	0.14792
1000	0.15138
1100	0.15640
1200	0.16496
1250	0.17358
1275	0.18221
1295	0.19947

Using the data of Table 11.1.1, which defines the thermal wavefront of the example at 25 sec, estimate the number of time steps needed by the explicit method to track the wave for another 5 min. Test your estimate by applying the explicit method to the sample problem.

3. Following Dendy, Swartz, and Wendroff [1977], one may consider the following one-dimensional model problem for the study of thermal waves: Find the dimensionless temperature $u(z, t)$ such that

$$u_t = u_{zz} + g(u), \qquad -\infty < z < \infty, \quad t > 0,$$

$$u(-\infty, t) = 0, \qquad u(\infty, t) = 1, \qquad u(z, 0) = u^0(z),$$

where

$$g(u) = \begin{cases} -Bu & \text{if } u \le u^*, \\ 0 & \text{if } u > u^*. \end{cases}$$

Here B is a dimensionless parameter known as the *Biot* number, and u^* is a dimensionless wetting temperature. Formulate the isotherm migration method for this problem, and develop an isotherm migration difference method that is analogous to the one of this section. The sample problem can be approximated by a model problem in which $B = 14$ and $u^* = 0.2$. Determine the approximate thermal wave speed in this case.

11.2 ACOUSTICAL WAVES IN AN AIRCRAFT CAVITY

The nature of the aerodynamics in and around structures such as spoilers and cavities is of interest to aeronautical engineers faced with the task of creating a new or modifying an old airplane design. Bomb bays provide examples of cavities in airplanes

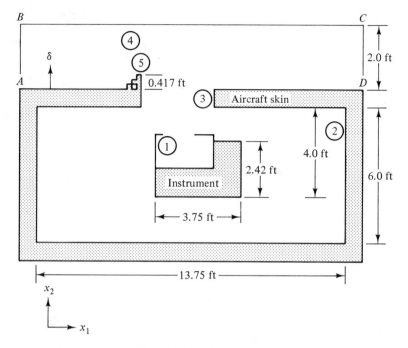

Figure 11.2.1 Aircraft cavity.

which are open during flight. Another example considered here is an aircraft cavity containing sensors (e.g., telescopes) which are to be activated while in flight. Figure 11.2.1 illustrates a two-dimensional model of such a cavity. The blockage in the cavity simulates instrumentation used during the observations. The spoiler ahead of the cavity opening is used to divert the airflow so as to stabilize the flow around the instrumentation. A solid spoiler is shown, although the results are for a spoiler with 58% porosity.

One way to study the possible effects of airflow on various design features is through the numerical solution of the conservation laws governing the dynamics of the airflow. The dependent variables are pressure, temperature, velocity, and density of the fluid as a function of position and time.

A mathematical model of this compressible fluid flow problem consists of the *continuity equation,*

$$\rho_t + (\rho v_j)_{x_j} = 0, \tag{11.2.1}$$

the *equations of motion,*

$$\rho(v_i)_t + \rho v_j(v_i)_{x_j} = -p_{x_i} + (\sigma_{ij})_{x_j} - f_i, \qquad i = 1, 2, \tag{11.2.2}$$

the *temperature equation,*

$$\rho c_v T_t + \rho c_v v_j T_{x_j} = k T_{x_j x_j} - p(v_j)_{x_j}, \tag{11.2.3}$$

and an *equation of state*,

$$\rho = \rho(p, T). \tag{11.2.4}$$

In the equations above, c_v is the heat capacity at constant volume, f_i a body force component, k the thermal conductivity, p the pressure, t the time, v_i a velocity component, x_i a Cartesian coordinate, T the temperature, ρ the density, and $[\sigma_{ij}]$ the viscous stress tensor,

$$[\sigma_{ij}] = \begin{bmatrix} 2\mu v_{1x_1} - \frac{2}{3}\mu v_{kx_k} & \mu(v_{1x_2} + v_{2x_1}) \\ \mu(v_{1x_2} + v_{2x_1}) & 2\mu v_{2x_2} - \frac{2}{3}\mu v_{kx_k} \end{bmatrix},$$

with μ, the viscosity of the fluid. Furthermore, a repeated index is to be summed over the values 1, 2. Note that if $\mu = 0$, then (11.2.1) and (11.2.2) are the two-dimensional equivalents of the equations developed in Section 2.5.

The functional form of the equation of state (11.2.4) is based on the ideal gas law for air,

$$\rho(p, T) = \frac{2.705p}{T + 459},$$

where the units of p are pounds force per square inch (psi), those of T are degrees Fahrenheit (°F), and those of density ρ are pounds mass per cubic feet (lbm/ft³). If the units of length, mass, and time are, respectively, feet (ft), pounds mass (lbm), and seconds (sec), the consistent units of pressure required in (11.2.2) and (11.2.3) are not psi, but poundals per square feet (pdl/ft²). To convert psi into pdl/ft², multiply the number of psi by 4633.056.

A typical study might require the determination of the pressure responses at the five positions indicated in Figure 11.2.1 when the flight Mach number is 0.75 at an altitude of 37,000 ft,[4] and the ambient pressure is 2.7 psi downstream from the cavity. The walls are assumed to be of no-slip[5] type and the upstream velocity profile is given by

$$v_1 = 750 \begin{cases} \left(\dfrac{\delta}{0.417}\right)^{1/7}, & 0 \le \delta < 0.417, \\ 1, & \delta \ge 0.417, \end{cases} \tag{11.2.5}$$

where δ is the distance from the aircraft skin into the free stream. The inlet temperature profile is given by

$$T = -56 \begin{cases} 1.1 - 0.1\left(\dfrac{\delta}{0.718}\right)^{1/7}, & 0 \le \delta < 0.718, \\ 1, & \delta \ge 0.718, \end{cases} \tag{11.2.6}$$

---

[4] At 37,000 ft, the speed of sound is about 1000 ft/sec, and hence Mach 0.75 corresponds to a speed of about 750 ft/sec.

[5] A *no-slip* condition means that the normal and tangential components of velocity are zero.

TABLE 11.2.1   PROPERTIES OF AIR

c_v	0.17	Btu/lbm-°F
k	0.47×10^{-5}	Btu/sec-ft-°F
μ	0.99×10^{-5}	lbm/ft-sec

where $-56°F$ is the ambient temperature of the air outside the aircraft. The properties of air are given in Table 11.2.1.

Simply stated, the boundary value problem is to find v_1, v_2, p, T, and ρ satisfying (11.2.1)–(11.2.4) subject to the boundary conditions (11.2.5) and (11.2.6) along $\overline{AB}$, and $p = 2.7$ psi along $\overline{CD}$. On all other boundaries, the no-slip condition is imposed. Finally, on all boundaries except $\overline{AB}$, the temperature flux is zero, that is, $\partial T/\partial \mathbf{n} = \mathbf{0}$, where $\mathbf{n}$ is an exterior unit normal. The body force term is assumed to be zero except within the spoiler, where $f_i = 10^4 v_i$, a linear friction term to simulate a porous material. One could just as well model the spoiler as a solid.

This is a time-dependent problem and the initial conditions on the interior of the domain are chosen as

$$v_2 = 0 \text{ everywhere,}$$

$$v_1 = \begin{cases} 750 & \text{outside the aircraft,} \\ 0 & \text{inside the aircraft,} \end{cases}$$

$$T = -56.0 \text{ everywhere,}$$

$$p = 2.7 \text{ (psi) everywhere.}$$

This problem was solved using a finite difference program ALGAE (see Frey, Hall, and Porsching [1987]).

Explicit and implicit finite difference discretizations of (11.2.1)–(11.2.4) are available in ALGAE. Both sets of finite difference equations utilize a staggered grid in which the discrete temperatures and pressures are located at cell (or mesh box) centers and the discrete velocity components in the ith coordinate direction are located on the sides of the cells that are normal to that coordinate direction. Details of the discretization can be found in Frey, Hall, and Porsching [1987].

To describe briefly the finite difference equations, it is convenient to introduce the mass fluxes, $G_i \equiv \rho v_i$, $i = 1, 2$. These are discretized on the same points as the corresponding v_i. If the mass fluxes and cell-centered densities are known, each velocity approximation may be determined as the quotient of a mass flux and a suitably interpolated cell side density.

For the explicit equations a discrete form of (11.2.3) is first used to advance the temperatures to the new time level. This is obtained by replacing the temporal derivative T_t by a forward difference and the Laplacian of the conduction term $T_{x_i x_i}$ by second-order divided differences. The divergence $(v_j)_{x_j}$ in the work term is approximated by differences that are centered on the cells, utilizing velocities obtained from the mass fluxes. The convection terms $v_j T_{x_j}$ are treated by upwind differences as determined by the signs of the velocities. Except for the forward difference in time, all information is at the current time level.

The discretized continuity equation is next used to obtain new time-level pressures. Equation (11.2.1) is written in the equivalent form,

$$\frac{1}{c^2} p_t + \rho_T T_t + (\rho v_j)_{x_j} = 0, \tag{11.2.7}$$

where c is the local sonic speed. Forward differences are again used for p_t and T_t. Now, however, the terms of the divergence $(\rho v_j)_{x_j}$ are regarded as conservative forms of a convection law, the convected quantity being the density. In this light they are discretized by the donor cell concept, where the quantity that is donated to the cell *side* is the appropriate cell *center* density. If all information except that of the temporal differences is taken at the current time level, the finite difference form of (11.2.7) explicitly determines the new pressure approximations.

Finally, the new mass flux components are obtained via (11.2.2). Obviously, this equation may be written as

$$\rho \left[\frac{G_i}{\rho} \right]_t + G_i \left[\frac{G_i}{\rho} \right]_{x_i} = -p_{x_i} + (\sigma_{ij})_{x_i} - f_i, \qquad i = 1, 2. \tag{11.2.8}$$

Forward, cell centered, and second divided differences are used, respectively, for the temporal, gradient, and viscous stress terms, $(G_i/\rho)_t$, $-p_{x_i}$, and $(\sigma_{ij})_{x_i}$. For each convection term $G_i(G_i/\rho)_{x_i}$, we employ a convex combination of a cell side centered difference and an upwind difference (see Hirt, Amsden, and Cook [1970]). This coupling of the stable, but dissipative upwind differences to the more locally accurate, but unstable central differences provides a means of preserving certain weak persistent unsteady motions present in the actual flow field. The choice of the weights defining the convex combination is critical if the discrete equations are to sustain such unsteady motions. For this problem the weight for the centered differences was 0.55 and the weight for the upwind differences was 0.45.

With the foregoing replacements in (11.2.8) we obtain a trivial system of equations for the new time mass flux approximations provided that the convection and viscous stress information is taken at the current time level. It appears that the discrete pressure gradient may be evaluated at either the current or new time level. However, a linear stability analysis shows that the finite difference equations are stable *only if* this term is evaluated using advanced time information, and this is what is done in ALGAE.

The overall system of explicit equations is stable provided that the time step is of the order of the cell transport time of a signal traveling at a speed $c + |v|$, where $|v|$ is the local particle speed.

For the implicit system the discrete temperatures are again the first variables to be advanced. Equation (11.2.3) is discretized as before, except that the temperature information appearing in the finite difference forms of the convection and conduction

Point 1

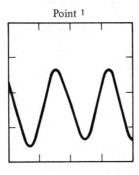

Point 2

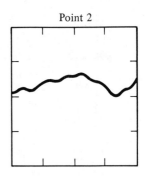

Point 3

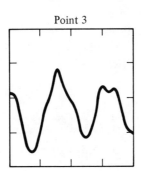

Point 4

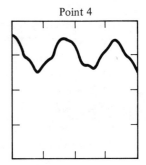

Point 5

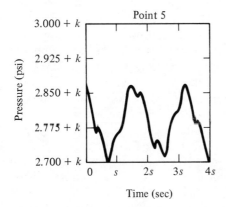

Time scale: $s = 0.0125$
Pressure scale: $k = 0.0$ except for point 4
where $k = 0.300$

Figure 11.2.2   Aircraft cavity pressure responses.

terms is now at the new time level. This results in a diagonally dominant system of linear equations.

Next finite difference forms of the continuity and momentum equations (in conjunction with the state equation) are solved simultaneously for the advanced time-level pressures and mass fluxes. The continuity equation is written as

$$\frac{1}{c^2} p_t + \rho_T T_t + G_{jx_j} = 0. \tag{11.2.9}$$

The differencing of the temporal terms is as before, but each divergence term is now replaced by a cell centered difference at the new time level. The differencing of the momentum equations (11.2.8) is as above, with the understanding that the mass flux and density information holds at the new time.

Unlike the discrete temperature equation, this new algebraic system is *nonlinear*. It is solved by a Picard-type iteration in which the convection coefficients are lagged one time step. The determination of each new set of pressure and mass flux iterates requires the solution of a *linear* system consisting of the coupled continuity and momentum finite difference equations.

The presence of an explicitly differenced work term in the discrete temperature equations renders the overall system conditionally stable. The stability condition on the time step is again related to the cell transport time except that now the signal speed is of order $|v|$ instead of the much higher $c + |v|$. This enables the computation to proceed with time steps that are larger than those of the explicit method.

The flow region was subdivided into 1167 flow cells with a fine mesh along the aircraft skin. The flow in the cavity was initialized by assuming that the fluid was incompressible for the first 100 sec of the transient. Once a reasonable flow regime was established in and around the cavity, the fluid was assumed to be compressible and a time step of 2.5×10^{-4} sec was used. Choosing a weight of 0.55 for the centered and 0.45 for the upwind difference approximations of the convective terms in the momentum equations produced a sustained unsteady behavior. Figure 11.2.2 illustrates the pressure responses at the five points requested.

SUGGESTIONS FOR FURTHER INVESTIGATIONS

1. Develop a difference method for (11.2.1)–(11.2.3) that is based on the discretizations discussed in this section. Use this method to determine the pressure responses in the sample problem when the spoiler is removed.

2. Study the effect of the boundary layer by replacing (11.2.5)–(11.2.6) by $v_1 = 750$ ft/sec and $T = -56°F$ at the inlet.

3. Determine the effect of varying the weights used in the convex combination of centered and upwind differencing.

11.3 ELECTRON DIFFUSION PARALLEL TO ELECTRIC FIELDS

The transport of electrons through a gas is of importance, for example, in the design of fluorescent lights, and this phenomenon has been studied by physicists for nearly a century (see Huxley and Crompton [1974]). Here we consider the case of a uniform stream of electrons being absorbed at a collecting electrode under the influence of an electric field. For pressures in excess of 1 torr, each electron experiences approximately 10^9 collisions per second. It was generally believed for over a half century that electron motion could be represented reasonably well by a drift velocity W and diffusion coefficient D that are independent of position. However, the work of Parker and Lowke [1969] and subsequent numerical experiments cited below concluded that near an absorbing boundary such an assumption leads to significant errors in the predicted electron density distribution. Hence for such regions, W and D should be regarded as functions of position.

The electron distribution function $f(\mathbf{r}, \mathbf{v}, t)$ plays a key role in the quantitative study of various properties of electrons moving through a gas and is characterized as a solution of a basic conservation law referred to as the Boltzmann transport equation. The quantity $f(\mathbf{r}, \mathbf{v}, t)\, d\mathbf{r}\, d\mathbf{v}$ denotes at time t the number of electrons at position $\mathbf{r}$ in volume $d\mathbf{r}$ with velocity $\mathbf{v}$ in the range $d\mathbf{v}$. To simplify the Boltzmann equation it is usually assumed that the distribution function f is almost spherically symmetric in velocity space, and hence is adequately represented by the first two terms of an expansion in spherical harmonics, that is,

$$f(\mathbf{r}, \mathbf{v}, t) = f^0(\mathbf{r}, \varepsilon, t) + f^1(\mathbf{r}, \varepsilon, t) \cos\theta, \qquad (11.3.1)$$

where ε is the electron energy and θ is the angle between $\mathbf{v}$ and the direction of the electric field.

With this approximation, the Boltzmann equation reduces to two partial differential equations in f^0 and f^1. The function f^1 can be eliminated from one equation to obtain an equation for f^0:

$$\frac{4\pi}{m}\left(\frac{2\varepsilon}{m}\right)^{1/2}\frac{\partial f^0}{\partial t} = \frac{16\pi}{mM}\frac{\partial}{\partial\varepsilon}\left[N\varepsilon^2 Q\left(f^0 + kT\frac{\partial f^0}{\partial\varepsilon}\right) + \frac{MeE}{6mN}\frac{\varepsilon}{Q}\left(eE\frac{\partial f^0}{\partial\varepsilon} + \frac{\partial f^0}{\partial z}\right)\right]$$

$$+ \frac{8\pi}{3m^2 N}\frac{\partial}{\partial z}\left[\frac{\varepsilon}{Q}\left(eE\frac{\partial f^0}{\partial\varepsilon} + \frac{\partial f^0}{\partial z}\right)\right]. \qquad (11.3.2)$$

The second coefficient function is then obtained from

$$f^1 = -\frac{1}{NQ}\left(\frac{\partial f^0}{\partial z} + eE\frac{\partial f^0}{\partial\varepsilon}k\right).$$

(see Parker and Lowke [1969] and Lowke, Parker, and Hall [1977]).

Equation (11.3.2) can be rewritten as

$$\frac{4\pi}{m}\left(\frac{2\varepsilon}{m}\right)^{1/2}\frac{\partial f^0}{\partial t} = \nabla\cdot(B\,\nabla f^0) + d_1\frac{\partial f^0}{\partial\varepsilon} + d_2\frac{\partial f^0}{\partial z} + d_3 f^0, \qquad (11.3.3)$$

where

m = electron mass

ε = electron kinetic energy

$\mathbf{V}$ = gradient operator $[\partial/\partial\varepsilon, \partial/\partial z]^T$

$$B = \frac{8\pi\varepsilon}{3m^2NQ} \begin{bmatrix} e^2E^2 + \dfrac{6mN^2\varepsilon^2QkT}{M} & eE \\ eE & 1 \end{bmatrix} \qquad (11.3.4)$$

z = distance along a given direction of propagation

$N(z)$ = total number density which is proportional to $P(293/T)$

P, T = pressure and temperature of the gas

$Q(\varepsilon)$ = momentum transfer cross section

e = electron charge

$E(z)$ = magnitude of the electric field $\mathbf{E} = E\mathbf{k}$, $\mathbf{k}$ a unit vector along the z-axis

M = atomic mass of the gas

k = Boltzmann constant

$$d_1 = \frac{16N\pi}{mM}\varepsilon^2 Q - \frac{8\pi e\varepsilon}{3m^2Q}\frac{\partial}{\partial z}\left(\frac{E}{N}\right), \qquad (11.3.5)$$

$$d_2 = -\frac{8\pi\varepsilon}{3m^2Q}\frac{\partial}{\partial z}\left(\frac{1}{N}\right) \quad \text{and} \quad d_3 = \frac{\partial d_1}{\partial \varepsilon}. \qquad (11.3.6)$$

The physical significance of the terms in (11.3.2) is as follows. Changes with respect to time of the electron distribution function f^0 can occur because the electrons change their energy. This is represented by the first group of terms within the brackets preceded by $\partial/\partial\varepsilon$. The distribution function can also change because electrons change their position. This is represented by the second group of terms in brackets preceded by $\partial/\partial z$. The terms in the first group represent, respectively, changes in electron energy due to collisions with gas atoms, collisions due to the gas temperature T, and collisions due to drift and diffusion within the electric field. The terms in the second group preceded by $\partial/\partial z$ represent changes in position due to drift and diffusion.

In view of the relative magnitudes of the parameters involved (i.e., $m \approx 10^{-27}$, $N \approx 10^{17}$, $M \approx 10^{-24}$, $e \approx 10^{-19}$, $P \approx 1$, $E \approx 1$, $Q \approx 10^{-15}$, and $k \approx 10^{-16}$, the matrix of coefficients

$$B \approx \varepsilon \begin{bmatrix} 10^{14} + 10^{37}\varepsilon T & 10^{33} \\ 10^{33} & 10^{52} \end{bmatrix}, \qquad (11.3.7)$$

$d_1 \approx 10^{54}\varepsilon^2$, and so on. It is computationally convenient to scale the independent variable energy, by dividing ε by 10^7e so that ε is in electron volts. The Boltzmann constant k is then replaced by $k/10^7e$. Finally, if we multiply (11.3.2) by m^2, the equation for steady state becomes

$$0 = \mathbf{\nabla} \cdot A \, \mathbf{\nabla} f^0 + c_1 \frac{\partial f^0}{\partial \varepsilon} + c_2 \frac{\partial f^0}{\partial z} + c_3 f^0, \qquad (11.3.8)$$

where

$$A = \frac{8\pi\varepsilon}{3NQ} \begin{bmatrix} E^2 + \dfrac{6mN^2\varepsilon^2 QkT}{M \, 10^7 e} & E \\ E & 1 \end{bmatrix}, \qquad (11.3.9)$$

$$c_1 = \frac{16NM\pi\varepsilon^2 Q}{M} - \frac{8\pi e\varepsilon}{3Q} \frac{\partial}{\partial z}\left(\frac{E}{N}\right), \qquad (11.3.10)$$

and

$$c_2 = \frac{8\pi\varepsilon}{3Q} \frac{\partial}{\partial z}\left(\frac{1}{N}\right), \qquad c_3 = \frac{\partial c_1}{\partial \varepsilon}. \qquad (11.3.11)$$

Note that the problem has been equilibrated and

$$A \approx \varepsilon \begin{bmatrix} 10^{-1} + 10^{-3}\varepsilon T & 10^{-1} \\ 10^{-1} & 10^{-1} \end{bmatrix}. \qquad (11.3.12)$$

We assume that the domain of definition of the partial differential equation (11.3.8) is $\Omega \equiv (0, \bar{\varepsilon}) \times (0, \bar{z})$ and that ε/Q is bounded in $\bar{\Omega}$. The cross section $Q(\varepsilon) > 0$ and hence (11.3.8) is *elliptic* for $T > 0$ (and *parabolic* for $T = 0$) in Ω since

$$\det A = \frac{16\pi Nmk\varepsilon^2 QT}{M \, 10^7 e}.$$

The boundary conditions imposed are that the distribution function f^0 is zero at the absorbing boundary $z = \bar{z}$ and also for high energy levels $\bar{\varepsilon}$. That is, there are negligible numbers of electrons for $z = \bar{z}$ and $\varepsilon = \bar{\varepsilon}$. At energy level zero, we require that $\partial f^0/\partial t$ be finite. From (11.3.2) it follows directly that for $\varepsilon = 0$ all the terms will drop out except $E(\partial f^0/\partial \varepsilon) + (\partial f^0/\partial z)$, which we force to be zero. Hence the conditions are

$$f^0 = 0, \qquad \varepsilon = \bar{\varepsilon}, \qquad 0 \le z \le \bar{z},$$

$$f^0 = 0, \qquad 0 \le \varepsilon \le \bar{\varepsilon}, \qquad z = \bar{z},$$

$$E \frac{\partial f^0}{\partial \varepsilon} + \frac{\partial f^0}{\partial z} = 0, \qquad \varepsilon = 0, \qquad 0 \le z < \bar{z}, \qquad (11.3.13)$$

and

$$f^0 = \exp\left\{\int_0^\varepsilon \frac{P(\varepsilon)\, d\varepsilon}{1 + (kT/10^7 e)P(\varepsilon)}\right\}, \qquad 0 \le \varepsilon \le \bar{\varepsilon}, \qquad z = 0,$$

where

$$P(\varepsilon) = \frac{6mN^2}{ME^2}[Q(\varepsilon)]^2\varepsilon.$$

The boundary condition at $z = 0$ is simply the value of f^0 obtained from assuming all gradient terms $\partial/\partial z$ are zero. This condition applies to a position in the electron stream far from the absorbing boundary.

Once the electron distribution function f^0 is approximated, the *electron current density* and *electron density* can be expressed in terms of f^0 as, respectively,

$$\Gamma(\bar{r}, t) = \frac{-8\pi}{3m^2 N} \int_0^{\bar{\varepsilon}} \frac{\varepsilon}{Q} \left(\frac{\partial^2 f^0}{\partial z^2} + eE \frac{\partial f^0}{\partial \varepsilon} \right) d\varepsilon,$$

and   (11.3.14)

$$n(\bar{r}, t) = \frac{4\pi}{m} \left(\frac{2}{m} \right)^{1/2} \int_0^{\bar{\varepsilon}} \varepsilon^{1/2} f^0 \, d\varepsilon,$$

(see Parker and Lowke [1969]).

Unfortunately, (11.3.8) is *non-self-adjoint* and finite difference equations are inherently *nonsymmetric*. Even though (11.3.8) is *essentially self-adjoint* (Ames [1971]), the transformations needed to simplify the equation are quite complex and unwieldy; so too are the standard transformations discussed in Chapter 2 for removal of the cross-derivative terms $\partial^2 f / \partial \varepsilon \, \partial z$. However, as we now show, an *almost* symmetric finite difference scheme can be developed (Hall and Lowke [1975]).

Consider the finite difference mesh Π shown in Figure 11.3.1. As indicated, a point of the grid and its eight closest neighbors are referred to generically according

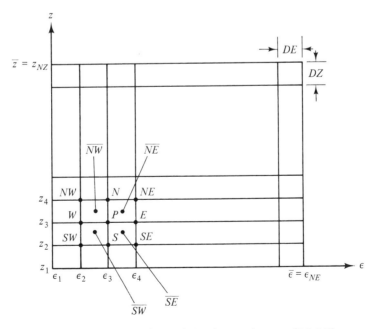

Figure 11.3.1   Rectangular mesh Π of gauge $h = \max \{DE, DZ\}$.

to compass designations (Chapter 10). The coefficients $A_{ij}(\varepsilon, z)$ of the matrix A in (11.3.12) are evaluated at *centroids* of mesh cells designated, respectively, $\overline{NW}$, $\overline{NE}$, $\overline{SW}$, $\overline{SE}$ so as to preserve *symmetry* of the second-order operator $(\nabla \cdot A\nabla)$.

The following finite difference approximation will prove useful. *If U is sufficiently differentiable, then*

$$\frac{\partial U}{\partial \varepsilon}(P) = (4DE)^{-1}[U(NE) + U(SE) - U(NW) - U(SW)] + O(h^2), \quad (11.3.15)$$

$$\frac{\partial U}{\partial z}(P) = (4DZ)^{-1}[U(NE) - U(SE) + U(NW) - U(SW)] + O(h^2), \quad (11.3.16)$$

as $h = \max(DE, DZ) \to 0$. The verification of (11.3.15) and (11.3.16) follows from standard Taylor series arguments.

To discretize the differential operator in (11.3.8) at the generic mesh point P, we first apply (11.3.15) and (11.3.16) with (SW, SE, P, NW, NE) replaced by $(\overline{SW}, \overline{SE}, P, \overline{NW}, \overline{NE})$ as follows:

$$\frac{\partial}{\partial \varepsilon}\left(A_{11}\frac{\partial f^0}{\partial \varepsilon} + A_{12}\frac{\partial f^0}{\partial z}\right) = (4DE)^{-1}\left[A_{11}(\overline{NE})\frac{\partial f^0}{\partial \varepsilon}(\overline{NE}) + A_{12}(\overline{NE})\frac{\partial f^0}{\partial z}(\overline{NE})\right.$$

$$+ A_{11}(\overline{SE})\frac{\partial f^0}{\partial \varepsilon}(\overline{SE}) + A_{12}(\overline{SE})\frac{\partial f^0}{\partial x}(\overline{SE})$$

$$- A_{11}(\overline{NW})\frac{\partial f^0}{\partial \varepsilon}(\overline{NW}) - A_{12}(\overline{NW})\frac{\partial f^0}{\partial z}(\overline{NW}) \quad (11.3.17)$$

$$\left. - A_{11}(\overline{SW})\frac{\partial f^0}{\partial \varepsilon}(\overline{SW}) - A_{12}(\overline{SW})\frac{\partial f^0}{\partial z}(\overline{SW})\right].$$

We use a similar expression to approximate $(\partial/\partial z)[A_{21}(\partial f^0/\partial \varepsilon) + A_{22}(\partial f^0/\partial z)]$. These approximations in turn necessitate approximating $\partial f^0/\partial \varepsilon$ and $\partial f^0/\partial z$ at the centroids $\overline{NE}$, $\overline{SE}$, $\overline{NW}$, and $\overline{SW}$, and again the finite difference approximations in (11.3.15) and (11.3.16) are applied with (SW, SE, P, NW, NE) being replaced by, for example, $(P, E, \overline{NE}, N, NE)$.

The coefficients $c_1(P)$ and $c_2(P)$ are approximated by an arithmetic average of the values of c_1 and c_2 (respectively) at the four neighboring centroids. Hence the functions N, Q, and E need only be specified at centroids. The linear terms $\partial f^0/\partial \varepsilon(P)$, $\partial f^0/\partial z(P)$, and so on, are also approximated using (11.3.15) and (11.3.16).

Following the discretization procedure above, the differential equation (11.3.8) is approximated at each mesh point P by the finite difference equation

$$L_h F^0 = \sum_Q A(P, Q)F^0(Q) = 0, \quad (11.3.18)$$

where at most nine couplings $A(P, Q)$ are nonzero. These couplings are tabulated below.

$$A(P, P) = \frac{1}{4DE^2} \left[-A_{11}(\overline{NE}) - A_{11}(\overline{SE}) - A_{11}(\overline{NW}) - A_{11}(\overline{SW}) \right]$$

$$+ \frac{1}{2DEDZ} \left[-A_{12}(\overline{NE}) + A_{12}(\overline{SE}) - A_{12}(\overline{NW}) - A_{12}(\overline{SW}) \right]$$

$$+ \frac{1}{4DZ^2} \left[A_{22}(\overline{NE}) - A_{22}(\overline{SE}) - A_{22}(\overline{NW}) - A_{22}(\overline{SW}) \right]$$

$$+ \frac{1}{2DE} \left[c_1(\overline{NE}) + c_1(\overline{SE}) - c_1(\overline{NW}) - c_1(\overline{SW}) \right],$$

$$A(P, E) = \frac{1}{4DE^2} \left[A_{11}(\overline{NE}) + A_{11}(\overline{SE}) \right] + \frac{1}{4DZ^2} \left[-A_{22}(\overline{NE}) - A_{22}(\overline{SE}) \right],$$

$$A(P, N) = \frac{1}{4DE^2} \left[-A_{11}(\overline{NE}) - A_{11}(\overline{NW}) \right] + \frac{1}{4DZ^2} \left[A_{22}(\overline{NE}) + A_{22}(\overline{NW}) \right],$$

$$A(P, S) = \frac{1}{4DE^2} \left[-A_{11}(\overline{SE}) - A_{11}(\overline{SW}) \right] + \frac{1}{4DZ^2} \left[A_{22}(\overline{SE}) + A_{22}(\overline{SW}) \right],$$

$$A(P, W) = \frac{1}{4DE^2} \left[A_{11}(\overline{NW}) + A_{11}(\overline{SW}) \right] + \frac{1}{4DZ^2} \left[-A_{22}(\overline{NW}) - A_{22}(\overline{SW}) \right],$$

$$A(P, NW) = \frac{A_{11}(\overline{NW})}{4DE^2} + \frac{A_{22}(\overline{NW})}{4DZ^2} - \frac{A_{12}(\overline{NW})}{2DE\,DZ} - EX + EZ,$$

$$A(P, NE) = \frac{A_{11}(\overline{NE})}{4DE^2} + \frac{A_{22}(\overline{NE})}{4DZ^2} + \frac{A_{22}(\overline{NE})}{2DE\,DZ} + EX + EZ,$$

$$A(P, SW) = \frac{A_{11}(\overline{SW})}{4DE^2} + \frac{A_{22}(\overline{SW})}{4DZ^2} + \frac{A_{12}(\overline{SW})}{2DE\,DZ} - EX - EZ,$$

$$A(P, SE) = \frac{A_{11}(\overline{SE})}{4DE^2} + \frac{A_{22}(\overline{SE})}{4DZ^2} - \frac{A_{12}(\overline{SE})}{2DE\,DZ} + EX - EZ,$$

$$EX = \frac{c_1(\overline{NW}) + c_1(\overline{NE}) + c_1(\overline{SE}) + c_1(\overline{SW})}{16DE},$$

$$EZ = \frac{c_2(\overline{NW}) + c_2(\overline{NE}) + c_2(\overline{SE}) + c_2(\overline{SW})}{16DZ}.$$

Consider the following example from Hall and Lowke [1975]. Let $E/N = 10^{-17}$ V cm^2, $N = 9.9 \times 10^{16}$, $P = 3$ torr, $T = 293$ K, for a gas of atomic weight 4. Other parameters in (11.3.2) are the physical constants, $m = 9.11 \times 10^{-28}$ g, $M = 6.68 \times 10^{-24}$ g, and $k = 1.38 \times 10^{-23}$ J/K. The cross section $Q(\varepsilon)$ was set equal to 60ε cm^2, where ε is in eV.

The solution corresponds to the physical situation of a continuous stream of electrons over an infinite plane being subjected to a uniform electric field of strength

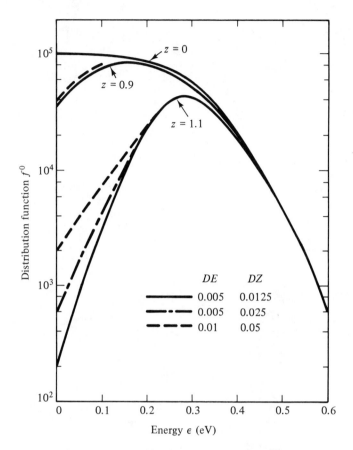

Figure 11.3.2   Electron distribution function $f^0(\varepsilon, z)$.

0.99 V/cm and being collected by a metal electrode. The absorbing metal electrode is at $\bar{z} = 1.2$ and the value of $\bar{\varepsilon}$ is taken to be 18 eV.

Figure 11.3.2 illustrates the finite difference approximations of f^0 for three mesh configurations as functions of energy and for three values of position z. Note that for low energy levels, the finite difference solution is quite sensitive to the size of mesh. However, it is the electron density which is the most significant physical quantity, and this integral of $\varepsilon^{1/2} f^0$ is virtually free from this sensitivity.

Figure 11.3.3 illustrates the electron density calculated from the finite difference solution of (11.3.2) and the formula for n given in (11.3.14). Also given in Figure 11.3.3 is the electron density calculated using the *steady-state electron continuity equation*

$$\frac{\partial}{\partial z}\left(nW - D\frac{\partial n}{\partial z}\right) = 0, \qquad (11.3.19)$$

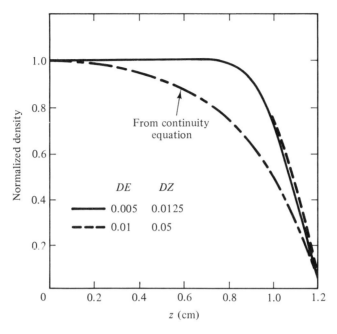

Figure 11.3.3 Calculated electron density.

where the electron drift velocity W is taken to be the constant 2.58×10^5 cm/sec and the electron diffusion coefficient D is taken to be the constant 8.4×10^4 cm^2/sec. Equation (11.3.19) is obtained by integrating (11.3.2) with respect to energy ε and setting $\partial n/\partial t = 0$. The terms of (11.3.2) in the first set of brackets are zero at both infinite energy and zero energy, assuming $Q(0)$ is finite. In general, W and D are functions of z defined by

$$nW = -\frac{8\pi e E}{3m^2 N} \int_0^\infty \frac{\varepsilon}{Q} \frac{\partial f^0}{\partial \varepsilon}\, d\varepsilon,$$

$$nD = \frac{8\pi}{3m^2 N} \int_0^\infty \frac{\varepsilon f^0}{Q}\, d\varepsilon,$$

(11.3.20)

where n is given in (11.3.14). However, for many applications W and D are assumed to be constant and n is approximated as the solution to the differential equation (11.3.19). The results of this case study indicate that the distribution of electrons is significantly different if W and D are allowed to depend on z. Note that for computations, $\bar{\varepsilon}$ is chosen to be some large energy value and the integral limits of ∞ in (11.3.20) are replaced by $\bar{\varepsilon}$.

Figure 11.3.4 illustrates the dependence of W and D on position z. The finite difference approximation F^0 to f^0 was used in (11.3.20) to calculate W and D.

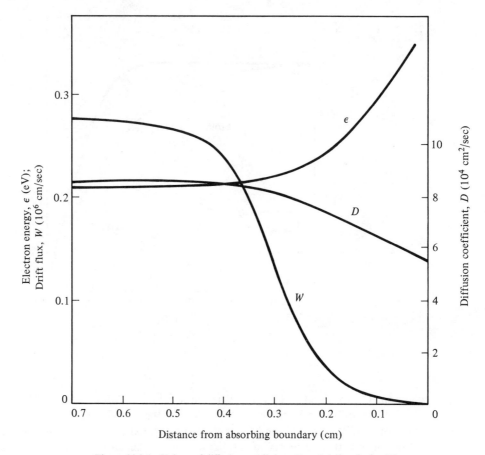

Figure 11.3.4   Values of diffusion coefficient D and drift velocity W.

SUGGESTIONS FOR FURTHER INVESTIGATIONS

1. Study the effect on the electron distribution function f^0 and the electron density $n(z)$ when the cross section $Q(\varepsilon)$ is a constant. Consider the problem above with $Q(\varepsilon) = 6 \times 10^{-16}$ cm^2, $E/N = 0.75 \times 10^{-17}$ V-cm^2, and $P = 4.5$ torr.

2. Study the effect on the finite difference solution if the temperature is reduced to 100 K, 25 K, 0 K.

11.4 NATURAL CONVECTION IN A GLASS BLOCK

Architects sometimes design translucent windows and walls using 4-in.-thick glass block to increase security, to provide privacy, or just for aesthetic reasons. Figure 11.4.1 shows a typical glass block used for such constructions. Since the block con-

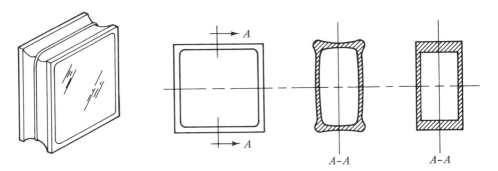

Figure 11.4.1 Glass block.

tains an air pocket, it is natural to expect that the glass block would also be a good insulating material. This case study involves an attempt to analyze the heat transfer processes within glass blocks and to determine the effect on heat loss through the face of the block when the thickness of the horizontal walls is decreased. It has been conjectured that reducing the thickness of the horizontal walls of the glass block would significantly reduce the heat flow through an exterior wall of a building composed in part of such blocks.

The current case study is similar to a standard test problem for computer programs that solve fluid flow models in which there are thermal effects. This test problem is referred to as the *natural convection in a cavity problem* and is given as follows. Consider the square cavity of side D as illustrated in Figure 11.4.2. The top and bottom are insulated, while the two sides are differentially heated. The walls of the cavity are assumed to be no-slip (i.e., the tangential, as well as the normal, component of the velocity vanishes on the wall). The problem is to determine the pressure p, the velocity $\mathbf{q}$, and the temperature T of the fluid within the cavity. The solution to

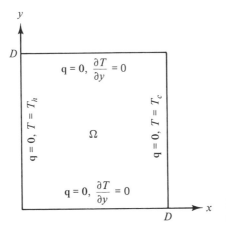

Figure 11.4.2 Natural convection in a closed cavity.

this problem is strongly dependent on the value of the *Rayleigh number*, defined by

$$Ra = \frac{\beta g(T_h - T_c)D^3}{\mu\alpha/\rho},$$
(11.4.1)

where

$\beta = -(1/\rho)(\partial\rho/\partial T) = $ coefficient of volumetric expansion

$\rho = $ fluid density

$g = $ gravitational constant

T_h and $T_c = $ the values of the temperature on the hot and cold sides of the cavity, respectively

$D = $ length of a side of the cavity

$\mu = $ viscosity

$\alpha = $ thermal diffusivity

It is well known that the problem becomes increasingly more diffcult to solve numerically as the Rayleigh number increases. By transforming the variables (see deVahl Davies [1983]) this problem can be solved in terms of the dimensionless equations[6]

$$\mathbf{V} \cdot \mathbf{q} = 0,$$

$$\frac{\partial\mathbf{q}}{\partial t} + \mathbf{q} \cdot \mathbf{Vq} = -\mathbf{V}p + \text{Pr } \mathbf{V}^2\mathbf{q} + \text{Pr Ra } T\begin{bmatrix} 0 \\ -1 \end{bmatrix},$$
(11.4.2)

$$\frac{\partial T}{\partial t} + \mathbf{V} \cdot (T\mathbf{q}) = \frac{1}{\text{Pr}} \mathbf{V}^2 T,$$

where $\mathbf{q}$ is the velocity vector, p the fluid pressure, T the fluid temperature, and Pr the Prandtl number. The Prandtl number is defined by

$$\text{Pr} = \frac{c\mu}{k},$$
(11.4.3)

where c is the specific heat and k is the thermal conductivity of the fluid.

A finite element approximation to the solution of (11.4.2) involves the approximation of the three primitive variables of pressure, velocity, and temperature. We approximate pressure by the four-node quadrilateral elements studied in Chapter 7,

---

[6] Note that to arrive at this form of the equations of fluid flow an approximation has been made relative to the state equation. The density ρ has been assumed to be a constant ρ_0 throughout, except in the buoyancy term ρg of the dimensioned momentum equation where $\rho = \rho_0 - \rho_0\beta(T - T_0)$ and T_0 is a reference temperature. This is the so-called *Boussinesq approximation*.

and approximate temperature and each of the velocity components by the eight-node isoparametric element presented in Chapter 8. Let Ω be the flow domain and $S^4(\Omega)$ the finite element space from which the pressure is approximated. Here we must assume that the pressure is specified at one node to eliminate what is termed the *hydrostatic pressure mode.*[7] Let $S^8(\Omega)$ be the finite element space from which the temperature and velocity components are approximated.

The finite element problem is: *Find q_1, q_2 and $T \in S^8(\Omega)$ and $p \in S^4(\Omega)$ satisfying the essential boundary conditions and such that*

$$\int_\Omega (\mathbf{V} \cdot \mathbf{q}) w_1 \, dx \, dy = 0,$$

$$\int_\Omega \left[\left(\frac{\partial \mathbf{q}}{\partial t} + \mathbf{q} \cdot \nabla \mathbf{q} + \nabla p - \text{Pr Ra } T \begin{bmatrix} 0 \\ -1 \end{bmatrix} \right) \cdot \begin{bmatrix} w_2 \\ w_3 \end{bmatrix} + \text{Pr } \nabla \begin{bmatrix} w_2 \\ w_3 \end{bmatrix} \cdot \nabla \mathbf{q} \right] dx \, dy = 0,$$

$$\int_\Omega \left[\left(\frac{\partial T}{\partial t} + \mathbf{V} \cdot (T\mathbf{q}) w_4 + \frac{1}{\text{Pr}} \nabla T \cdot \nabla w_4 \right) \right] dx \, dy = 0,$$

where $w_1 \in S_0^4(\Omega)$, and w_2, w_3, and $w_4 \in S_0^8(\Omega)$. The subscript 0 designates that the functions have value zero wherever the essential boundary conditions are specified. Note that the coefficients (nodal values) of the finite element approximations are functions of time and that time derivatives of these coefficients appear in the formulation above. This system of ordinary differential equations can then be solved by standard backward or forward differencing in time.

A typical benchmark experiment is to solve this natural convection problem for Rayleigh numbers ranging from 10^3 to 10^6, and determine the isotherms (lines of equal temperature). If dimensioned equations are used and the fluid is air, typical values for the parameters involved are $\rho = 0.08634$ lbm/ft^3, $g = 4.2 \times 10^8$ ft/hr^2, $\beta = 0.218 \times 10^{-2}$ (°F)$^{-1}$, $\mu = 0.05639$ lbm/(hr-ft), $c = 0.243$ Btu/(lbm-°F), and $k = 0.01939$ Btu/(ft-hr-°F). Further, if $T_h = 1$ and $T_c = 0$ then $\alpha = 0.256 \times 10^{-3}$ ft^2/hr, Pr $= 0.71$, and Ra $= (0.151 \times 10^7)D^3$. The desired parameter study can then be accomplished by varying the size of the cavity; for example, $D = 0.08717$ corresponds to Ra $= 10^3$ while $D = 0.1878$ corresponds to Ra $= 10^4$, and so on. Figure 11.4.3 contains plots of the isotherms as functions of Ra.

For the standard differentially heated cavity problem just described, the numerical solution becomes quite difficult to compute as the Rayleigh number increases much beyond 10^6. For realistic values of the problem parameters involved in modeling the glass block problem, the Rayleigh number is between 10^6 and 10^7. Figure 11.4.4 illustrates the results of a finite element solution using eight-node velocity approximations and four-node pressure approximations. The properties of air have been

---

[7] Note that the pressure does not appear in (11.4.2) directly, only the gradient of pressure appears. Thus these equations determine the pressure only up to a constant, and pressure must be specified for at least one point to remove this indeterminacy.

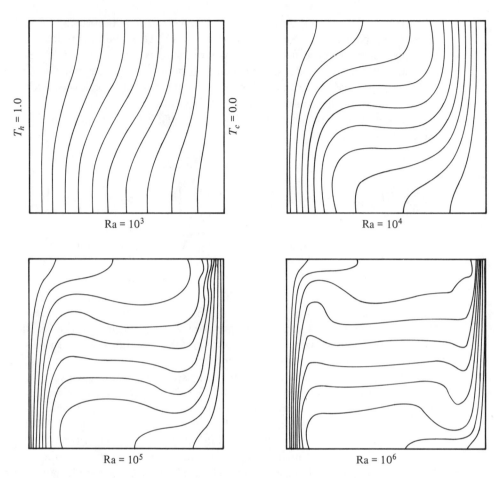

$T_h = 1.0$

$T_c = 0.0$

Ra = 10^3

Ra = 10^4

Ra = 10^5

Ra = 10^6

Figure 11.4.3   Isotherms for various choices of the Rayleigh number.

given earlier, while for glass we assume that $\rho = 110$ lbm/ft^3, $c = 0.18$ Btu/lbm-°F, and $k = 1.0$ Btu/ft-hr-°F. The pressure of the air inside the cavity is initially 12.7 psi, and its temperature is 45°F. The constant temperatures on the left and right walls are 70°F and 20°F, respectively. This corresponds to a Rayleigh number Ra = 1.9×10^7 and a Prandtl number Pr = 0.71.

To assess the effect of reducing the size of the horizontal walls on the flux across the face of a block, the simpler model of a glass block illustrated in Figure 11.4.5, which ignores the curvature of the walls, was considered. A 12 × 16 grid was used; the horizontal glass walls were modeled as being three elements thick while the vertical walls were one element thick. Figure 11.4.6 contains isotherms for this finite element idealization at 0.115 hr. The flux across the wall designated $\overline{AB}$ was calculated to be

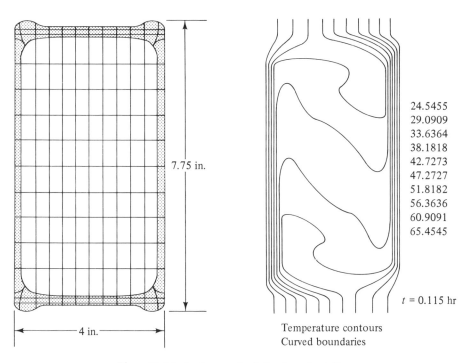

24.5455
29.0909
33.6364
38.1818
42.7273
47.2727
51.8182
56.3636
60.9091
65.4545

$t = 0.115$ hr

Temperature contours
Curved boundaries

Figure 11.4.4   Isotherms of a finite element solution.

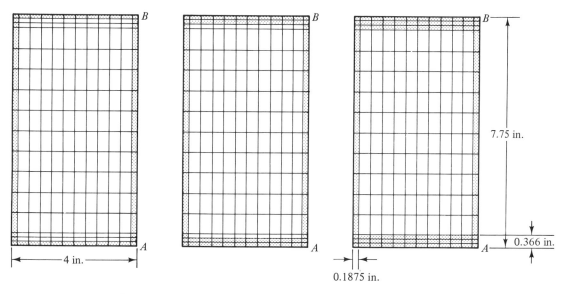

Figure 11.4.5   Rectangular glass block subdivided into 192 elements.

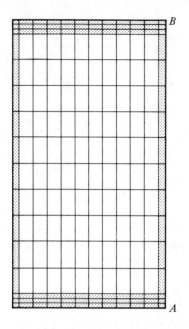
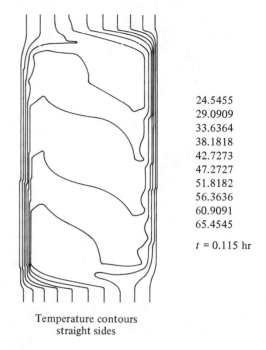

24.5455
29.0909
33.6364
38.1818
42.7273
47.2727
51.8182
56.3636
60.9091
65.4545

$t = 0.115$ hr

Temperature contours
straight sides

Figure 11.4.6   Isotherms.

22.74 Btu/hr. Reducing the thickness of the walls to two-thirds of the original thickness reduced the flux to 19.45 Btu/hr, resulting in a reduction of 14.5%.

SUGGESTIONS FOR FURTHER INVESTIGATIONS

1. Consider other thickness reductions of the horizontal walls and develop a correlation of this reduction to a reduction in the flux across $\overline{AB}$.

2. Replace the fixed temperature boundary conditions with a radiation or mixed boundary condition of the form

$$-k \, \nabla T \cdot \mathbf{n} = h_0 (T - T_s)$$

where $\mathbf{n}$ is the unit outward normal, T_s is the temperature of the surrounding medium (70°F on the left and 20°F on the right), and h_0 is the surface conductance or convective heat transfer coefficient. Choose $h_0 = 0.59$ Btu/(hr-ft^2-°F). When the horizontal walls are reduced in thickness to two-thirds the original thickness, show that the reduction in surface flux is roughly 40%.

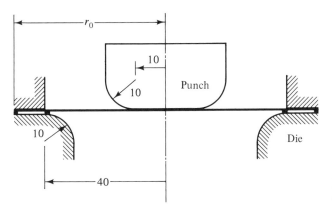

Figure 11.5.1 Plane strain punch stretching geometry.

11.5 PUNCH STRETCHING OF SHEET METAL

Computerized mathematical models that produce accurate and efficient simulations of a sheet-metal forming process are valuable to the automobile industry (for example) as a means of predicting the success or failure of a punch-die design, or for evaluating formability properties of new materials. The basic geometry considered here is shown in Figures 11.5.1 and 11.5.2 with representative dimensions in millimeters (mm). The sheet is assumed to be flat initially and is stretched over a die by a punch with curved edges. For a plane strain problem, no quantity varies in the direction perpendicular to the plane of the paper. Therefore, the strain component in this direction is zero. Points on the material are identified by their initial distances ξ from the z-axis, and the sheet initially lies in the interval $\xi_L \leq \xi \leq \xi_R$. The current horizontal and vertical

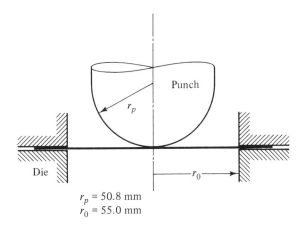

$r_p = 50.8$ mm
$r_0 = 55.0$ mm

Figure 11.5.2 Hemispheric punch stretching geometry.

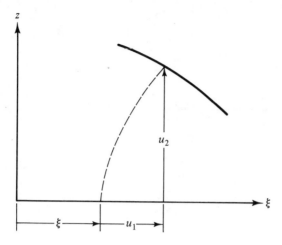

Figure 11.5.3 Displacement (u_1, u_2).

displacements are u_1 and u_2, respectively, and are functions of ξ and time t (see Figure 11.5.3).

The principal logarithmic strain components for the plane strain problem are

$$\varepsilon_1 \equiv \ln\left[\left(1 + \frac{\partial u_1}{\partial \xi}\right)^2 + \left(\frac{\partial u_2}{\partial \xi}\right)^2\right]^{1/2}, \tag{11.5.1}$$

$$\varepsilon_2 \equiv 0, \tag{11.5.2}$$

where subscript 1 is tangential to the sheet (ξ-direction) and 2 is normal to the plane of the paper.

For axisymmetric problems ε_1 is as in (11.5.1), but the circumferential component of strain is

$$\varepsilon_2 = \ln\left(1 + \frac{u_1}{\xi}\right). \tag{11.5.3}$$

During punch stretching, the sheet may be divided into a punch contact region, a die contact region, and a noncontact region. We assume that the shape $S_D(\xi)$ of the fixed (in time) die and the shape $S_P(\xi, t)$ of the moving punch have been specified. For our purposes the punch is moving vertically with a rate $V(t)$ and

$$S_P(\xi, t) = S_0(\xi) + \int_0^t V(t') \, dt'. \tag{11.5.4}$$

where $S_0(\xi)$ is the initial shape of the punch. For ξ in the punch (or die) contact region the displacements u_i must satisfy one of the constraints

$$u_2(t) = S_P(\xi + u_1(t), t) \quad \text{or} \quad u_2(t) = S_D(\xi + u_1(t)). \tag{11.5.5}$$

For punch-sheet or die-sheet interaction we assume Coulomb friction effects. Furthermore, we assume that the horizontal and vertical components of force are, respectively,

$$f_1(\xi, t) = \begin{cases} (-\sin\theta_P - (\text{sgn } \dot{u}_1)\mu_P \cos\theta_P)p, & \text{punch contact,} \\ (-\sin\theta_D + (\text{sgn } \dot{u}_1)\mu_D \cos\theta_D)p, & \text{die contact,} \\ 0, & \text{noncontact,} \end{cases}$$

and   (11.5.6)

$$f_2(\xi, t) = \begin{cases} (\cos\theta_P - (\text{sgn } \dot{u}_1)\mu_P \sin\theta_P)p, & \text{punch contact,} \\ (\cos\theta_D + (\text{sgn } \dot{u}_1)\mu_D \sin\theta_D)p, & \text{die contact,} \\ 0, & \text{noncontact,} \end{cases}$$

where $(\cos\theta_P, \sin\theta_P)$ is the unit tangent vector to the punch (and die for subscript D), μ_P is the coefficient of friction between the sheet and punch (and die for subscript D), and the component of force normal to the sheet is $p(\xi, t)$.

Three basic boundary conditions are considered:

1. *Clamped condition.* $u_i(\xi, t) = 0$ for $\xi = \zeta_R$ (and/or ζ_L), $i = 1, 2$, and all time t.

2. *Drawing condition.* This is the same as (1) for $t < t_D$, where t_D is the first value of t at which the reaction force parallel to the sheet at ξ_R (and/or ξ_L) exceeds a specified drawing force Q_R (and/or Q_L). For $t \geq t_D$, the boundary point is now free to move but an external force Q_R is applied (see Figure 11.5.4).

3. *Symmetry condition.* $u_1(\xi_L, t) = 0$ for all time t.

We use the equilibrium equations of shell membrane theory (see Budiansky [1968] and Wang and Wenner [1982]) and follow the formulation presented in Cavendish et al. [1988]. If the sheet is in equilibrium under external loading, then the strain energy must equal the work done by the external forces. This leads to the following variational formulation: *For arbitrary admissible variations δu_α of the components of displacement u_α we have*

$$h_0 \int_\Omega \tau_\alpha \, \delta\varepsilon_\alpha \, d\Omega = \int_\Omega f_\alpha \, \delta u_\alpha \, d\Omega + [Q_\alpha \, \delta u_\alpha]_{\xi_L}^{\xi_R}, \qquad (11.5.7)$$

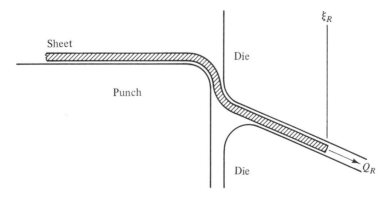

Figure 11.5.4 Drawing boundary condition.

where

$h_0 = $ *initial sheet thickness*

$\Omega = $ *undeformed domain of the sheet*

$d\Omega = d\xi$ *for plane strain and* $d\Omega = 2\pi\xi \, d\xi$ *for the axisymmetric punch problems*

$\varepsilon_\alpha = $ *principal logarithmic strain components*

$\tau_\alpha = $ *Kirchhoff stress components*

$f_\alpha = $ *components of the external forces per unit undeformed area due to punch and/or die contact*

$Q_\alpha = $ *components of external drawing forces,* $\alpha = 1, 2$ *(repeated indices designate summation)*

$\delta\varepsilon_\alpha = $ *variations of the components of strain corresponding to* δu_α *derived from* (11.5.1), (11.5.2) *or* (11.5.1), (11.5.3)

Equation (11.5.7) is the so-called *principle of virtual work* and is equivalent to nonlinear equilibrium equations analogous to (2.4.12),(2.4.13) for linear elastic deformation.

Two types of stress–strain relations are generally considered:

1. *Rate-sensitive equations* (Wang and Wenner [1978]). The material response is assumed to depend on the plastic strain rate $\dot{\bar{\varepsilon}}$. It is also assumed that the total strain rates are obtained as sums of the elastic and viscoplastic parts. Solving for stress rates, we have

$$\dot{\tau}_1 - \frac{E}{1 - v^2}\dot{\varepsilon}_1 - \frac{vE}{1 - v^2}\dot{\varepsilon}_2 + g_1(\tau_1, \tau_2, \bar{\varepsilon}) = 0,$$

$$\dot{\tau}_2 - \frac{vE}{1 - v^2}\dot{\varepsilon}_1 - \frac{E}{1 - v^2}\dot{\varepsilon}_2 + g_2(\tau_1, \tau_2, \bar{\varepsilon}) = 0, \qquad (11.5.8)$$

$$\dot{\bar{\varepsilon}} + g_3(\tau_1, \tau_2, \bar{\varepsilon}) = 0,$$

where

E is Young's modulus, v is Poisson's ratio,

$$g_1(\tau_1, \tau_2, \bar{\varepsilon}) \equiv \frac{E\alpha(1 - vc)g(\tau_e, \varepsilon)}{(1 - v^2)\tau_e}\left(\tau_1 - \frac{c - v}{1 - vc}\tau_2\right),$$

$$g_2(\tau_1, \tau_2, \bar{\varepsilon}) = g_1(\tau_2, \tau_1, \bar{\varepsilon}),$$

$$g_3(\tau_1, \tau_2, \bar{\varepsilon}) = -\alpha g(\tau_e, \bar{\varepsilon}),$$

$c \equiv r/(1 + r)$, r is the anisotropy coefficient,

$\tau_e \equiv (\tau_1^2 + \tau_2^2 - 2c\tau_1\tau_2)^{1/2}$ is the effective stress,

$$\alpha = \begin{cases} 0 & \text{for elastic region,} \\ 1 & \text{for plastic region,} \end{cases}$$

$\bar{\varepsilon}$ is the effective plastic strain,

and

$$g(\tau_e, \bar{\varepsilon}) = \gamma \left\{ \exp \left[\frac{\tau_e - K(\bar{\varepsilon} + \varepsilon_0)^n}{K\eta} \right] - 1 \right\}, \tag{11.5.9}$$

where K, η, γ, n, and ε_0 are material parameters.

Normally, the strain-hardening and strain-rate hardening of a material are specified by a relation which expresses effective stress as a function of effective strain and its rate, that is,

$$\tau_e = F(\bar{\varepsilon}, \dot{\bar{\varepsilon}}). \tag{11.5.10}$$

This is called the *hardening law*. Many forms of F have been proposed. We follow Wang and Wenner [1978] and use

$$F(\bar{\varepsilon}, \dot{\bar{\varepsilon}}) = K \left[(\bar{\varepsilon} + \varepsilon_0)^n + \eta \ln \left(1 + \frac{\dot{\bar{\varepsilon}}}{\gamma} \right) \right]. \tag{11.5.11}$$

The function $g(\tau_e, \bar{\varepsilon})$ is obtained by solving (11.5.10) for $\dot{\bar{\varepsilon}}$.

The material response is elastic or plastic as determined by

$$\alpha = \begin{cases} 0 & \text{for } \tau_e \leq K(\bar{\varepsilon} + \varepsilon_0)^n \quad \text{(elastic deformation)}, \\ 1 & \text{for } \tau_e > K(\bar{\varepsilon} + \varepsilon_0)^n \quad \text{(plastic deformation)}. \end{cases} \tag{11.5.12}$$

2. *Rate-insensitive equations.* The material response is assumed to be independent of strain rate, and (11.5.10) becomes

$$\tau_e = K(\bar{\varepsilon} + \varepsilon_0)^n. \tag{11.5.13}$$

The decision, in this case, as to whether the material response is plastic or elastic depends on the current yield stress, τ_y, defined to be the larger of an initial yield stress and $(\tau_e)_{max}$, the largest value of τ_e reached in the deformation history. We have

$$\alpha = \begin{cases} 0 & \text{if } \tau_e < \tau_y \\ & \text{or if } \tau_e = \tau_y \text{ and } \dot{\tau}_e \leq 0, \\ 1 & \text{if } \tau_e = \tau_y \text{ and } \dot{\tau}_e > 0. \end{cases} \tag{11.5.14}$$

Our problem then is to find displacements $u_i(\xi, t)$, $i = 1, 2$, stresses $\tau_i(\xi, t)$, $i = 1, 2$, pressure $p(\xi, t)$, and effective strain $\bar{\varepsilon}(\xi, t)$ which satisfy the principle of virtual work (11.5.7) (the equilibrium equations), the constitutive laws (11.5.8), the boundary conditions, and the constraints due to punch and/or die contact. In addition, we specify initial conditions, for example,

$$u_i(\xi, 0) = 0, \qquad i = 1, 2,$$

$$\tau_1(\xi, 0) = \theta, \qquad \tau_2(\xi, 0) = \nu\theta \quad \text{(plane strain)}, \tag{11.5.15}$$

$$\tau_2(\xi, 0) = \theta \quad \text{(axisymmetric)},$$

and

$$p(\xi, 0) = 0, \qquad \bar{\varepsilon}(\xi, 0) = 0,$$

where θ is some small number.

The DEM (differential equation on a manifold) approach of Cavendish et al. [1988] is based on the observation that the constitutive equations (11.5.8) represent a differential equation defined on a manifold determined by the *basic* equilibrium equation (11.5.7). We refer to the set of all solutions to (11.5.7) as the *equilibrium manifold*. Our problem then is to determine the trajectory of a curve lying on the equilibrium manifold. This curve is determined as the solution curve of the constitutive differential equation (11.5.8) passing through the given initial point. Since this solution curve is on the manifold, the DEM formulation guarantees that equilibrium will be satisfied for all values of time.

The steps of the DEM approach are as follows.

1. Introduce finite element approximations to the displacements u_α, $\alpha = 1, 2$, as

$$u_\alpha(\xi, t) \approx \sum_{i=1}^n u_{\alpha i}(t)\phi_i(\xi), \tag{11.5.16}$$

where $\phi_i(\xi)$ are the piecewise linear chapeau functions presented in Section 1.3 and $u_{\alpha i}(t) \approx u_\alpha(\xi_i, t)$. In addition to these approximations to the displacement components, we also approximate the stresses, effective strain, and pressure, respectively, by

$$\tau_\alpha(\xi, t) \approx \sum_{j=1}^m \tau_{\alpha j}\eta_j(\xi). \qquad \alpha = 1, 2, \tag{11.5.17}$$

$$\bar{\varepsilon}(\xi, t) \approx \sum_{j=1}^m \bar{\varepsilon}_j\eta_j(\xi), \tag{11.5.18}$$

and

$$p(\xi, t) \approx \sum_{j=1}^n p_j\gamma_j(\xi), \tag{11.5.19}$$

where η_j are chosen as piecewise constant basis functions associated with finite elements with one node at the center of the element. The γ_j are taken to be piecewise constant basis functions associated with finite elements with nodes at each end of the element. Of course, there are many choices that one could make for these basis functions.

The DEM method is a variant of the so-called mixed finite element method, although the solution scheme is not typical of mixed methods. It was demonstrated in Cavendish et al. [1988] that the inherent liability arising from an increase in the number of unknowns is offset by an attendant improvement in the efficiency of the computation and in the accuracy of the computed approximations.

2. Discretize the equilibrium equation (11.5.7) using the approximations in step 1 and the variations

$$\delta u_1 = \phi_j, \qquad \delta u_2 = 0,$$
$$\delta u_1 = 0, \qquad \delta u_2 = \phi_j, \quad j = 1, \ldots, n. \tag{11.5.20}$$

This yields $2n$ *nonlinear algebraic* equations,

$$\mathbf{F}_1(\mathbf{Y}, t) = 0, \tag{11.5.21}$$

in the $3m + 3n$ variables $\mathbf{Y} = (\mathbf{U}_1, \mathbf{U}_2, \mathbf{T}_1, \mathbf{T}_2, \mathbf{E}, \mathbf{P})^T$, where for $1 \leq i \leq n$, $1 \leq j \leq m$, and $\alpha = 1, 2$, we have $\mathbf{U}_{\alpha i} = u_{\alpha i}$, $\mathbf{T}_{\alpha j} = \tau_{\alpha j}$, $\mathbf{E}_j = \bar{\varepsilon}_j$, $\mathbf{P}_i = p_i$.

3. Introduce constraints to model the punch/sheet and die/sheet interaction to obtain n *nonlinear algebraic* equations

$$\mathbf{F}_2(\mathbf{Y}, t) = 0. \tag{11.5.22}$$

These constraints are formulated as follows. Assume that the pressure node ξ_j has deformed to the point $\mathbf{P}_j \equiv (\xi_j + u_{1j}, u_{2j})$, and $\mathbf{Q}_P \equiv (\xi_P, z_P)$ and $\mathbf{Q}_D \equiv (\xi_D, z_D)$ are the closest points to $\mathbf{P}_j$ on the punch and die, respectively. Then for a specified tolerance δ,

$$\mathbf{F}_{2j} = \begin{cases} d(\mathbf{P}, \mathbf{Q}_P) & \text{if } d(\mathbf{P}, \mathbf{Q}_P) < \delta, \\ d(\mathbf{P}, \mathbf{Q}_D) & \text{if } d(\mathbf{P}, \mathbf{Q}_D) < \delta, \\ p_j & \text{otherwise}, \end{cases} \tag{11.5.23}$$

where $d(\mathbf{A}, \mathbf{B})$ is the Euclidean distance between points $\mathbf{A}$ and $\mathbf{B}$. The tolerance $\delta \ll h_0$, so only one of the above can hold since $d(\mathbf{Q}_P, \mathbf{Q}_D) > h_0$. Condition (11.5.23) simply says that if the sheet is within δ units of the punch (or die), it is considered to be in contact. Otherwise, the condition that the normal component of external force is zero is imposed.

Let $r = 3m + 3n$ and $\mathbf{F} = (\mathbf{F}_1, \mathbf{F}_2)$. Then the set $S = \{(\mathbf{Y}, t) \mid \mathbf{F}(\mathbf{Y}, t) = 0\}$ is a $(3m + 1)$-dimensional manifold in R^{r+1}. S is called the (discrete) equilibrium manifold.

4. Approximate the constitutive equations (11.5.8) by collocating at the m stress nodes. The resulting $3m$ equations are a matrix differential equation of the form

$$B(\mathbf{Y}, t)\dot{\mathbf{Y}} = G(\mathbf{Y}, t). \tag{11.5.24}$$

This differential equation defines a direction field on the manifold S. We seek a path on S through the starting point for which the tangent at each point equals the direction vector of the field at that point; that is, we seek to solve the differential equation (11.5.24) on the manifold

$$\mathbf{F}(\mathbf{Y}, t) = 0. \tag{11.5.25}$$

We note also that (11.5.24) and (11.5.25) constitute what are termed differential-algebraic equations (DAE) (see Rheinboldt [1984a, 1984b], Petzold [1982], and Gear [1971b]).

5. Integrate the DAE (11.5.24)–(11.5.25) using, for example, a software package such as LSODI (Hindmarsh [1983]). LSODI is a Fortran code for integrating stiff systems of implicit differential/algebraic equations. To describe the LSODI solution scheme for (11.5.24)–(11.5.25), let

$$\mathbf{H}(\dot{\mathbf{Y}}, \mathbf{Y}, t) = \begin{pmatrix} B(\mathbf{Y}, t)\dot{\mathbf{Y}} - G(\mathbf{Y}, t) \\ \mathbf{F}(\mathbf{Y}, t) \end{pmatrix},$$

and denote by $\mathbf{Y} = \mathbf{Y}(t)$ the desired solution for a specific initial condition $\mathbf{Y}(t_0) = \mathbf{Y}_0$. For the next step from the current approximation $\mathbf{Y}_{k-1} \approx \mathbf{Y}(t_{k-1})$, the predictor is based on the interpolating polynomial $\mathbf{Q} = \mathbf{Q}(t)$ that passes through the $s_k + 1$ ($s_k \geq 1$) most recently computed points along the path. This polynomial is used to evaluate the predicted point $\mathbf{Q}(t_k)$, $t_k = t_{k-1} + \Delta t_k$, corresponding to a suitably chosen steplength Δt_k. For $k = 1$ we utilize $\dot{\mathbf{Y}}(t_0)$ directly. For the corrector phase the derivative $\dot{\mathbf{Y}}$ in $\mathbf{H}$ is replaced by a backward difference formula (BDF) of order s_k. At t_k this produces an equation of the form

$$\mathbf{H}(\alpha_k \mathbf{Y}_k + \mathbf{b}_k, \mathbf{Y}_k, t_k) = 0 \tag{11.5.26}$$

involving some nonzero real number α_k and vector $\mathbf{b}_k$, as, for example, $\alpha_k = 1/\Delta t_k$, $\mathbf{b}_k = -\alpha_k \mathbf{Y}_{k-1}$ when $t_k = 1$. Equation (11.5.26) for the new point $\mathbf{Y}_k$ is solved by means of a chord-Newton process started at the predicted point $\mathbf{Q}(t_k)$. The code controls both the order s_k of the process and the step length Δt_k adaptively on the bases of certain local error estimates. Note that when the corrector process applied to (11.5.26) converges, the new point $(\mathbf{Y}_k, t_k)$ does satisfy the equilibrium equations (11.5.25).

Some general comments concerning the DEM method are appropriate. The contact equation (11.5.22) changes form at a node as that node moves from the non-contact region into the punch contact (or die contact) region, or vice versa. If a node comes in contact during the prediction stage of LSODI, it may move out of contact during the correction stage, or vice versa. This means that the Newton corrections are for a system of equations, some of which are of radically different form than those for which the Jacobian was calculated. For some situations this may produce an erratic performance by LSODI. One way to resolve this is to force the corrector stage of LSODI to accept the choices in (11.5.23) made during the predictor stage. Note also that the hardening law (11.5.10), or more explicitly the form of the function $g(\tau_e, \bar{\varepsilon})$ in (11.5.9), causes the differential equation (11.5.24) to be extremely stiff (Gear [1971a]).

Consider the flat-bottomed punch illustrated in Figure 11.5.1 with dimensions as indicated. A punch velocity of 1 mm/sec is used and other parameters are[8]

$$n = 0.22, \quad K = 482.7 \text{ MPa}, \quad r = 1.8,$$

$$\gamma = 0.000137, \quad \eta = 0.018, \quad \varepsilon_0 = 0.0077, \tag{11.5.27}$$

$$E = 206841 \text{ MPa}, \quad \mu_P = \mu_D = 0.1, \quad \delta = 0.$$

Taking advantage of symmetry, we can choose the problem domain to be the region $\xi_L = 0.0 \leq \xi \leq 50.0 = \xi_R$, where $\xi = \xi_L$ is the centerline of the punch. The sheet is clamped at $\xi = \xi_R$, and $\xi = \xi_L$ is a line of symmetry. The domain is decomposed

---

[8] MPa is the abbreviation for *megapascal*. One megapascal $= 10^6$ pascal $= 10^6$ newtons per square meter. The pascal is the consistent unit of pressure in the MKS system.

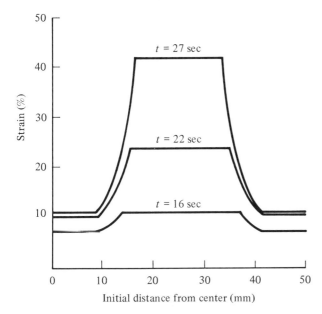

Figure 11.5.5 Strain distributions for clamped case at three times.

into 20 linear elements ($n = 21$) for the displacements by a uniform mesh, and using the same mesh, 20 constant elements ($m = 20$) for the stresses and effective strain. The pressure is approximated by linear elements centered on the displacement nodes.

The results for a 27-sec transient are as follows. For rate-sensitive laws, Figure 11.5.5 illustrates the strain as a function of initial position for three different times. Figure 11.5.6 presents the peak strain (which occurs in the unsupported region of the sheet) and the floor strain (i.e., the strain under the punch) as functions of time,

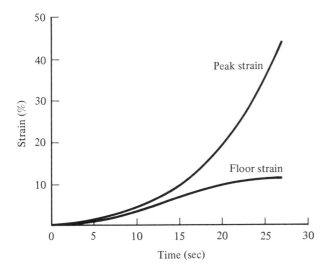

Figure 11.5.6 Peak and floor strains as functions of time for clamped problem.

or equivalently, as functions of punch depth. These results compare well with those presented in Wang and Wenner [1978].

The geometry of Figure 11.5.1 can also be used for a drawing problem. For this calculation the right-hand boundary is moved to $\xi_R = 63$ mm and the draw force Q_R is specified so that drawing begins when the stress τ_1 reaches 300 MPa. The parameters in (11.5.27) are used, except for friction, which is changed to 0.2. A uniform mesh with $n = 41$ and $m = 40$ is used, with linear elements for the displacements and pressure and constant elements for the stresses and effective strain.

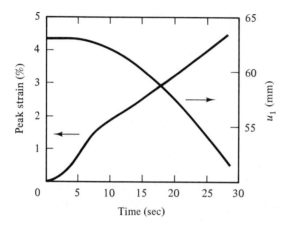

Figure 11.5.7 Peak strain and the location of right boundary for drawing problem.

Plotted in Figure 11.5.7, as functions of time or punch depth, are the peak strain (which occurs again in the unsupported region) and the location of the right-hand boundary node. After drawing begins, this node moves to the left. Note that drawing begins at about 6.5 sec, the time at which the stress reaches 300 MPa. Due to the drawing-in, the strains in this case are much smaller than for the clamped condition.

SUGGESTIONS FOR FURTHER INVESTIGATIONS

1. Analyze the examples above using the rate-insensitive laws.
2. Solve these examples if the sheet is assumed to be elastic for all time, that is, $\alpha = 0$ for all time.
3. Consider the effect of increasing or decreasing the friction factor μ on the stresses and strains. This corresponds to varying the lubrication between the punch and sheet.
4. Investigate the use of other DAE solvers such as DASSL (see Petzold [1982]).

Bibliography

ADAMS, R. A. [1975], *Sobolev Spaces*, Academic Press, New York.

AMES, W. F. [1971], *Numerical Methods for Partial Differential Equations*, Barnes & Noble, New York.

ARGYRIS, J. H. [1954–1955], "Energy Theorems and Structural Analysis, Part I: General Theory," *Aircr. Eng.* 26, 347–356, 383–387, 394; 27, 42–58, 80–94, 125–134.

ARGYRIS, J. H., and I. FRIED [1968], "The LUMINA Element for the Matrix Displacement Method (Lagrangian Interpolation)," *Aeronaut. J. Roy. Aeronaut. Soc.* 72, 514–517.

ASHRAE HANDBOOK, AMERICAN SOCIETY OF HEATING, REFRIGERATING AND AIR CONDITIONING ENGINEERS, INC, [1978], ASHRAE, New York.

AUBIN, J. P. [1967], "Behavior of the Error of the Approximate Solutions of Boundary Value Problems for Linear Elliptic Operators by Galerkin's and Finite Difference Methods," *Ann. Scuola Norm. Sup. Pisa Cl. Sci.* (3)21, 599–637.

AXELSSON, O., and V. A. BARKER [1984], *Finite Element Solution of Boundary Value Problems, Theory and Computation*, Academic Press, New York.

AXELSSON, O., S. BRINKKEMPER, and V. P. IL'IN [1974], "On Some Versions of Incomplete Block-Matrix Factorization Iterative Methods," *Linear Algebra Appl.* 58, 3–15.

BANK, R. E. [1977], "Marching Algorithms for Elliptic Boundary Value Problems, 2: The Variable Coefficient Case," *SIAM J. Numer. Anal.* 14, 950–970.

BANK, R. E. [1978], "Algorithm 527. A Fortran Implementation of the Generalized Marching Algorithm," *ACM Trans. Math. Software* 4, 165–176.

BANK, R. E., and D. J. ROSE [1977], "Marching Algorithms for Elliptic Boundary Value Problems, 1: The Constant Coefficient Case," *SIAM J. Numer. Anal.* 14, 792–829.

BATCHELOR, G. K. [1967], *An Introduction to Fluid Dynamics*, Cambridge University Press, New York.

BECKER, E., G. CAREY, and J. T. ODEN [1981], *Finite Elements, An Introduction*, Vol. 1, Prentice-Hall, Englewood Cliffs, N.J.

BICKLEY, W. G. [1948], "Finite-Difference Formulas for the Square Lattice," *Quart. J. Mech. Appl. Math.* 1, 35–42.

BIRD, R. B., W. E. STEWART, and E. N. LIGHTFOOT [1960], *Transport Phenomena*, Wiley, New York.

BIRKHOFF, G. [1971], *The Numerical Solution of Elliptic Equations*, SIAM, Philadelphia.

BIRKHOFF, G., and C. DEBOOR [1965], "Error Bounds for Spline Interpolation," *J. Math. Mech.* 13, 827–836.

BIRKHOFF, G., M. H. SCHULTZ, and R. S. VARGA [1968], "Piecewise Hermite Interpolation in One and Two Variables with Applications to Partial Differential Equations," *Numer. Math.* 11, 232–256.

BOISVERT, R. F. [1981], "Families of High Order Accurate Discretizations of Some Elliptic Problems," *SIAM J. Sci. Statist. Comput.* 2, 268–284.

BRAMBLE, J., and B. HUBBARD [1963], "A Theorem on Error Estimation for Finite Difference Analogues of the Dirichlet Problem for Elliptic Equations," *Contributions to Differential Equations* 2, 319–340.

BRANDT, A. [1973], "Generalized Local Maximum Principles for Finite Difference Operators," *Math. Comp.* 27, 685–718.

BRANDT, A. [1977], "Multi-level Adaptive Solutions to Boundary Value Problems," *Math. Comp.* 31, 333–390.

BROWDER, F. E. [1964], "Non-linear Equations of Evolution," *Ann. of Math.* 80. 485–523.

BUCHANAN, M. L. [1963], "A Necessary and Sufficient Condition for Stability of Difference Schemes for Initial Value Problems," *SIAM J. Appl. Math.* 11, 919–935.

BUDIANSKY, B. [1968], "Notes on Nonlinear Shell Theory," *J. Appl. Mech. ASME* 35, 393–401.

BUTLER, D. S. [1960], "The Numerical Solution of Hyperbolic Systems of Partial Differential Equations in Three Independent Variables," *Proc. Roy. Soc. London Ser. A* 255, 232–252.

BUZBEE, B. L., G. H. GOLUB, and C. W. NIELSON [1970], "On Direct Methods for Solving Poisson's Equations," *SIAM J. Numer. Anal.* 7, 627–656.

CAREY, G. F., and J. T. ODEN [1984], *Finite Elements, Computational Aspects*, Vol. 3, Prentice-Hall, Englewood Cliffs, N.J.

CARSLAW, H. S., and J. C. JAEGAR [1959], *Conduction of Heat in Solids*, Oxford, London.

CAVENDISH, J. [1972], "A Collocation Method for Elliptic and Parabolic Boundary Value Problems Using Cubic Splines," Ph.D. thesis, University of Pittsburgh.

CAVENDISH, J. [1974], "Automatic Triangulation of Arbitrary Planar Domains for the Finite Element Method," *Internat. J. Numer. Methods Engrg.* 8, 679–697.

CAVENDISH, J., D. FIELD, and W. FREY [1985], "An Approach to Automatic Three-Dimensional Finite Element Mesh Generation," *Internat. J. Numer. Methods Engrg.* 21, 329–347.

CAVENDISH, J., M. WENNER, J. BURKARDT, C. HALL, and W. RHEINBOLDT [1988], "Punch Stretching of Sheet Metal and Differential Equations on Manifolds," *Internat. J. Numer. Methods Engrg.* 25, 269–282.

CEA, J. [1964], "Approximation variationnelle des problèmes aux limits," *Ann. Inst. Fourier (Grenoble)* 14, 345–444.

CHRISTIE, I. D., D. F. GRIFFITHS, A. R. MITCHELL, and O. C. ZIENKIEWICZ [1976], "Finite Element Methods for Second Order Differential Equations with Significant First Derivatives," *Internat. J. Numer. Methods Engrg.* 10, 1389–1396.

CHURCHILL, R. V. [1941], *Fourier Series and Boundary Value Problems*, McGraw-Hill, New York.

CIARLET, P. G. [1970], "Discrete Maximum Principles for Finite-Difference Operators," *Aequationes Math.* 4, 338–352.

CIARLET, P. G. [1978], *The Finite Element Method for Elliptic Problems*, North-Holland, Amsterdam.

CIARLET, P. G., and P.-A. RAVIART [1972], "Interpolation Theory over Curved Elements with Applications to Finite Element Method," *Comput. Methods Appl. Mech. Engrg.* 1, 217–249.

CLOUGH, R. W. [1960], "The Finite Element Method in Plane Stress Analysis," *Proc. 2nd ASCE Conf. Electron. Comput.*, Pittsburgh, Pa., pp. 345–378.

CODY, W., G. MEINARDUS, and R. VARGA [1969], "Chebyshev Rational Approximations to e^{-x} in $[0, +\infty]$ and Applications to Heat-Conduction Problems," *J. Approx. Theory* 2, 50–65.

COLELLA, P., and P. R. WOODWARD [1984], "The Piecewise Parabolic Method (PPM) for Gas Dynamical Simulations," *J. Comput. Physics* 54, 174–201.

COLLATZ, L. [1960], *The Numerical Treatment of Differential Equations*, 3rd ed., Springer-Verlag, Berlin.

COLLATZ, L. [1966], *Functional Analysis and Numerical Mathematics*, Academic Press, New York.

CONCUS, P., and G. H. GOLUB [1973], "Use of Fast Direct Methods for the Efficient Numerical Solution of Non-separable Elliptic Equations," *SIAM J. Numer. Anal.* 10, 1103–1120.

COOLEY, J. W., and J. W. TUKEY [1965], "An Algorithm for the Machine Calculation of Complex Fourier Series," *Math. Comp.* 19, 297–301.

COURANT, R. [1943], "Variational Methods for the Solution of Problems of Equilibrium and Vibrations," *Bull. Amer. Maths. Soc.* 49, 1–23.

COURANT, R., and D. HILBERT [1953], *Methods of Mathematical Physics*, Vol. 1, Interscience, New York.

COURANT, R., and D. HILBERT [1962], *Methods of Mathematical Physics*, Vol. 2, *Partial Differential Equations*, Interscience, New York.

COURANT, R., K. FRIEDRICHS, and H. LEWY [1928], "Über die partiellen Differenzengleichungen der mathematischen Physik," *Math. Ann.* 100, 32–74.

COURANT, R., E. ISAACSON, and M. REES [1952], "On the Solution of Nonlinear Hyperbolic Differential Equations by Finite Differences," *Comm. Pure Appl. Math.* 5, 243–255.

COWPER, G. R. [1973], "Gaussian Quadrature Formulas for Triangles," *Internat. J. Numer. Methods Engrg.* 7, 405–408.

CRANK, J., and P. NICOLSON [1947], "A Practical Method for Numerical Evaluation of Solutions of Partial Differential Equations of the Heat-Conduction Type," *Proc. Cambridge Philos. Soc.* 43, 50–67.

CRYER, C. W. [1982], *Numerical Functional Analysis*, Clarendon Press, Oxford.

CULLEN, C. [1966], *Matrices and Linear Transformations*, Addison-Wesley, Reading, Mass. (To be reprinted by Dover Publications, New York, 1990.)

DAVIES, A. J. [1980], *The Finite Element Method: A First Approach*, Clarendon Press, Oxford.

DEBOOR, C. [1978], *A Practical Guide to Splines*, Vol. 27, *Springer-Verlag Applied Mathematical Sciences*, Springer-Verlag, New York.

DE LA VALLEE POUSSIN, C. [1926], *Cours d'analyse infinitesimale*, Vol. 1, Gauthier-Villiars, Paris.

DENDY, J. E., JR., B. SWARTZ, and B. WENDROFF [1977], "Computing Traveling Wave Solutions of a Nonlinear Heat Equation," in *Topics in Numerical Analysis*, Vol. 3, J. J. H. Miller, ed., Academic Press, London.

DENY, J., and J. L. LIONS [1953–1954], "Les espaces du type de Beppo Levi," *Ann. Inst. Fourier (Grenoble)* 5, 305–370.

DEVAHL DAVIS, G. [1983], "Natural Convection in a Square Cavity," *Internat. J. Numer. Methods Fluids* 3, 249–264.

DIX, R. C., and J. CIZEK [1971], "The Isotherm Migration Method for Transient Heat Conduction Analysis," *Proc. 4th Internat. Heat Transfer Conf.*, Paris, Vol. 1, American Society of Mechanical Engineers, New York.

DONGARRA, J. J., J. R. BUNCH, C. B. MOLER, and G. W. STEWART [1979], *LINPACK User's Guide*, SIAM, Philadelphia.

DOOR, F. W. [1970], "The Direct Solution of the Discrete Poisson Equation on a Rectangle," *SIAM Rev.* 12, 248–263.

DOUGLAS, J., and T. DUPONT [1970], "Galerkin Methods for Parabolic Equations," *SIAM J. Numer. Anal.* 7, 575–626.

DUFFEY, R. B., and D. T. C. PORTHOUSE [1973], "The Physics of Rewetting in Water Reactor Emergency Core Cooling," *Nuclear Engrg. Design* 25, 379–394.

DURACK, D., and B. WENDROFF [1977], "Computing a Two-Dimensional Quench Front," *Nuclear Sci. Engrg.* 64, 187–191.

ERGATOUDIS, I., B. M. IRONS, and O. C. ZIENKIEWICZ [1968], "Curved Isoparametric 'Quadralateral' Elements for Finite Element Analyses," *Internat. J. Solids and Structures* 4, 31–42.

EVANS, D. J., ed. [1983], *Preconditioning Methods: Analysis and Applications*, Vol. 1, *Topics in Computer Mathematics*, Gordon and Breach, New York.

FADDEEVA, V. N. [1949], "The Method of Lines Applied to Some Boundary Problems," *Trudy Mat. Inst. Steklov* 28, 73–103 (Russian).

FINDLAYSON, B. A. [1972], *The Method of Weighted Residuals and Variational Principles*, Academic Press, New York.

FISCHER, E. [1907], "Sur la convergence en moyenne," *C. R. Acad. Sci. Paris* 144, 1022–1024, 1148–1150.

FORSYTHE, G. E., and W. R. WASOW [1960], *Finite Difference Methods for Partial Differential Equations*, Wiley, New York.

FREY, A. E., C. A. HALL, and T. A. PORSCHING [1978], "Some Results on the Global Inversion of Bilinear and Quadratic Isoparametric Finite Element Transformations," *Math. Comp.* 32, 725–749.

FREY, A. E., C. A. HALL, and T. A. PORSCHING [1987], "Numerical Simulation of Confined Unsteady Aerodynamical Flows," *Internat. J. Numer. Methods Engrg.* 24, 1–18.

FRIEDLANDER, F. G. [1982], *Introduction to the Theory of Distributions*, Cambridge University Press, Cambridge.

FRIEDMAN, A. [1964], *Partial Differential Equations of Parabolic Type*, Prentice-Hall, Englewood Cliffs, N.J.

FRIEDMAN, A. [1969], *Partial Differential Equations*, Holt, Rinehart and Winston, New York.

GALLAGHER, R. H. [1975], *Finite Element Analysis Fundamentals*, Prentice-Hall, Englewood Cliffs, N.J.

GANTMACHER, F. R. [1959], *The Theory of Matrices*, Vol. 1, Chelsea, New York.

GARABEDIAN, P. R. [1986], *Partial Differential Equations*, 2nd ed., Chelsea, New York.

GEAR, C. W. [1971a], *Numerical Initial Value Problems in Ordinary Differential Equations*, Prentice-Hall, Englewood Cliffs, N.J.

GEAR, C. W. [1971b], "Simultaneous Numerical Solution of Differential-Algebraic Equations," *IEEE Trans. Circuit Theory* CT-18, 89–95.

GERSCHGORIN, S. [1930], "Fehlerabschätzung für das Differenzenverfahren zur Lösung partieller Differentialgleichungen," *Z. Angew. Math. Mech.* 10, 373–382.

GLASSTONE, S., and M. EDLUND [1952], *The Elements of Nuclear Reactor Theory*, D. Van Nostrand, Princeton, N.J.

GODUNOV, S. K. [1959], "Finite Difference Method for Numerical Computation of Discontinuous Solutions of the Equations of Fluid Dynamics," *Mat. Sb.* 47, 271–306.

GORDON, W. J. [1971], "'Blending-Function' Methods of Bivariate and Multivariate Interpolation and Approximation," *SIAM J. Numer. Anal.* 8, 158–177.

GORDON, W. J., and C. A. HALL, [1973], "Transfinite Element Methods: Blending-Function Interpolation over Arbitrary Curved Element Domains," *Numer. Math.* 21, 109–129.

GRISVARD, P. [1985], *Elliptic Problems in Nonsmooth Domains*, Pitman, Marshfield, Mass.

GUNN, J. E. [1965], "The Solution of Difference Equations by Semi-explicit Iterative Techniques," *SIAM J. Numer. Anal.* 2, 24–55.

GURCAK, A. W., T. A. PORSCHING, and A. C. SPENCER [1980], "Implicit Isotherm Migration: A Numerical Method for the Two-Dimensional Quench Front Problem," *Nuclear Engrg. Design* 61, 25–31.

HACKBUSCH, W. [1985], *Multi-grid Methods and Applications*, Springer-Verlag, Berlin.

HACKBUSCH, W., and U. TROTTENBERG, eds. [1982], *Multi-grid Methods*, Springer-Verlag, Berlin.

HAGEMAN, L. A., and D. M. YOUNG [1981], *Applied Iterative Methods*, Academic Press, New York.

HALL, C. A. [1968], "On Error Bounds for Spline Interpolation," *J. Approx. Theory* 1, 209–218.

HALL, C. A., and J. J. LOWKE [1975], "A Non-Self-Adjoint Finite Difference Model of Electron Diffusion Parallel to Electric Fields," *J. Comput. Phys.* 19, 297–310.

HALL, C., M. RAYMUND, and S. PALUSAMY [1979], "A Macro Element Approach to Computing Stress Intensity Factors for Three Dimensional Structures," *Internat. J. Fracture* 15, 231–245.

HALMOS, P. [1951], *Introduction to Hilbert Space and the Theory of Spectral Multiplicity*, Chelsea, New York.

HAMMER, P. C., O. P. MARLOWE, and A. H. STROUD [1956], "Numerical Integration over Simplices and Cones," *Math. Tables Aids Comput.* 10, 130–137.

HARTEN, A. [1984], "On a Class of High Resolution Total-Variation-Stable Finite Difference Schemes," *SIAM J. Numer. Anal.* 21, 1–23.

HARTEN, A., and P. D. LAX [1981], "A Random Choice Finite Difference Scheme for Hyperbolic Conservation Laws," *SIAM J. Numer. Anal.* 18, 289–315.

HEINRICH, J., and O. C. Zienkiewicz [1977], "Quadratic Finite Element Schemes for Two-Dimensional Convective Transport Problems," *Internat. J. Numer. Methods Engrg.* 11, 1831–1844.

HINDMARSH, A. C. [1983], "ODE Solvers for Time-Dependent PDE Software," Report UCRL-89311, Lawrence Livermore National Laboratory, Livermore, Calif.

HINTON, E., and D. R. OWEN [1977], *Finite Element Programming*, Academic Press, New York.

HIRT, C. W., A. A. AMSDEN, and J. L. COOK [1974], "An Arbitrary Lagrangian-Eulerian Computing Method," *J. Comput. Phys.* 14, 227–253.

HOCKNEY, R. W. [1965], "A Fast Direct Solution of Poisson's Equation Using Fourier Analysis," *J. Assoc. Comput. Mach.* 12, 95, 113.

HRENNIKOFF, A. [1941], "Solution of Problems in Elasticity by the Framework Method," *J. Appl. Mech.* A8, 169–175.

HUXLEY, L. G. H., and R. W. CROMPTON [1974], *The Diffusion and Drift of Electrons in Gases*, Wiley, New York.

IMSL [1980], *Library Reference Manual*, 8th ed., IMSL Inc., Houston.

IRONS, B. M. [1970], "A Frontal Solution Program for Finite Elements," *Internat. J. Numer. Methods Engrg.* 2, 5–32.

ISAACSON, E., and H. KELLER [1966], *Analysis of Numerical Methods*, Wiley, New York.

JOHNSTON, R. L., and S. K. PAL [1972], "The Numerical Solution of Hyperbolic Systems Using Bicharacteristics," *Math. Comp.* 26, 377–392.

KANTOROVICH, L. V., and V. I. KRYLOV [1958], *Approximate Methods in Higher Analysis*, translated from Russian by C. D. Benster, Interscience, New York.

KERNER, M. [1933], "Die Differentiale in der allgemeinen Analysis," *Ann. of Math.* 34, 546–572.

KINCAID, B. R., and D. M. YOUNG [1979], "Survey of Iterative Methods," in *Encyclopedia of Computer Science and Technology*, Vol. 13, J. Belzer, A. Holzman, and A. Kent, eds., Marcel Dekker, New York.

KINCAID, D., R. GRIMES, J. RESPESS, and D. YOUNG [1981], "ITPACK 2B: A Fortran Implementation of Adaptive Accelerated Iterative Methods for Solving Large Sparse Linear Systems," CNA-173, Center for Numerical Analysis, University of Texas, Austin.

KORN, A. [1907], "Sur les équationes d'élasticité," *Ann. Ec. Nosm.* 24, 9–75.

KREISS, H. O. [1962], "Über die Stabilitätsdefinition für Differenzengleichungen die partielle Differentialgleichungen approximieren," *Nordisk Tidskr. Informationsbehandling* 2, 153–181.

KREYSZIG, E. [1978], *Introductory Functional Analysis with Applications*, Wiley, New York.

LADYZHENSKAYA, O. A. [1952], "On Integration of the Cauchy Problem for Hyperbolic Systems by the Difference Method," Thesis for a candidate's dissertation. Leningrad University, March 1949; *Učen. Zapiski Leningrad, Univ. Ser. Math.* 23, 192–246.

LADYZHENSKAYA, O. A. [1969], *The Mathematical Theory of Viscous Incompressible Flow*, Gordon and Breach, New York.

LADYZHENSKAYA, O. A. [1985], *The Boundary Value Problems of Mathematical Physics*, Springer-Verlag, New York.

LAX, P. D. [1954], "Weak Solutions of Nonlinear Hyperbolic Equations and Their Numerical Computation," *Comm. Pure Appl. Math.* 7, 159–193.

LAX, P. D. [1967], "Hyperbolic Difference Equations: A Review of the Courant, Friedrichs, Lewy Paper in the Light of Recent Developments," *IBM J. Res. Develop.* 11, 235–238.

LAX, P. D. [1972], *Hyperbolic Systems of Conservation Laws and the Mathematical Theory of Shock Waves*, SIAM, Philadelphia.

LAX, P. D., and B. WENDROFF [1960], "Systems of Conservation Laws," *Comm. Pure Appl. Math.* 13, 217–237.

LIONS, J. L. [1961], *Équations differentielles opérationnelles et problemes aux limites*, Springer-Verlag, Berlin.

LORD RAYLEIGH (STRUTT, J. W.) [1870], "On the Theory of Resonance," *Trans Roy. Soc. London* A161, 77–118.

LOWKE, J. J., J. H. PARKER, JR., and C. A. Hall [1977], "Electron Diffusion under the Influence of an Electric Field near Absorbing Boundaries," *Phys. Rev. A* 15, No. 3, 1237–1245.

LYNCH, R. E., and H. R. RICE [1978], "High Accuracy Finite Difference Approximations to Solutions of Elliptic Partial Differential Equations," *Proc. Nat. Acad. Sci. USA* 75, 2541–2544.

MASSAU, J. [1899], *Mémoire sur l'intégration graphique des équations aux dérivées partials*, F. Meyer-Van Loo, Ghent.

McCORMICK, S., ed. [1987], *Multigrid Methods*, Frontiers of Applied Mathematics Series, No. 3, SIAM, Philadelphia.

McHENRY, D. [1943], "A Lattice Analogy for the Solution of Plane Stress Problems," *J. Inst. Civ. Eng.* 21, 59–82.

MEIJERINK, J. A., and H. A. VAN DER VORST [1977], "An Iterative Solution Method for Linear Systems of which the Coefficient Matrix is a Symmetric M-Matrix," *Math. Comp.* 31, 148–162.

MEIS, T., and U. MARCOWITZ [1981], *Numerical Solution of Partial Differential Equations*, Springer-Verlag, New York.

MEYERS, N., and J. SERRIN [1964], "$H = W$," *Proc. Nat. Acad. Sci. USA* 51, 1055–1056.

MIKHLIN, S. G. [1965], *The Problem of the Minimization of a Quadratic Functional*, Holden-Day, San Francisco.

MILNE-THOMSON, L. M. [1955], *Theoretical Hydrodynamics*, Macmillan, New York.

MOORE, R. E. [1985], *Computational Functional Analysis*, Ellis Horwood, Chichester, West Sussex, England.

MOTZKIN, T. S., and W. WASOW [1953], "On the Approximation of Linear Elliptic Differential Equations by Difference Equations with Positive Coefficients," *J. Math. Phys.* 31, 253–259.

MUNROE, M. E. [1953], *Introduction to Measure and Integration*, Addison-Wesley, Cambridge, Mass.

NEČAS, J. [1967], *Les méthodes directes en théorie des équations elliptiques*, Masson, Paris.

NAG [1980], *Fortran Library Manual Mark 8*, NAG Central Office, Oxford.

NITSCHE, J. [1968], "Ein Kriterium für die Quasi-optimalitet des ritzchen Verfahrens," *Numer. Math.* 11, 346–348.

O'BRIEN, G. G., M. A. HYMAN, and S. KAPLAN [1951], "A Study of the Numerical Solutions of Partial Differential Equations," *J. Math. Phys.* 29, 223–251.

ODEN, J. T., and J. N. REDDY [1976], *An Introduction to the Mathematical Theory of Finite Elements*, Wiley, New York.

O'LEARY, D. P., and O. WIDLUND [1979], "Capacitance Matrix Methods for the Helmholtz Equation on General Three-Dimensional Regions," *Math. Comp.* 33, 849–880.

ORTEGA, J. M., and W. C. RHEINBOLDT [1970], *Iterative Solution of Nonlinear Equations in Several Variables*, Academic Press, New York.

PARKER, J. H., and J. J. LOWKE [1969], "Theory of Electron Diffusion Parallel to Electric Fields, 1: Theory," *Phys. Rev.* 181, No. 1, 290–300.

PETZOLD, L. R. [1982], "Differential-Algebraic Equations Are Not ODE's," *SIAM J. Sci. Statist. Comput.* 3, 367–384.

PEYRET, R., and T. D. TAYLOR [1983], *Computational Methods for Fluid Flow*, Springer-Verlag, New York.

PRESS, W. H., B. P. FLANNERY, S. A. TEUKOLSKY, and W. T. VETTERLING [1986], *Numerical Recipes, the Art of Scientific Computing*, Cambridge University Press, Cambridge.

PRICE, H. S., and R. S. VARGA [1970], "Error Bounds for Semidiscrete Galerkin Approximations of Parabolic Problems with Application to Petroleum Reservoir Mechanics." *Numerical Solution of Field Problems in Continuum Physics*, G. Birkhoff and R. S. Varga, eds., SIAM-AMS Proceedings, Vol. 2, American Mathematical Society, Providence R.I., pp. 74–94.

PROSKUROWSKI, W. [1979], "Numerical Solution of Helmholtz's Equation by Implicit Capacitance Methods," *ACM Trans. Math. Software* 5, 36–59.

PROTTER, M., and H. WEINBERGER [1984], *Maximum Principles in Differential Equations*, Springer-Verlag, New York.

REID, J. K. [1977], "Sparse Matrices," in *The State of the Art in Numerical Analysis*, D. A. H. Jacobs, ed., Academic Press, London.

REID, J. K. [1987], "Sparse Matrices," in *The State of the Art in Numerical Analysis*, A. Iserles and M. J. D. Powell, eds., Clarendon Press, Oxford.

RHEINBOLDT, W. C. [1984a], "Differential-Algebraic Systems as Differential Equations on Manifolds," *Math Comp.* 43, 473–482.

RHEINBOLDT, W. C. [1984b], "On Some Methods for the Computational Analysis of Manifolds," in *Numerical Methods for Bifurcation Problems*, J. Knepper et al. eds., Birkhäuser Verlag, Basle.

RICE, J. R., and R. F. BOISVERT [1985], *Solving Elliptic Problems Using ELLPACK*, Springer-Verlag, Berlin.

RICHTMYER, R. D., and K. W. MORTON [1967], *Difference Methods for Initial-Value Problems*, Interscience, New York.

RIESZ, F. [1907a], "Sur les systèms orthogonaux de fonctions," *C. R. Acad, Sci. Paris* 144, 615–619, 734–736.

RIESZ, F. [1907b], "Über orthogonale Funktionensysteme," *Gottinger Nachr.* 1907, 116–122.

RIESZ, F., and B. SZ-NAGY [1955], *Functional Analysis*, Ungar, New York.

RITZ, W. [1908], "Über eine neue Methode zur Lösung gewisser Variationsprobleme der mathematischen Physik," *J. Reine Angew. Math.* 135, 1–61.

ROACHE, P. J. [1972], *Computational Fluid Dynamics*, Hermosa, Albuquerque, N. Mex.

RUDIN, W. [1973], *Functional Analysis*, McGraw-Hill, New York.

SAUER, R. [1952], *Anfangswertprobleme bei partiellen Differentialgleichungen*, Springer-Verlag, Berlin.

SAUER, R. [1963], "Differenzenverfahren für hyperbolische Anfangswertprobleme bei mehr als zwei unabhängigen Veränderlichen mit Hilfe von Nebencharakteristiken," *Numer. Math.* 5, 55–67.

SCHNEIDER, P. J [1963], *Temperature Response Charts*, Wiley, New York.

SCHOENBERG, I. J. [1946], "Contributions to the Problem of Approximation of Equidistant data by Analytic Functions," *Quart. Appl. Math.* 4, 45–99, 112–141.

SCHOENBERG, I. J., ed. [1969], *Approximations with Special Emphasis on Spline Functions*, Academic Press, New York.

SCHULTZ, M. H. [1973], *Spline Analysis*, Prentice-Hall, Englewood Cliffs, N.J.

SCHWARTZ, L. [1966], *Thèorie des distributions*, Hermann, Paris.

SMITH, G. D. [1978], *Numerical Solution of Partial Differential Equations: Finite Difference Methods*, Clarendon Press, Oxford.

STEPLEMAN, R. S. [1971], "Difference Analogues of Quasi-linear Elliptic Dirichlet Problems with Mixed Derivatives," *Math. Comp.* 25, 257–269.

STEWART, G. W. [1973], *Introduction to Matrix Computations*, Academic Press, New York.

STRANG, G., and G. J. FIX [1973], *An Analysis of the Finite Element Method*, Prentice-Hall, Englewood Cliffs, N.J.

SWARTZ, B. [1968], "$O(h^{2n+2-l})$ Bounds on Some Spline Interpolation Errors," *Bull. Amer. Math. Soc.* 74, 1072–1078.

SWARTZ, B., and R. S. VARGA [1972], "Error Bounds for Spline and L-spline Interpolation," *J. Approx. Theory* 6, 6–49.

SWARZTRAUBER, P. N. [1977], "The Methods of Cyclic Reduction, Fourier Analysis and the FACR Algorithm for the Discrete Solution of Poisson's Equation on a Rectangle," *SIAM Rev.* 19, 490–501.

TEMPERTON, C. [1980], "On The FACR(l) Algorithm for the Discrete Poisson Equation," *J. Comput. Phys.* 34, 314–329.

THACKER, W. C. [1980], "A Brief Review of Techniques for Generating Irregular Computational Grids," *Internat. J. Numer. Methods Engrg.* 15, 1335–1341.

THOMAS, L. H. [1954], "Computation of One-Dimensional Flows Including Shocks," *Comm. Pure Appl. Math.* 7, 195–206.

THOMPSON, T. S. [1974], "On the Process of Rewetting a Hot Surface by a Falling Liquid Film," *Nuclear Engrg. Design* 31, 234–245.

TIMOSHENKO, S. P., and J. N. GOODIER [1970], *Theory of Elasticity*, 3rd ed., McGraw-Hill, New York.

TURNER, M. J., R. W. CLOUGH, H. C. MARTIN, and L. J. TOPP [1956], "Stiffness and Deflection Analysis of Complex Structures," *J. Aeronaut. Sci.* 23, 805–823.

VARGA, R. S. [1962], *Matrix Iterative Analysis*, Prentice-Hall, Englewood Cliffs, N.J.

VARGA, R. S. [1966], "Hermite Interpolation-Type Ritz Methods for Two-Point Boundary Value Problems," in *Numerical Solution of Partial Differential Equations*, J. H. Bramble, ed., Academic Press, New York, pp. 365–373.

VARGA, R. S. [1971], *Functional Analysis and Approximation Theory in Numerical Analysis*, Regional Conference Series in Applied Mathematics, SIAM, Philadelphia.

VEMURI, V., and W. J. KARPLUS [1981], *Digital Computer Treatment of Partial Differential Equations*, Prentice-Hall, Englewood Cliffs, N.J.

VON NEUMANN, J., and R. D. RICHTMYER [1950], "A Method for the Numerical Calculation of Hydrodynamic Shocks," *J. Appl. Phys.* 21, 232–257.

WANG, N. M., and M. L. WENNER [1978], "Elastic-Viscoplastic Analyses of Simple Stretch Forming Problems," *Proc. General Motors Research Laboratories Symposium on Mechanics of Sheet Metal Forming*, D. Koistinen and N. Wang, eds., Plenum Press, New York.

WANG, N. M., and M. L. WENNER [1982], "Effects of Strain-Hardening Representation in Sheet Metal Forming Calculations of 2036-74 Aluminum," *ASTM Special Technical Publication* 753, J. R. Newby and B. A. Niemeierr, eds., American Society for Testing and Materials, Philadelphia.

WERNER, W. [1968], "Numerical Solutions of Systems of Quasilinear Hyperbolic Differential Equations by Means of the Method of Nebencharacteristics in Combination with Extrapolation Methods," *Numer. Math.* 11, 151–169.

WILKINSON, J. H. [1965], *The Algebraic Eigenvalue Problem*, Clarendon Press, Oxford.

WOODWARD, P. R., and P. COLELLA [1984], "The Numerical Simulation of Two-Dimensional Fluid Flow with Strong Shocks," *J. Comput. Phys.* 54, 115–173.

YOSIDA, K. [1965], *Functional Analysis*, Springer-Verlag, Berlin.

YOUNG, D. M. [1971], *Iterative Solution of Large Linear Systems*, Academic Press, New York.

ZALESAK, S. T. [1979], "Fully Multidimensional Flux-Corrected Transport Algorithms for Fluids," *J. Comput. Phys.* 31, 335–362.

ZEIDLER, E. [1988], *Nonlinear Functional Analysis and Its Applications*, Springer-Verlag, New York.

ZIENKIEWICZ, O. C. [1977], *The Finite Element Method*, McGraw-Hill, Maidenhead, Berkshire, England.

ZLAMAL, M. [1968], "On the Finite Element Method," *Numer. Math.* 12, 394–409.

Conversion Factors

Density	$1 \text{ lbm/ft}^3 = 16.0185 \text{ kg/m}^3$
Diffusivity	$1 \text{ ft}^2/\text{sec} = 0.0929 \text{ m}^2/\text{sec}$
Energy	$1 \text{ J} = 1 \text{ W} \cdot \text{sec} = 1 \text{ N} \cdot \text{m}$
	$1 \text{ Btu} = 1055.04 \text{ J}$
	$1 \text{ Btu} = 252 \text{ cal}$
	$1 \text{ cal} = 4.1868 \text{ J}$
Force	$1 \text{ lbf} = 32.1739 \text{ pdl}$
	$1 \text{ lbf} = 4.4482 \text{ N}$
Heat flux	$1 \text{ Btu/(hr} \cdot \text{ft}^2) = 3.1537 \text{ W/m}^2$
Heat transfer coefficient	$1 \text{ Btu/(hr} \cdot \text{ft}^2 \cdot {}^\circ\text{F}) = 5.677 \text{ W/(m}^2 \cdot {}^\circ\text{C})$
	$1 \text{ Btu/(hr} \cdot \text{ft}^2 \cdot {}^\circ\text{F}) = 4.882 \text{ kcal/(hr} \cdot \text{m}^2 \cdot {}^\circ\text{C})$
Length	$1 \text{ in.} = 2.54 \text{ cm}$
	$1 \text{ ft} = 0.3048 \text{ m}$
Mass	$1 \text{ lbm} = 0.4536 \text{ kg}$
Power	$1 \text{ hp} = 745.7 \text{ W} = 745.7 \text{ J/sec}$
	$1 \text{ hp} = 550 \text{ ft} \cdot \text{lbf/sec}$
	$1 \text{ Btu/hr} = 3.93 \times 10^{-4} \text{ hp}$

(continued)

Pressure

$$1 \text{ Pa} = 1 \text{ N/m}^2$$
$$1 \text{ lbf/in.}^2 = 1 \text{ psi}$$
$$1 \text{ psi} = 6894.76 \text{ Pa}$$
$$1 \text{ atm} = 14.696 \text{ psi}$$
$$1 \text{ psi} = 4633.056 \text{ pdl/ft}^2$$

Specific heat

$$1 \text{ Btu/(lbm} \cdot {}^\circ\text{F)} = 4186.69 \text{ J/(kg} \cdot {}^\circ\text{C)}$$
$$1 \text{ Btu/(lbm} \cdot {}^\circ\text{F)} = 1 \text{ cal/(g} \cdot {}^\circ\text{C)}$$

Temperature

$$T_{{}^\circ\text{F}} = 1.8 T_{{}^\circ\text{C}} + 32$$

$$T_\text{K} = \frac{1}{1.8}(T_{{}^\circ\text{F}} + 459.67)$$

$$T_\text{K} = \frac{1}{1.8} T_{{}^\circ\text{R}}$$

Thermal conductivity

$$1 \text{ Btu/(hr} \cdot \text{ft} \cdot {}^\circ\text{F)} = 1.7303 \text{ W/(m} \cdot {}^\circ\text{C)}$$
$$1 \text{ Btu/(hr} \cdot \text{ft} \cdot {}^\circ\text{F)} = 0.4132 \text{ cal/(sec} \cdot \text{m} \cdot {}^\circ\text{C)}$$

Viscosity

$$1 \text{ lbm/(ft} \cdot \text{sec)} = 1.4882 \text{ kg/(m} \cdot \text{sec)}$$
$$1 \text{ lbm/(ft} \cdot \text{sec)} = 14.882 \text{ P}$$

Glossary
of Symbols

Symbol	Meaning	Page
	Sets	
$\bar{D}$	closure of D	87
supp u	support of u	108
Ω	bounded region	108
$\partial\Omega$	boundary of Ω	108
dist (A, B)	distance from set A to set B	108
$\partial\Omega_h$	boundary strip of Ω	108
	Vectors and Matrices	
n	unit normal vector	22
R^n	real Euclidean n-space	39
Diag $(\cdot)$	diagonal matrix	49
Tridiag $\{\cdot\}$	tridiagonal matrix	78
$\rho(A)$	spectral radius of matrix A	80
Block-Tridiag $\{\cdot\}$	block tridiagonal matrix	216
Seven-diag $\{\cdot\}$	seven diagonal matrix	217

(continued)

311

Symbol	Meaning	Page
	Operators	
∇	gradient operator	22
∇^2	Laplacian operator	23
$T: X \to Y$	T maps X into Y	87
I	identity operator	91
$\tilde{\gamma}$	trace operator	112
L	differential operator	119
$P_\xi[\cdot]$	transfinite interpolating operator	178
$P_\xi P_\eta[\cdot]$	tensor product interpolating operator	178
$P_\xi \oplus P_\eta[\cdot]$	Boolean sum interpolating operator	178
L_h	finite difference operator	232
	Function Spaces	
$C^m(\cdot)$	space of m times continuously differentiable functions	108
$C^m(\bar{\Omega})$	restrictions of $C^m(R^2)$ to $\bar{\Omega}$	108
$C_0^m(\Omega)$	functions in $C^m(\Omega)$ having compact support in Ω	108
$L_2(\Omega)$	space of square integrable functions on Ω	110
$H^m(\Omega)$	Sobolev space of functions with square integrable generalized derivatives on Ω	111
$H_0^m(\Omega)$	closure of $C_0^\infty(\Omega)$ in $H^m(\Omega)$	111
ker T	kernel of T	112
$S_0(\bar{\Omega})$	subspace of $H^1(\Omega)$	125
$V_k(\cdot)$	Cartesian product space	168
H_E	energy space	172
S_0	subspace of $H^1(\Omega)$	202
S^h	finite dimensional subspace of S_0	202
$P^n(\bar{I}, \Pi)$	piecewise polynomial space	209
$H^n(\bar{I}, \Pi)$	smooth Hermite space of order n	209
$H_0^n(\bar{I}, \Pi)$	subspace of $H^n(\bar{I}, \Pi)$	210
$S^n(\bar{I}, \Pi)$	spline subspace of $H^n(\bar{I}, \Pi)$	211
$S_0^n(\bar{I}, \Pi)$	subspace of $S^n(\bar{I}, \Pi)$	212
	Inner Products	
$(\cdot, \cdot)$	generic inner product	109
$((\cdot, \cdot))_k$	Sobolev semi-inner product	110
$(\cdot, \cdot)_m$	Sobolev inner product	110
$\langle \cdot, \cdot \rangle$	inner product on $H_0^1(\Omega)$	122
$[\cdot, \cdot]$	energy inner product	172
	Norms	
$\|\cdot\|_\infty$	vector or matrix infinity norm	49
$\|\cdot\|_2$	vector or matrix Euclidean norm	81
$\|\cdot\|$	generic norm	87
$|\cdot|_k$	Sobolev seminorm	110
$\|\cdot\|_m$	Sobolev norm	110
$\|\cdot\|_{0,\partial\Omega}$	norm on $L_2(\partial\Omega)$	111
$\|\cdot\|_{m,\Omega'}$	Sobolev norm	113
$\|\cdot\|_{j,\infty}$	infinity norm on $C^j(\bar{\Omega})$	114

Symbol	Meaning	Page
	Norms (continued)	
$\lvert \cdot \rvert_E$	norm induced by $\langle \cdot, \cdot \rangle$	122
$\lvert \cdot \rvert_{m,M}$	Sobolev seminorm	138
$\lvert \cdot \rvert_{m,M,\infty}$	Sobolev seminorm	138
$\lVert \cdot \rVert_s$	Sobolev norm	169
$\lVert \cdot \rVert_E$	energy norm	172
	Finite Differences	
M_D	abstract finite difference method	90
$\partial \Omega_h$	set of boundary mesh points	231
Ω_h	set of interior mesh points	231
$\bar{\Omega}_h$	set of interior and boundary mesh points	231
U	grid function	232
	Finite Elements	
$S_0^h(\bar{\Omega})$	finite dimensional subspace of $S_0(\bar{\Omega})$	129
$S^h(\bar{\Omega})$	finite dimensional finite element space	136
u^h	finite element solution	129
u^*	solution of Galerkin problem	123
e^h	finite element error	132
h_j	element diameter	140
ρ_j	element in-diameter	140
h	mesh gauge	141
	Elasticity	
σ_x, σ_y	normal stress components	25
δ	displacement vector	25
τ_{xy}, τ_{yx}	shear stress components	25
γ_{xy}	shear strain	27
$\varepsilon_x, \varepsilon_y$	strain components	27
E	Young's modulus	28
ν	Poisson's ratio	29
G	shear modulus	29
$E(\delta)$	potential energy	168
δ_j	element displacement vector	174
N_i	shape function	175
K	global stiffness matrix	176
K_j^e	element stiffness matrix	177
$\mathbf{F}_j^e$	element force vector	177
	Fluid Flow	
v	velocity	32
p	pressure	33
c	sound speed	40
E	internal energy	62

(continued)

Symbol	Meaning	Page
	Heat Conduction	
ρ	density	21
c	specific heat	22
k	thermal conductivity	22
h	heat transfer coefficient	24
u_s	sink temperature	24
D	thermal diffusivity	29
	Miscellaneous	
$D^x u$	generalized derivative of u	109
$J_\rho * u(\mathbf{x})$	regularization of u	113
$J_\rho(\mathbf{x})$	averaging kernel	113
$D\mathbf{F}$	Jacobian matrix of transformation $\mathbf{F}$	134
v_I	interpolant of v	137

Index